The Logic of COMPUTER
ARITHMETIC

PRENTICE-HALL INTERNATIONAL SERIES
IN ELECTRICAL ENGINEERING
William L. Everitt, editor

PRENTICE-HALL, INC.
PRENTICE-HALL INTERNATIONAL, INC., UNITED KINGDOM AND EIRE
PRENTICE-HALL OF CANADA, LTD., CANADA

Blackwell & Kotzebue, *Semiconductor-Diode Parametric Amplifiers*
Boisvert, Robichaud & Robert, *Signal Flow Graphs and Applications*
Chang, *Energy Conversion*
Flores, *The Logic of Computer Arithmetic*
Gray, *Digital Computer Engineering*
Kuo, *Analysis and Synthesis of Sampled-Data Control Systems*
Maley & Earle, *The Logic Design of Transistor Digital Computers*
Nussbaum, *Semiconductor Device Physics*

PRENTICE-HALL INTERNATIONAL, INC., *London*
PRENTICE-HALL OF AUSTRALIA, PTY., LTD., *Sydney*
PRENTICE-HALL OF CANADA, LTD., *Toronto*
PRENTICE-HALL OF JAPAN, INC., *Tokyo*

The Logic of COMPUTER ARITHMETIC

IVAN FLORES

Consultant
Norwalk, Connecticut

and

Adjunct Professor of Electrical Engineering
New York University

PRENTICE-HALL, INC.

Englewood Cliffs, N. J.

This book is dedicated to the technology which will free man from the menial so that his creativity may be applied to happiness and benevolence.

Current printing (last digit):

11 10 9 8 7 6 5 4 3 2

Library of Congress Catalog Card Number: 63–14727

Printed in the United States of America

C 54003

PREFACE

This book is a complete, exhaustive, yet readable exposition of high-speed, binary digital computer arithmetic hardware and its rationale. In order to be tutorial without sacrifice to rigor, the emphasis leaves less to the reader's imagination at the risk of being repetitious.

Originally, my purpose was to write a book, using my first book *Computer Logic* (Prentice-Hall, Inc., 1960) as a "jumping-off" place, that would lead the reader from the novice to the expert class, to an understanding of the frontiers of computer design. A basic requirement was, and still is, to keep the text readable by avoiding all such phrases as "it can be shown" or "it is easily proved" and by writing reasonable explanations. The objective of clarity restricted the scope of my work which then became a complete coverage of arithmetic units. Since parallel, natural, binary arithmetic is used in all of the fastest, largest computers available, it is the primary topic of interest here. The result is a thorough, though somewhat specialized text.

The discussion of high-speed arithmetic is not historically oriented, but it covers the early classical methods, the methods employed in currently available machines, the methods employed in machines now on the drawing boards which will be produced within the next five years, the methods still in the laboratory stage, and esoteric methods which are still in the investigational stage (radix representation).

The reader should have an understanding of basic logical design. The work is intended for practicing engineers or logical designers in the computer field or those who have completed a course in computer design. One who has diligently read *Computer Logic* should be prepared for this book.

In Chapter 1 some of the principles of logical design are reviewed and my methodology for such design is discussed. Also, some of the pros and cons of alternate methods are presented. The chapter ends with a discussion of symbols.

Next, in Chapters 2 and 3, various binary representations for signed numbers are examined together with an outline of how arithmetic is performed using these notations. The reader may not be able to absorb all this material at one sitting but may find it a useful reference in coping with unfamiliar representations.

The adder is fundamental to the arithmetic unit; therefore, three chapters are devoted to a thorough discussion of the presently available fast adders. Both the carry lookahead and the conditional sum adders are of such complexity that a full chapter is devoted to each. In Chapter 7 a typical adder is incorporated in the design of a complete, simple parallel arithmetic unit. This allows the reader to see the big picture before jumping into multiplication and division.

The next few chapters go into detail to develop the algorithms necessary for multiplication and division; the rationale behind the algorithms is thoroughly presented. From these algorithms, typical multiplication and division functional units are built up. For the first time, a complete comparison of hardware and timing is presented for these methods of multiplication and division.

In Chapters 15 and 16, I develop the algorithms necessary to perform floating-point arithmetic. Although rapidly replacing all other kinds, references to this topic, especially its design aspects, are almost nonexistent in the present comparative literature. The problems of constructing and designing floating-point hardware, as they apply to the several alternatives available to the arithmetic unit designer, are discussed in these chapters.

Often, special-purpose function generators could perform special operations in less time than conventional arithmetic units. Although these require more hardware, such functions are occasionally incorporated in special-purpose machines where the particular function is frequently required. Two such functions are presented in Chapter 17. Although the square-root operation has been discussed briefly in the literature, no one, to my knowledge, has discussed a polynomial evaluator. Since this is an operation frequently requiring a mathematical analysis, it may find use in future general-purpose computers.

Residue or radix arithmetic, covered in Chapter 18, is a fairly new concept in the computer field, although it is familiar to mathematicians who specialize in number theory. Since carry propagation is virtually eliminated, this is an attractive method of computer design, provided other obstacles can be eliminated.

Nothing is said in this text of the relation of the arithmetic unit or, less specifically, the computer, to the problem to be solved. The two are related by the program, of course. How the program, the computer, and the software are related is the topic for at least one other book which I am currently writing.

A group of my friends have helped me in writing *The Logic of Computer Arithmetic*. They have read and reread the manuscript, making innumerable comments and suggestions so that it might be readable. I wish to express my appreciation to André Godefroy, Burton Walder, Saul Teichman, Julian Reitman, Alvin Brooks, Leon Steiner, and Ralph Townsend. High praises are also in order to my secretary, Mrs. Patricia Maestri, for her efficiency and intelligence. My thanks also go to Chester Abend for his fine cover and jacket design.

IVAN FLORES

CONTENTS

ix

The Logic of COMPUTER

ARITHMETIC

1

INTRODUCTION

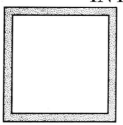

1.1 COMPUTER SYSTEM STRUCTURE

The System Hierarchy

The purpose of a computer system is to solve a problem or a class of problems. The approach of the atomist is to completely comprehend the function of the components and the wires that connect them. From this he can determine how any system or supersystem works. This approach is too much for me. I prefer to look at a problem by building up larger and larger units in intermediate steps. The old approach of Aristotle of analysis followed by synthesis still seems to contain quite a bit of wisdom.

Figure 1.1.1 shows how larger and larger units are assembled from the tinier building blocks, the components. The components are interconnected with wire, of course, and larger units are assembled, so that we go from circuits to large computer systems and even supersystems.

The Supersystem

The supersystem consists of a general problem class. These problems are comprehended by one or more computing devices. In addition, other data-handling, transmitting, and receiving devices are included. Such supersystems are best discussed by examining some examples.

1

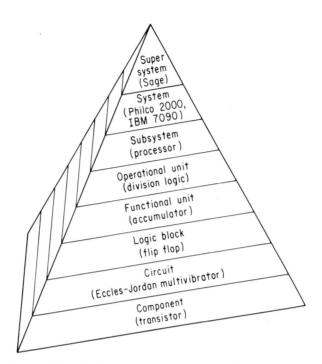

FIGURE 1.1.1 Building larger computer units (apex) from
smaller ones (base). Examples are in parentheses

sage

Most technical people are aware of the original data-processing system
set up to alert us of an impending enemy attack. This system, entitled
SAGE (Semi-Atomatic Ground Environment), was used to relay information about approaching aircraft which might endanger our country from
far distant points to a central point where a computer was stationed.
This computer took cognizance of all events relating to air security.
It matched these events against criteria and determined whether and what
friendly aircraft should be alerted to intercept or monitor the unknown
aircraft. SAGE is a data-processing system surrounded by a number of
other devices and humans. The goal of the entire system is clear. In this
particular supersystem the computer is approximately equal in stature to
the other components of the supersystem.

process control

In the small type of supersystem used for processing, the computer
monitors an on-going process. It receives information from a manu-

facturing process, chemical or mechanical, relates this to control criteria, and transmits information to controllers which effect changes in the processing so that the end product is of the required uniformity. In such a supersystem the computer may be minor in comparison to the elaborate control equipment required.

payroll system

A payroll system is also a supersystem. Consider the human employees who create the information regarding the payroll. The amount of time which they work is recorded in some fashion on a time record. This time record may contain information about production rather than time, but in any case it is a document upon which earnings are based. The rules for payment are incorporated in the computer which then produces the output documents—the paychecks—which are returned to the employee to complete the loop. The supersystem must make elaborate provisions to accommodate the many changes which take place. These changes consist of employees who leave the concern, new employees who join the firm, changes in wages which occur frequently, changes in deduction status due to marriage, birth, and death, and changes in the rules which occur within the organization are also due to givernmental changes in tax structure or in reporting procedures.

The System

The computer system is thoroughly discussed in most introductory computer texts. The arrangement of Figure 1.1.2 applies to the configuration of the subsystems within the system. In general, computer systems are configurated as in Figure 1.1.2. The differences among computers consist in subsystem capabilities and layout. It should be remembered that multiple subsystems are possible in most computer systems.

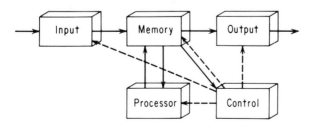

FIGURE 1.1.2 Subsystem arrangement in the computer system

Subsystems—System Components

To reiterate, each subsystem may appear in multiple. For instance, most computer systems include, as input subsystems, magnetic tape units, punched paper tape units, punched card units, and operator consoles. New input subsystems, such as magnetic cards, magnetic character readers, and optical character recognition devices, are becoming more prevalent.

The criteria for choice of any given subsystem are several: when high speed can be achieved, it must be weighed against cost; often special abilities are required; sometimes versatility of performance is a desired characteristic.

When interconnecting sybsystems, **buffering** is always a problem. We cannot expect speeds and capacities of subsystems to be immediately comparable. To allow for these discrepancies, buffer units are interposed. These compensate for the differences in speed or capacity.

1.2 SUBSYSTEM STRUCTURE

The subsystem consists of operational units which are logically interconnected.

Operational Units

The performance of the subsystem can be broken down into operations. These operations can usually be localized to the function of an **operational unit**. As an example, consider the control unit. Its function may be broken down into many operations. Among these are the fetch operation wherein the command to be executed next is procured from the memory unit. Another operation which can be localized is the index operation where the operand address is modified, when necessary, before the operand is obtained from memory.

In a similar fashion, processing may be broken down into operational processes such as arithmetic and editing. Most of this book, of course, is devoted to the operational unit known as the **arithmetic unit**.

In most computers we are able to discriminate between the different operational units; however, functions are frequently shared by operational and functional units. The extent to which this occurs is a function of many factors in computer design,

1. Variety of functions performed.
2. Restriction of problem classification.
3. Asynchronism.
4. Function-sharing among operational units.

Operational units are made from functional units which are inter-connected by logic. We could go down the line in Figure 1.1.1 and even-tually get to the bottom, the components. Instead of proceeding in that direction, it will be more informative to proceed upward from the com-ponent level at this point.

Components

Once we have an operational unit in view, we are in a position to assemble it from smaller units. The very smallest items are the com-ponents. These are of three types: simple interconnections or wiring; passive elements such as resistors, capacitors, and inductances; and active elements used as energy sources or sinks. Another category of components is most important in the computer field; these are storage elements of various types. These include magnetic cores, magnetic films, electrostatic elements, and virtually anything which will store energy for later reference. These components are important only insofar as they perform logical storage and time-binding functions. They must be in-corporated into circuits to do so.

Circuits

Circuits fall into several categories. There are the logical circuits which perform the work, set up by the logical designer, to exercise a function required by the computer. These logical circuits are, of course, the &-gates and the ∨-mixers or other logical functions required by the logical de-signer. The &-gate is a multi-input block for which the single output is activated only when *all* inputs are activated; the ∨-mixer is a similar block which produces an output when *any* input is present.

Then there are storage circuits where the smallest atom of information may be placed for future reference—the bit storage device discussed in Section 1.5. Similar circuits are used to offset information in time—these are delay circuits.

Another category of circuits consists of those which provide nonlogical functions. They assure that information in the form of electrical pulses is shaped correctly. Thus, amplifiers are used to assure pulses of correct amplitude; shapers are used to produce pulses of the proper length; delays are used to assure the pulses occurring at the proper time. Since circuits are connected one to the other, matching is an important factor.

Although there are many exceptions, it is usually possible for the logical designer to ignore the questions posed by circuitry, at least in the earliest phases of logical design.

Logical Blocks

Logical blocks perform logical functions without regard to circuit considerations. Of course, certain rules must be observed in interconnecting these blocks so that a given block may be connected to a limited number of other blocks. Even this consideration may be disregarded, in the strict sense of logical design, as long as a later design stage is provided whereby amplifiers or other appropriate circuits may be inserted between these blocks.

We assume in this book, in order to simplify the discussion, that the logical designer can manipulate logical blocks as he chooses with utter disregard to the following factors:

1. Energy gain or loss.
2. Signal amplitude degradation.
3. Shape degradation.
4. Signal polarity.
5. Impedance matching.
6. Driving capabilities.
7. Capabilities for being driven.

Functional Units

Combinations of logical blocks, as described above, can be made which perform specific functions required in the computer and are called **functional units**. Such functions have already been treated in *Computer Logic.** For instance, an encoder is a functional unit which translates information in baseless form into binary, binary-coded decimal, or other coded form. A decoder provides the reverse function. A full adder performs addition of two binary digits, taking into consideration the carry from the previous stage. A comparator determines which piece of coded information is of the larger magnitude. This usage should now be familiar to the reader.

---

* Ivan Flores, *Computer logic: the functional design of digital computers* (Englewood Cliffs, N. J.: Prentice-Hall, Inc., 1960).

1.3 PROCESSING AND ARITHMETIC

The Processing Subsystem

The **processing subsystem** is sometimes referred to by the computer manufacturer as a processor or **processing unit**. It usually contains two subsystems: the first of these performs the control function and the other processes information. Processing consists of performing arithmetic, editing and formating information, performing comparisons, and making decisions which affect the future behavior of the computer. All of these processing functions are important. In this volume, we are primarily concerned with arithmetic.

The Arithmetic Unit

A block diagram of a portion of the computer is shown in Figure 1.3. The bottom section of this diagram is referred to as the arithmetic unit; it performs several functions. It receives the data, transmitted under the

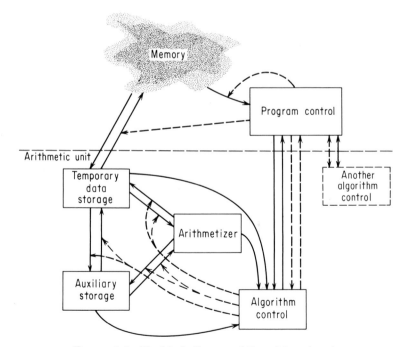

FIGURE 1.3   The block diagram of the arithmetic unit

supervision of the control unit, which is to be processed. It receives a processing specification, also as directed by the control unit. This specification determines how arithmetic will be performed by it. In so doing, the control unit selects an algorithm control unit which will operate autonomously when so directed by the control unit.

The reader may wonder how the name algorithm control arose. "Algorithm" is the name used by the mathematician to describe a set of numerical procedures by which a given result is obtained from given operands. The **algorithm control unit** is the unit which supervises the activity indicated in the procedures set forth in the algorithm.

When the arithmetic unit has completed its activities, the main control unit is signaled by the algorithm control unit. The main control unit is then at liberty to return the answer to the section of memory specified by the computer program.

Makeup of the Arithmetic Unit

The arithmetic unit contains a number of registers which contain the operands, intermediate results, and the final result. Several algorithm control units are provided, one for each process to be carried on by the arithmetic unit.

Auxiliary information units are used for many purposes. They summarize intermediate results such as a sign of a product. They indicate the relative timing of the present moment to the chain of events in progress. They summarize the state of affairs of intermediate results. They store things which have yet to be done.

Another unit is required to perform actual processing. This unit, which is usually an **adder**, takes one or more pieces of information and converts it into another piece of information. This translation process must be distinguished from data transfer. This is one of the few places in the computer where parity checks are no longer valid. Information is being transformed and parity is not an adequate means for checking.

The Algorithm Control Unit

Each algorithm control unit is, in truth, a miniature control unit: it is autonomous. Its purpose is to direct the flow and conversion of information within the arithmetic unit by using a wired-in procedure—the algorithm. In so doing, it refers to auxiliary storage devices mentioned above. It also sets these devices according to the progress of the process which it is directing.

There is no denying that it is possible to vastly increase the number of commands available by storing in memory different "wiring tables" corresponding to different algorithms. This has been done in the militarized computer made by Thompson Ramo-Wooldridge, Inc., the AN/UYK–1. Since the benefits of this concept remain to be demonstrated, we restrict our discussion to permanent logic.

Study of the Arithmetic Unit

To begin our study of the arithmetic unit, we assume that certain information has already been supplied; that is, the algorithm control unit has been set in motion by having specified to it the process which it is about to direct. The operands have been delivered to the appropriate registers. A ready signal has been given. Provisions have been made for the results to be retrieved from the arithmetic unit when they are posted as available.

We will investigate the numerical procedures by which the desired results may be obtained. We will set up one of a few possible configurations by which the results may be obtained. This means the type of registers for operands, auxiliary results, and final results will be specified, as will their interconnections. Provisions will also be made for auxiliary results.

We are then ready to determine the general data flow. Repetitive processes may be performed with one or another condition prevailing. The flow of information will be indicated according to the conditions prevailing.

Next we can set up, in words, the auxiliary and control conditions which apply. It is then a simple matter to convert from words to equations. It then remains only to convert the equations into hardware logic.

Scope of this Volume

Obviously, arithmetic unit design is the objective of this work. Such a unit can be designed with one of several objectives in mind. If cost is the main obstacle, simplicity results and speed is sacrificed. If speed is paramount and cost is no obstacle, it may be achieved by two methods.

Decreasing the response time of the building blocks by using more expensive components will fulfill the aim. There is a state-of-the-art limit to this procedure where no further expense produces a time reduction.

Changing the organization of the arithmetic unit can also afford an improvement. It is then necessary to take several simultaneous actions upon the participants in the arithmetic process. Hence, compound decisions are required which, in turn, impose a more complex organization upon the arithmetic unit.

We are not concerned with affecting the speed of the building blocks. This is a matter of improving components and circuits and is a specialty unto itself. Given the building blocks, what alternatives are available for the organization of the arithmetic section and what are the trade-offs?

Serial organization requires only one full adder for binary or one digit adder for binary coded decimal and so entails less expense than the parallel organization. Detailed discussion of this kind of logic abounds.

For given block speeds, the fastest arithmetic is done by parallel organization, not by serial or hybrid (serial-parallel) organization. By adding more logic for more complex decision and action, speed can be increased. Here, too, there is a limit. We investigate how to improve speed by organization and what the limiting factors are.

The most efficient representation of numerical information is binary. Most of the fastest scientific computers use a binary representation. Therefore, the principles discussed here are in terms of a binary machine. The extension to decimal machines and even to serial or hybrid machines should be well within the capability of the reader when he finishes this volume.

1.4   LOGICAL DESIGN

The Logical Design Program

The purpose of logical design is to bring the design of the subsystem from a simple sketch to a state where the relative position of each fundamental logical block is prescribed. Usually, this is continued further, to the point where each module is specified, assigned a number, and given a physical location on a physical chassis. This stage would include enumeration of all interconnections between the modules. The term **module** refers to one or more logical blocks in physical juxtaposition within a small detachable unit. The contents of a given module depends upon the designer and manufacturer. Some modules contain only one or two logical blocks in a small unit, such as those used by Philco in their Model 212 computer; others have ten, twenty, or more logical blocks, as in the Honeywell 800. Some designers use small modules, placing them on a large "mother" board which is also detachable from the main hardware.

The province of the logical design group differs from one organization to another; this difference occurs in several areas. The first is the extent to which logical design is performed, that is, how much system design is performed by the group and how much of the job of converting the logical description into physical hardware is performed by the group. Another facet is the amount of detail evolved by the logical design group. Frequently, some of the detail is left either to a manufacturing design group, or, when this phase has been automated, programmers can frequently perform hardware layout with the aid of a large digital computer. Another point of difference among groups is the extent to which Boolean equations are depended upon and the phase of logical design during which they are incorporated. Despite the argument which may have existed between the Eastern and the Western schools of logical design, it is evident that both schools use both an equation approach and a block-diagram approach. It is only the extent and the time factor which distinguishes these schools of thought.

Design Philosophy

We now discuss the essential steps in logical design. First these steps are enumerated, then each one in turn is discussed in greater detail.

1. A preliminary operational and functional configuration is constructed as a jumping-off point, with the understanding that it may change radically during future developments.
2. The sequence of events which occurs in the subsystem under inspection is carefully examined, and a preliminary timing plan is evolved.
3. The set of units which are required and the sequence in which they are activated are examined with emphasis upon the dependency of one upon the other.
4. A set of logic-time equations is generated.
5. The requirements for auxiliary logical devices apart from the main functional units are listed.
6. Boolean equations are written for each and every functional unit not already specified.
7. Hardware equations are derived and the hardware configuration is planned.

The System Configuration

The layout of the subsystem depends most intimately on the system specification. The subsystem does not exist in isolation but, rather, in symbiosis with the system for which it was designed. The subsystem specification is usually generated during or just after the system specification is determined. Such a specification indicates the time and quanity of information to be processed by the subsystem as well as other details of the process.

One of the most important areas to consider is the interface between the subsystem and other subsystems within the system. How is information transmitted to and from *this* subsystem? How is the processing of information controlled? If the subsystem control is autonomous, the means by which control is transferred from another subsystem to this subsystem must be specified as well as the means by which main control is relinquished. Timing is always of importance when units are talking together; the conversion must not only be comprehensible to both units, but it must occur when the computers have time to "listen" to each others' message!

Before further design commences, the algorithms by which processing is performed must be investigated and the proper ones specified. This is obvious for the arithmetic unit. Comparable to algorithms, other subsystems have organizing principles which set forth the interrelation of the functional units. For instance, for the control unit we concern ourselves with the method by which sequential instructions are procured, how indexing is performed, how operands are fetched, how instructions are decoded and delegated, and so forth. The algorithm or organizational principles must be set forth before the quantity and relation among the functional units can be specified.

The Functional Units

The type and internal organization of the functional units depend upon many factors related to data and control:

1. What is the format of the data as it enters and leaves the subsystem and during processing by the subsystem?
2. Is serial, parallel, or a combination of the two the method by which data is handled?
3. What kind of processing is required at the various stages?
4. How is the timing of the functional unit initiated, maintained, and terminated?
5. What means is used to control the processing and the flow of information among the functional units?
6. The design experience of the logical design group undoubtedly affects to a large extent the choice of the functional units used by that group in their design.

Having chosen the functional units, they must be interrelated. This process is governed by the algorithm or the organizing principle of the subsystem. It is also affected by other considerations such as

1. Speed.
2. Other system specifications.
3. The interfaces.
4. Economy.
5. The ability and past history of the design group.

The Event Sequence

The sequence in which events take place is primarily determined by the algorithm or organizational principle. At this stage of the game, we should be able to determine how data flows among the various functional units. Usually, data is held in registers (temporary storage devices), therefore these are the units with which we will be most concerned. However, we wish to consider when the other functional units will be occupied. Events will take place in two realms—time and space. Thus, we associate, with each event, a place (or functional unit) and a time in the subsystem history at which it is taking place.

Frequently, events will take place conditionally in the sense that their nature is determined by other events which may have preceded them. Thus, in multiplication an addition is performed upon the sum-so-far in some cases if a 1 appears as the multiplier bit; another action such as a shift takes place if this bit is a 0 instead.

A list of events and alternative actions is necessary. However, a visual aid, a flow diagram of the activities, usually clarifies the designer's understanding of the subsystem requirements. Such flow diagrams are used in explaining arithmetic and control in many introductory texts including *Computer Logic*; this device will be resorted to in the future when the complexity of the system structure is such as to warrant it.

Logic-Time Equations

One policy we might adopt is to express time with respect to the initiation of the subsystem. Usually the start pulse, ST, is the handy little reference. A later time, $T1$, is indicated by

$$T1 = \Delta ST \tag{1.4.1}$$

A later time than $T1$ would be indicated by $T2$,

$$T2 = \Delta T1 \tag{1.4.2}$$

and so forth.

From the configuration, the functional requirements, and the event sequence, we are now able to specify for each functional unit its inputs by referring to:

1. Data entering the given unit—whether a bit is 0 or 1.
2. Control equations—information in the form of control voltages from one or more control units.
3. Time as indicated above.
4. Auxiliary settings—data or control information is frequently distilled into the setting of specific auxiliary devices which are referred to in controlling given functional units.
5. Algorithm in progress—this is necessary when a unit performs one or more procedures.

A given functional unit relates the inputs in a way characteristic to it and thus produces an output. This output can be expressed as a Boolean equation involving time and the specific inputs.

Auxiliary Units

As touched on above, auxiliary storage units may distill a large amount of information into a single setting. A unit may refer to control information, intermediate results, and a time factor, and compress these into one or a few settings. Similar to the functional unit, the auxiliary unit has an equation which specifies its input in terms of data, control, and time. When such units are bistable devices, specifying its two inputs indicates when each of its mutually exclusive states prevails.

In some cases such auxiliary devices may be time-shared; that is, they may be used to store several auxiliary functions at different times within the operating sequence of the subsystem.

Boolean Equations

Each functional unit has a Boolean equation which describes its characteristic. The logical designer working on a complicated subsystem deals most frequently with functional units which are already fixed and hence have specific Boolean equations. These units may be described either by their function or by their equation. In addition, he must make up some special purpose, functional units; in that case, a description in Boolean equation form is usually preferable. Such an equation, together with a Karnaugh map, provides simplification not immediately apparent in most other forms. The logic-time equations are occasionally amenable to simplifications after they have been put into the Boolean form. Such equations arise throughout, especially in connection with the auxiliary units, but also in connection with the control processing and auxiliary processing units.

Hardware Phase

Once the subsystem has been specified, as described in the previous subsections, we are ready to pass into what frequently consists of a separate phase. This phase converts the paper which is specifying a system into paper which is specifying a machine layout. This is done in several subphases. The Boolean equations and logic-time equations have to be converted into available logic-block form. The logic-block form may require rewriting, especially if we are converting from ∨, & logic into **Nor** logic. This conversion process must heed the **fan-in** and **fan-out** precautions relative to each logic block. The fan-in is the maximum number of circuits which may drive a given block; the fan-out is the maximum number of circuits which the given block may drive. The logic thus generated may require the addition of nonlogical elements. Thus, when a logic block is required to drive more than its allowable fan-out, this may be achieved by inserting an amplifier between this block and the one that it drives.

After this conversion, another look should be made to see if simplifications can be made to reduce the design in its new form. Now we must convert from blocks to modules. A module comprises several similar or dissimilar blocks. The blocks must be assigned to specific modules with an allotment for spares which inevitably are required.

Along with the module assignment is the module arrangement. The geometric arrangement of the modules on the backboard is of crucial importance when we get into the area of very high-speed computers. The difference in delay incurred by transmitting some pulses over a few feet of wire while others travel only a few inches may be enough to jeopardize the proper functioning of the subsystem. Some work has been done on this topological problem, but much more should be done in the future to develop an effective science of module placement.

The final step in the hardware phase is the pin assignment for each module and the wiring layout which indicates where each wire of the computer begins and ends and how long it should be. From this information, cable layouts can be made and the wiring done.

1.5 SYMBOLS

This section is especially for those who have passed the novice grade and have not found it necessary to read or refer to *Computer Logic*. The original choice of symbols for *Computer Logic* arose from an attempt to predict a set of symbols which would become the convention for the field. However, the committee that suggested these symbols for adoption did not prove successful and at present there are still no universally accepted standards. For consistency, we will continue to use the symbols presented in the first volume. The total set of symbols used here is displayed in Figure 1.5.

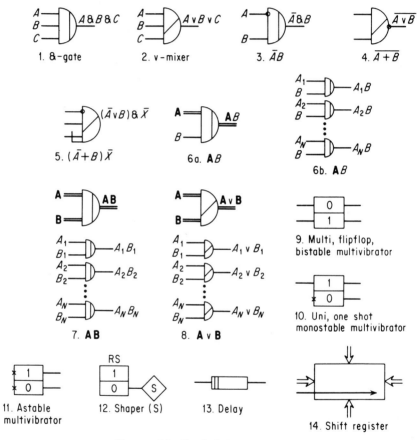

FIGURE 1.5 Symbols for logic design

Gates and Mixers

D-**symbols** are used throughout for combinatorial logic. Inputs to the D-symbol are always on the flat side; the output is taken from the semi-circular side. The multiple input &-**gate** is indicated as in Figure 1.5.1.

There it is seen that the &-function is designated by drawing a line within the D parallel to the input entry line, the diameter of the semi-circle, and spacing this line about two-thirds away from the diameter. The multiple input ∨-**mixer** is indicated, as in Figure 1.5.2, by a diagonal line oblique to the diameter. **Inversion** is indicated by a small circle at the termination of an input line or at the start of an output line. Examples are found in Figures 1.5.3 and 1.5.4. The **inhibit function** is indicated as shown in Figure 1.5.5.

Notice that for the D-symbols no directional arrows are required since signals *enter* the D-symbol only at the diameter and leave only at the side opposite.

The Boolean connective *and* is symbolized by the ampersand, &. It is defined by a truth table where A & B *is true* only when A *is true and* B *is true*. The Boolean connective *or* is symbolized by "vel" or inclusive *or*, ∨. It is defined by a truth table where A ∨ B is true for all entries *except* when A *is false and* B *is false*. The overbar is used to deny a variable (the *not* function); thus, $\bar{A}$ *is true* only when A *is false*.

A hardware block which performs a logical function is refered to in the text by the proper symbol followed by a numerical designation: &6 refers to a block which performs *and* and is designated 6; 15 is a denial block designated as 15; a block performing both negation and conjunction is indicated by a "primed" ampersand, &'23.

In dealing with multiple logical devices so common in parallel processing, we have adopted the pipeline notation. First consider a number of parallel signals indicated by the use of bold type as **A**. If all of these are gated by single signal B, the logical symbol and its equivalent are indicated in Figure 1.5.6. When multiple signals gate multiple signals this is indicated as in Figure 1.5.7 where the inputs **A** and **B** are gated by the compound &-block shown there. Finally, multiple signals can be mixed in a similar fashion, as shown in Figure 1.5.8.

Bit Storage

Devices which store single bits of information are called **bit storage devices**. They are also commonly referred to as **flip-flops**, **bi-stable multivibrators**, or simply **multis**. My symbol for the bit storage device is found in Figure 1.5.9. Note several aspects of this symbol. It may seem confusing at first that no arrows are shown. Since the symbol is not used in a vacuum, however, signals entering the device will have their direction indicated by their source; those leaving the device will have their direction indicated by their termination. Only when the source or destination lies off the paper are arrowheads necessary. The bit storage symbol is independent of the circuitry used and the polarity of the signals manipulated. For instance, when the line entering the bit storage device at the one input contains a pulse signal, it will cause the device to change state or remain in its present state, depending on its present condition and provided that the signal is of the proper amplitude and duration (this always being assumed here). We attach the output wire corresponding to the 1-state to the terminal of the device which yields the signal polarity that we desire. This requires that the other terminal be of the opposite polarity. It also requires that a signal which resets the device to its 0-state will cause the one output to become reversed.

The **uni**, **single shot** or **delay flip-flop** is shown in Figure 1.5.10. This device can be set to the 1-state by an incoming signal. After a fixed period of time, it resets itself to the alternate state. Arbitrarily, we say that *the signal* sets it to the *1-state* and then *it resets* itself *to 0*. Therefore, all inputs to the device enter the 1 half-box; the 0 half-box has an X at its input to indicate that no input is required here—that the uni resets without intervention. Where a time constant is explicitly required, it is placed close to the box to which it applies.

The **astable multi-vibrator** or **pulse generator** is a flip-flop which is self-triggering. It is indicated in Figure 1.5.11 where both input X's are in corresponding half-boxes to show that no input signal is supplied.

Shaper

The **shaper** is attached to a bit storage device to recover a pulse when the bit storage device switches to a given state, Figure 1.5.12. When the bit storage device is set to 1 by a pulse, there is no output from the shaper, S; when RS is reset to 0 a pulse is emitted from S such that the pulse front of the pulse emitted from S corresponds to the time at which RS assumes the 0-state.

Delay

The symbol for **delay** is shown in Figure 1.5.13. Any signal at the input (the left-hand side of the symbol as shown) appears at the output in exactly the same form but delayed a fixed length of time according to the parameter associated with the delay symbol. In my approach to logical design, I have omitted all references to amplifiers and like circuits. Thus it is assumed that the designer will compensate for any attenuation and distortion presented by the delay by incorporating the required circuitry, although the symbols for such additional circuits are omitted throughout.

Registers

The **register** symbol is found in Figure 1.5.14. The directed pipelines indicate inputs and outputs, both series and parallel, whose direction is determined by the associated arrowheads. A single line which enters the box and has attached an arrowhead within the box indicates that this is the means by which the register is set to the incoming signal.

It is unnecessary to dwell on the register symbol since we will elaborate upon it to a large extent in Section 4.1.

2

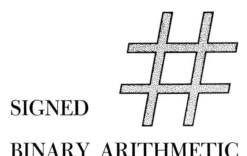

SIGNED

BINARY ARITHMETIC

2.1 INTRODUCTION

Unfortunately, some things just have to be learned by rote. Remember the arithmetic tables, "Two times two is four, two times three is six, $\cdots$"? Well, this chapter is devoted to arithmetic in various notations. Although they do not have to be learned by heart, still the rules that apply to them have to be understood in depth.

The chapters which follow develop the methods by which Arithmetic Units of various extant computers perform arithmetic. These methods, numerical manipulations, founded upon mathematical justification and realized in hardware, are called **algorithms**.* Naturally, the correctness of any algorithm depends on the representation of the numbers and form of the desired result.

In the first section of this chapter, the three main representations for signed numbers are explained. A design group must decide which of these representations is best suited to the computer under consideration. There is no immediate clear-cut choice; there are advantages and disadvantages to each representation; each is used as the basis for at least one machine. Although some of the newer machines have chosen 2's complement nota-

---

* I use the term in this seemingly broad way. Actually, Webster's present definition is even broader and, referring to a treatise by al-Khurar-izmi, applies to the study of *decimal* arithmetic.

tion, it should not be concluded that this notation should now be used universally. On the contrary, often the choice is made solely on the basis of compatability of the machine being designed with the previous product of the manufacturer.

To contrast the representations of signed numbers requires an understanding of how arithmetic is done in each, and this is presented in this and the next chapter.

Although three representations are presented here, for brevity, chapters on high-speed arithmetic are based entirely on 2's complement notation. It will best serve the reader's need to comprehend the workings of the representations presenting the most hardware problems—then he should certainly understand the others! The tools, in the form of comprehension and use of the different representations, are furnished here to enable the reader to complete a design using any of them.

Besides developing a comprehension of available representations, the reader may gain two things more from these chapters:

1. A reference for later chapters. For instance, in discussing high-speed multiplication of two negative 2's complement numbers using Method 2, Figure 3.3.5 may be used as an example and page 55 gives a step-by-step description of what occurs there.

2. Practice in thinking in binary. Following each example, although a chore, is amazingly helpful in that respect. The first few examples will demand intensive concentration, but, near the close of the chapter, things fall into place and soon the problems can be worked without referring to the book.

Since Chapters 15 and 16 are devoted to floating-point arithmetic, expansion of binary notation to floating-point numbers is tabled until then. Suffice it to say that the conventions established here are applicable and need only be extended.

2.2   REPRESENTATIONS

Introduction

The discussion of arithmetic and of binary numbers, found in Chapters 6 and 7 of *Computer Logic*, was confined to the sign and magnitude notation. In the sign and magnitude notation, numbers which have the same absolute value are represented identically, except for the sign position. There are other representations for negative numbers which provide a greater facility of manipulation when performing arithmetic; such representations are frequently used in current computers. Therefore, it is appropriate to study how arithmetic is performed using these other notations. Also, since an understanding of these representations is basic to the comprehension of how computers perform fast arithmetic, it must be acquired before we discuss the logic of high-speed arithmetic.

Binary Point

The binary point is implicit in the manipulation of numbers in most modern computers. It is the same as a decimal point in every-day notation, except that it applies to binary numbers. That is, it separates a number into a whole part and a fraction; the whole part is to the left of the binary point and the fraction is to the right.

The conventions in many modern computers, as we will see later, requires that all numbers handled internally by the computer be less than unity; therefore, these numbers are proper binary fractions. Hence, we might expect that the position to the left of the binary point would always contain 0. However, this position is used to indicate the sign of the number and therefore may contain 0 or 1, according to the sign of the number represented. Customarily, a 0 indicates a positive number and a 1 a negative number.

Using these conventions, all numbers consist of a sign bit at the left, followed (proceeding to the right) by a binary point, and then a number of bits which determine the magnitude of the number. One objection to the binary point notation is that, in reality, the computer can only manipulate truth values or binary information. Since this binary information is limited in extent, it can be said to correspond to a limited range of integers, a subset of the numbers of counting with a sign associated. Consequently, the binary point representation might easily make fractions seen to be acceptable numbers when only a *small range* of fractions are acceptable to the computer. However, there are advantages which might outweigh the disadvantages mentioned above: this notation permits one to keep track of numbers easily during discussion; it facilitates scaling during programming; and it provides a left-hand-oriented system, which is of advantage in high-speed division, for instance. An automatic signle-bit rough approximation of the comparative size of two numbers is thus available.

Let us adopt the binary point notation, and from here on we will consider that all numbers are less than one, that the sign indication is at the left-hand bit of the computer word, and that the binary point is just to the right of the sign bit. A negative number has a 1 in the sign position and a positive number contains a 0 in the sign position.

note

In this section and those that follow, upper-case letters indicate the signed number under discussion, and lower-case letters indicate magnitude. Thus we say $a = |A|$ where $-1 \leq A < +1$.

Also note that "$\simeq$" in this chapter is used to convey "is represented by."

Sign and Magnitude Notation

In the sign and magnitude notation, numbers of the same magnitude are identical to the right of the binary point; they differ only in the sign bit. Thus,

$$+26(2^{-5}) \simeq 0.11010 \tag{2.2.1}$$

$$-26(2^{-5}) \simeq 1.11010 \tag{2.2.2}$$

1's Complement Notation

A positive number in 1's complement notation is identical with its form in the sign and magnitude notation. In fact, in the three systems discussed, positive numbers are represented identically. To form the representation of a negative number in 1's complement notation, we subtract the magnitude of the number from W, where we define W as the largest numerical word that can be stored in a one-word register (ignoring the sign bit).

In practice, this means that negative and positive numbers of equal magnitude in the 1's complement notation are exact complements of each other. That is, wherever a 1 appears in the first number, including the sign position, a 0 appears in its negative counterpart, and vice versa. Thus,

$$+26(2^{-5}) \simeq 0.11010 \tag{2.2.3}$$

$$-26(2^{-5}) \simeq 1.00101 \tag{2.2.4}$$

Another way to look at this in mathematical terms is to define the value of the least significant bit of the computer word, e, in terms of the largest computer word W:

$$e = 1 - W \tag{2.2.5}$$

Then,

$$W = 1 - e = 1 - 2^{-N} \tag{2.2.6}$$

where there are N numerical bits in the computer word. Also,

$$e = 2^{-N} \qquad (2.2.7)$$

For the five-bit case above, $W = 0.11111$. We can then say that the negative number, $-a$, is represented as

$$-a \simeq 2 - a - e \qquad (2.2.8)$$

Any number and its complement, when added together, will equal $1 + W$ ($1.1111\cdots11$). This means that two numbers of the same magnitude but opposite sign, when added together, will form a word consisting entirely of 1's. We must therefore additionally adopt the convention that the word $1 + W$ is equal to 0 (since the sum of a number and its complement is 0).

2's Complement Notation

Again, positive numbers are represented in the same form as that discussed under sign and magnitude notation. A negative number is formed by taking its positive counterpart and subtracting it from 2. We then have

$$+26(2^{-5}) \simeq 0.11010 \qquad (2.2.9)$$

$$-26(2^{-5}) \simeq 1.00110 \qquad (2.2.10)$$

When a number and its complement are added together, naturally, they will sum to 2. Since this exceeds the word size of the register, it will be stored there in the form of all 0's, which is desirable.

A simple rule for finding the 2's complement is: find the 1's complement and add e. Truly it is quite simple but requires an addition. An alternate rule, especially applicable to multiply and divide where serial right-to-left examination is done anyway, is:

Starting at the right, examine bits of the positive number in turn. For each 0 in the positive number place a 0 in its negative counterpart. When the first 1 is reached, place a 1 in the negative counterpart. Thereafter, for each 0, place a 1 in the negative quantity and for each 1 in the original word place a 0 in the negative quantity for all bits including the sign bit.

This method also works in converting negative numbers to their positive equivalents. For example, examine (2.29) and (2.2.10) above for that purpose. A negative number in 2's complement notation is given as

$$-a \simeq 2 - a \qquad (2.1.11)$$

Peculiarities

Each notation has peculiarities which are of interest to the user. These pertain to the largest and smallest number represented by each and the representation of 0. These peculiarities are summarized in Table 2.2.

TABLE 2.2 Peculiarities of binary notational systems

		Representation		
		Sign and Magnitude	*1's Complement*	*2's Complement*
Largest number	is	$0.11\cdots11$	$0.11\cdots11$	$0.11\cdots11$
	stands for	$1-e$	$1-e$	$1-e$
Smallest number	is	$1.11\cdots11$	$1.00\cdots00$	$1.00\cdots00$
	stands for	$-(1-e)$	$-(1-e)$	-1
Zero	$+$	$0.00\cdots00$	$0.00\cdots00$	$0.00\cdots00$
	$-$	$1.00\cdots00$	$1.11\cdots11$	(unsigned)

In some cases, it is convenient to have two representations for 0. Subtraction of a number from itself or the addition of a number to its complement may produce a bit combination not otherwise used. Therefore, this combination also may be used for 0. The resulting confusion is more than compensated for by the ease of handling this problem. In 2's complement, the 0 resulting from arithmetic is the same as the normal 0; namely, $0.00\cdots00$. Hence, only one 0 is required in this system.

largest number

In all systems the largest number is represented as $0.11\cdots11$ and is $1-e$ or $1-2^N$.

smallest number

It is clear that $-(1-e)$ is the smallest number represented in both the sign and magnitude and 1's complement notation. These take the form, respectively, of $1.00\cdots00$ and $1.11\cdots11$, corresponding in absolute values to the largest representable numbers.

In the 2's complement notation, the representation of $-(1-e)$ is $1.00\cdots01$. Subtracting e from this we have $1.00\cdots00$, which may be used to represent -1. Alternatively, we may use it to represent -0. Unfortunately, it is conventional to use $1.00\cdots00$ to represent -1 in the 2's complement notation. Although the convention solves some problems, like normalizing $-\frac{1}{2}$, it creates others. One problem is that the range of numbers for the 2's complement machine is then

$$-1 \leq X \leq 1 - e$$

instead of

$$-(1-e) \leq X \leq 1 - e$$

as for the other systems.

Hence, provision must be made to handle (or prevent) addition, subtraction, multiplication, and division for -1. Notice, for instance, that multiplication is closed for the numbers represented in sign and magnitude or 1's complement. That is, the product of any two numbers is a representable number. But for 2's complement we have $(-1) \times (-1) = +1$ and there is no representation for $+1$!

2.3 SIGN AND MAGNITUDE ADDITION

Positive Numbers

The addition of positive numbers is the same in all three notations. Addition is done in the conventional manner for binary numbers; see Figure 2.3. The one precaution to be observed is that the sum must not exceed 1. In that case, the sum of the numbers we are adding exceeds the word size of the register, W. The computer must detect this and prevent further computations using this number. Overflow detection by some computers automatically causes them to jump to a subroutine in the program to correct the error. Other computers, not automatically equipped, simply stop for operator intervention to remedy the condition. The sum of two positive numbers is then given as

$$A + B \simeq a + b \qquad a + b < 1, \quad A, B \geq 0 \qquad (2.3.1)$$

Negative Numbers

To add two negative numbers we add only their magnitudes, observing that the sign of the numbers being added is the same. We preserve the sign and place it in the sign position of the sum. Again, we must beware of numbers whose sum exceeds the numerical word size of the register.

				Notes
+13:	0.01101	−13:	1.01101	Add magnitudes
+11:	0.01011	−11:	1.01011	Duplicate sign
+24:	0.11000	−24:	1.11000	

1. *Positive Numbers*   2. *Negative Numbers*

+13:	0.01101	−13:	1.01101	
−11:	1.01011	+11:	0.01011	
+ 2:		− 2:		
	01101		01101	To augend magnitude
	10100		10100	Add addend complement magnitude
	00001		00001	End around carry occurs
	↳1		↳1	Add it to above
	00010		00010	
	0.00010		1.00010	Give result sign of augend

3. *Differently Signed—*
Augend Magnitude Larger

+11:	0.01011	−11:	1.01011	
−13:	1.01101	+13:	0.01101	
	01011		01011	To augend magnitude
	10010		10010	Add addend complement magnitude
	11101		11101	There's no end around carry
				Complement result
	1.00010		0.00010	Give it sign of addend

4. *Differently Signed*
Addend Magnitude Larger or Equal

FIGURE 2.3   Sign and magnitude addition
of fractions (thirty-seconds)

The sum of two negative numbers is then given as

$$A + B \simeq 1 + a + b \qquad a + b < 1, \quad A, B < 0 \qquad (2.3.2)$$

An example of such an addition is given in Figure 2.3.2.

Oppositely Signed Numbers

When the signs of the numbers to be added are different, the result and the procedure depend upon which is larger, the augend or the addend.

augend magnitude larger

First, examine a case where we have a positive augend larger, in absolute size, than the addend. We add the addend, in 1's complement form, to the augend, as in the examples given in Figure 2.3. This produces an end-around carry, which is added to the sum-so-far. The sign bit is that of the augend. The equation for this process is

$$A + B \simeq a + (1 - b - e) + e \qquad (2.3.3)$$

where a is the magnitude of A; $1 - b - e$ is the 1's complement of the magnitude of B; e is the number $0.0\cdots01$. How are you sure a carry occurs? Well, the complement of b is larger than the complement of a; hence, when the former is added to a, the result must be greater than 1. Now,

$$A + B \simeq 1 + a - b \qquad (2.3.4)$$

$$A + B \simeq a - b \ (\text{mod } 1) \qquad a > b, \quad A \geq 0, \quad B < 0 \qquad (2.3.5)$$

The carry from the sign position indicates to the computer that e should be added, which the computer then does. This is described more succinctly and less accurately as "adding in the end-around carry." Throughout the text we say "the carry is added" to mean "when the carry is detected e is added."

I use the notation "(mod 1)" to mean that, when the word size W of the register is exceeded, we use whatever is then contained in the register. That is, we add numbers into the numerical portion of the register and do not transmit carries, if they should occur, into the sign bit. This manipulation is defined as **addition modulo 1** and is recorded as in (2.3.5).

For a negative augend with magnitude larger than the addend, we perform addition as above. We take the 1's complement of the addend and add it to the augend. The end-around carry is added to the sum-so-far and the sign of the result is that of the augend. Here we have

$$A + B \simeq 1 + [a + (1 - b - e) + e] \ (\text{mod } 1) \qquad (2.3.6)$$

$$\simeq 1 + a - b \qquad a > b, \quad A < 0, \quad B \geq 0 \qquad (2.3.7)$$

addend magnitude larger

To add two numbers of different signs where the addend is larger than the augend, take the 1's complement of the addend and add it to the augend, as illustrated in the examples of Figure 2.3. The result should not produce a carry. Why? Because the result is negative and it is produced in the form of the 1's complement of the proper sum. In order to find the proper sum, we must take the 1's complement of the sum-so-far. The sign of the sum is that of the addend.

Let us see how this looks in equation form. For b larger than a and with A negative, B positive, we have

$$A + B \simeq 1 - [a + (1 - b - e) + e] \qquad (2.3.8)$$

$$\simeq b - a \qquad a < b, \quad A < 0, \quad B \geq 0 \qquad (2.3.9)$$

The parentheses enclose the 1's complement of the addend. The result inside the brackets is not correct; it must be complemented, which is indicated by subtracting the number in the brackets from 1.

For the case of b greater than a, A positive and B negative, we have

$$A + B \simeq 1 + [1 - \{a + (1 - b - e) + e\}] \qquad (2.3.10)$$

$$\simeq 1 + b - a \qquad a > b, \quad A \geq 0, \quad B < 0 \qquad (2.3.11)$$

The parentheses surround the 1's complement of the addend. The braces hold the sum of the augend, and the complement of the addend magnitude brackets indicate the complementation of the sum. Finally, 1 is added to form a negative number.

2.4 1's COMPLEMENT ADDITION

Both Positive

Two positive numbers are added in the same manner in all representations. Thus,

$$A + B \simeq a + b \qquad A, \quad B \geq 0 \qquad (2.4.1)$$

Both Negative

Two negative numbers are added as shown in Figure 2.4. All the bits of the numbers are added including the sign bit. The carry which must be

Notes

```
−13:  1.10010
−11:  1.10100          Add numbers including sign bit

      1.00110          There is end around carry
           1           Add it to result

−24:  1.00111
```

1. *Negative Numbers*

```
−13:  1.10010     +11:  0.01011     Add numbers including sign bit
+11:  0.01011     −13:  1.10010     No end around carry

− 2:  1.11101     − 2:  1.11101     Result remains correct
```

2. *Oppositely signed numbers,*
   negative result

```
+13:  0.01101     −11:  1.10100     Add numbers including sign bit
−11:  1.10100     +13:  0.01101

      0.00001           0.00001     There is end around carry
           1                1       Add it in

+ 2:  0.00010     + 2:  0.00010
```

3. *Oppositely signed numbers,*
   positive result

FIGURE 2.4   1's complement addition
of fractions (thirty-seconds)

produced is then added to the partial sum. The result should then be correct. Since both numbers are negative, they are shown as

$$A \simeq (2 - a - e) \tag{2.4.2}$$

$$B \simeq (2 - b - e) \tag{2.4.3}$$

Adding these numbers will definitely cause a carry from the sign position since, you recall, the register size is $1 + W$. The equations for adding two negative numbers are then

$$A + B \simeq [(2 - a - e) + (2 - b - e)] + e \ (\text{mod } 2) \qquad (2.4.3)$$

$$\simeq (4 - a - b - e) \ (\text{mod } 2) \qquad (2.4.4)$$

$$\simeq 2 - a - b - e \qquad a + b < 1 \qquad A, \quad B < 0 \qquad (2.4.5)$$

The expression "(mod 2)," above, indicates that the limit in the full register size (including the sign bit this time) has the effect of subtracting 2 from the partial sum. The final result should be a negative number, indicated by a 1 in the sign position. Care must be taken that $a + b$ is not greater than W; in that case, the result will appear incorrectly as a positive number. This discrepancy cannot be detected by observing the carryout from the sign position; rather, the carryout from the most significant bit of the sum must be monitored to be sure it occurs.

Oppositely Signed Numbers

To add numbers of different signs, the procedure depends, to some extent, on sign of the result. In any case, we add the number bit by bit, including the sign bit.

negative result

When the sign of the result is negative, no carry is produced. The result should then be correct, as illustrated in Figure 2.4. The equations for a negative result are as follows:

$$A + B \simeq (2 - a - e) + b \qquad (2.4.6)$$

$$\simeq 2 - a + b - e \qquad a > b, \quad A < 0, \quad B \geq 0 \qquad (2.4.7)$$

where A is negative, B is positive, and $a > b$. For A positive, B negative, and $b > a$,

$$A + B \simeq a + (2 - b - e) \qquad (2.4.8)$$

$$\simeq 2 + a - b - e \qquad a \leq b, \quad A \geq 0, \quad B < 0 \qquad (2.4.9)$$

positive result

To add two numbers where the result is positive, we add the numbers bit by bit, as above, including the sign bit. This time, a carry should be produced from the sign position and is added into the least significant position of the partial sum. The result, including the sign, should then be correct. (See Figure 2.4.) We have

$$A + B \simeq [(2 - a - e) + b + e] \pmod 2 \qquad (2.4.10)$$

$$\simeq (2 - a + b) \pmod 2 \qquad (2.4.11)$$

$$\simeq b - a \qquad a \leq b, \quad A < 0, \quad B \geq 0 \qquad (2.4.12)$$

where A is negative, B is positive, and $b \geq a$. "$(\mod 2)$" indicates that the size of the register has been exceeded and, therefore, 2 is automatically subtracted so that it reads the proper quantity. In other words, the representations are added together, and the result is stored in the register. In the addition, a carry occurs from the *sign* positions; this carry is disregarded. The result register now records a number which is shown by (2.4.11). When the extra 2 is accounted, the register is found to hold the proper representation of the result (2.4.12).

For the case of A positive, B negative, and $a \geq b$,

$$A + B \simeq (a + (2 - b - e) + e) \pmod 2 \qquad (2.4.13)$$

$$\simeq 2 + a - b \pmod 2 \qquad (2.4.14)$$

$$\simeq a - b \qquad a \geq b, \quad A \geq 0, \quad B < 0 \qquad (2.4.15)$$

2.5 2's COMPLEMENT ADDITION

Positive Numbers

As in sign and magnitude addition, addition of positive numbers is performed bit by bit so that we have

$$A + B \simeq a + b \qquad a + b < 1 \quad A, \quad B \geq 0 \qquad (2.5.1)$$

Negative Numbers

To add negative numbers, we add the respective bits of the two numbers together, including the sign bit, and ignore the carryout of the sign portion (see Figure 2.5). The equations are

$$A + B \simeq [(2 - a) + (2 - b)] \pmod 2 \qquad (2.5.2)$$

$$\simeq 4 - a - b \pmod 2 \qquad (2.5.3)$$

$$\simeq 2 - a - b \qquad a + b < 1 \quad A, \quad B < 0 \qquad (2.5.4)$$

Here the inevitable overflow of the register reduces the 4 to a 2 for the final result.

Notes

-13:	1.10011
-11:	1.10101
-24:	1.01000

Add numbers including the signs; neglect carry from sign position if it occurs.

$+13$:	0.01101	-13:	1.10011
-11:	1.10101	$+11$:	0.01011
$+2$:	0.00010	-2:	1.11110
-11:	1.10101	$+11$:	0.01011
$+13$:	0.01101	-13:	1.10011
$+2$:	0.00010	-2:	1.11110

FIGURE 2.5 Addition of binary numbers in 2's complement representation (thirty-seconds)

Oppositely Signed Numbers

Differently signed numbers are also added in a straightforward manner; they are added bit by bit, including the sign portion. Carryout of the sign bit is *always* ignored. There are four possible cases: For A positive and a larger than b,

$$A + B \simeq [a + (2 - b)] \;(\mathrm{mod}\, 2) \tag{2.5.5}$$

$$\simeq (2 + a - b) \;(\mathrm{mod}\, 2) \tag{2.5.6}$$

$$\simeq a - b \qquad a > b, \quad A \geq 0, \quad B < 0 \tag{2.5.7}$$

For A positive and a less than b,

$$A + B \simeq a + (2 - b) \tag{2.5.8}$$

$$\simeq 2 + a - b \qquad a < b, \quad A \geq 0, \quad B < 0 \tag{2.5.9}$$

For A negative and a larger than b,

$$A + B \simeq (2 - a) + b \tag{2.5.10}$$

$$\simeq 2 - a + b \qquad a > b, \quad A < 0, \quad B \geq 0 \tag{2.2.11}$$

For A negative and a smaller than b,

$$A + B \simeq (2 - a) + b \;(\mathrm{mod}\, 2) \tag{2.5.12}$$

$$\simeq b - a \qquad a \leq b, \quad A < 0, \quad B \geq 0 \tag{2.5.13}$$

TABLE 2.5 Addition in All Representations

Entry	Augend A	Addend B	Larger	Result represented by	What is happening	Restriction	Notation
1	+	+	Either	$a + b$	$a + b$	$a + b < 1$	Sign and magnitude
2	−	−	Either	$1 + a + b$	$1 + a + b$	$a + b < 1$	
3	+	−	a	$a - b$	$[a + (1 - b - e) + e] (\text{mod } 1)$		
4	+	−	b	$1 + b - a$	$1 + [1 - \{a + (1 - b - e)\} - e] (\text{mod } 1)$		
5	−	+	a	$1 + a - b$	$1 + [a + (1 - b - e) + e] (\text{mod } 1)$		$-a \simeq 1 + a$
6	−	+	b	$b - a$	$1 - [a + (1 - b - e) + e]$		
7	+	+	Either	$a + b$	$a + b$	$a + b < 1$	1's complements
8	−	−	Either	$2 - (a + b) - e$	$[(2 - a - e) + (2 - b - e) + e] (\text{mod } 2)$	$a + b < 1$	
9	+	−	a	$a - b$	$[a + (2 - b - e) + e] (\text{mod } 2)$		
10	+	−	b	$2 - (b - a) - e$	$a + (2 - b - e)$		
11	−	+	a	$2 - (a - b) - e$	$(2 - a - e) + b$		
12	−	+	b	$b - a$	$[(2 - a - e) + b + e] (\text{mod } 2)$		$-a \simeq 2 - a - e$
13	+	+	Either	$a + b$	$a + b$	$a + b < 1$	2's complements
14	−	−	Either	$2 - (a + b)$	$[(2 - a) + (2 - b)] (\text{mod } 2)$	$a + b < 1$	
15	+	−	a	$a - b$	$[a + (2 - b)] (\text{mod } 2)$		
16	+	−	b	$2 - (b - a)$	$a + (2 - b)$		
17	−	+	a	$2 - (a - b)$	$(2 - a) + b$		
18	−	+	b	$b - a$	$[(2 - a) + b] (\text{mod } 2)$		$-a \simeq 2 - a$

Mod 1 means neglect carries into sign position
Mod 2 means neglect carries out of sign position

Summary

A summary of the equations for the three representations is found in the Table 2.5. Columns 1 and 2 indicate, respectively, the sign of the augend and addend. The third column indicates which of these is larger. The fourth column indicates the proper form the sum should take. The fifth column indicates the equation for arriving at this sum. Here e is added (a 1 in the least significant bit position) to the partial sum when the end-around carry is detected. The sixth column indicates the correction to the sum which may be required to put the result into proper form. The last column gives the representation of the final result.

2.6 SIGN AND MAGNITUDE SUBTRACTION

Subtraction is performed in a parallel binary machine by complement addition for all representations.

Oppositely Signed Numbers

First consider two differently signed numbers. The old rule for subtraction says, "Change the sign of the subtrahend and add." For differently signed numbers, when the sign of one of the numbers is changed, we have two similarly signed numbers. This calls for the *addition* of the magnitude of the numbers as shown at the top of Figure 2.6. As soon as we detect that the numbers have different signs, we add the numerical positions and give the result the sign of the minuend. For the minuend positive,

$$A - B \simeq a + b \qquad a + b < 1, \quad A \geq 0, \quad B < 0 \quad (2.6.1)$$

For the minuend negative,

$$A - B \simeq 1 + a + b \qquad a + b < 1, \quad A < 0, \quad B \geq 0 \qquad (2.6.2)$$

Similarly Signed Numbers

In subtracting numbers of the same sign, we must determine which number has the larger magnitude. The method we adopt is to first find the 1's complement of the magnitude of the subtrahend and add it to the minuend. If an overflow from the most significant bit occurs, e is added and the result is correct. If there is no overflow from the most significant bit, then the sum is incorrect, because it is in 1's complement form. The sum must

Notes

13:	0.01101	−13:	1.01101	
− (−11):	1.01011	− (+11):	0.01011	
	01101		01101	Add magnitudes; sum has sign
	01011		01011	of minuend
	———		———	
	11000		11000	
——		——		No carry into sign position
26:	0.11000	−26:	1.11000	allowed

1. *Differently Signed Numbers*

+13:	0.01101	−13:	1.01101	
− (+11):	0.01011	− (−11):	1.01011	Numbers
				Add subtrahend complement to
				minuend magnitude
	01101		01101	
	10100		10100	
	———		———	
	⌐1.00001		⌐1.00001	For carry into sign position, add
	→1		→1	1 to sum; sign is that of
——	———	——	———	minuend
+2:	0.00010	−2:	1000010	

2. *Similarly Signed Numbers, Minuend Larger Magnitude*

+11:	0.01011	−11:	1.01011	
− (+13):	0.01101	− (−13):	1.01101	
	01011		01011	For no carry into sign position
	10010		10010	sum is complement; sign is
	———		———	that of minuend reversed
	11101		11101	
——	———	——	———	
−2:	1.00010	+2:	0.00010	

3. *Similarly Signed Numbers, Subtrahend Larger Magnitude*

FIGURE 2.6 Subtraction of binary numbers using sign and magnitude representation

be complemented to obtain the proper representation of the difference. For an overflow, the sign of the difference is that of the minuend; for no overflow, the sign of the difference is that of the minuend reversed.

larger minuend magnitude

The complement of the subtrahend is in the form $1 - b - e$. Where the numbers are positive and a is greater than b,

$$A - B \simeq [a + (1 - b - e) + e] \pmod 1 \qquad (2.6.3)$$

$$\simeq (1 + a - b) \pmod 1 \qquad (2.6.4)$$

$$\simeq a - b \qquad a \geq b \quad A, B \geq 0 \qquad (2.6.5)$$

"(mod 1)" requires that, when the *numerical* size of the register has been exceeded, the result stored in the register is one less than the algebraic quantity indicated in (2.6.5). An example of this appears in Figure 2.6.2. When the numbers are negative and a is larger than b,

$$A - B \simeq 1 + [a + (1 - b - e) + e] \pmod 1 \qquad (2.6.6)$$

$$\simeq 1 + (1 + a - b) \pmod 1 \qquad (2.6.7)$$

$$\simeq 1 + (a - b) \qquad (2.6.8)$$

$$\simeq 1 + a - b \qquad a > b \quad A, B < 0 \qquad (2.6.9)$$

as demonstrated in Figure 2.6.2.

larger subtrahend magnitude

Where the numbers are negative and a is smaller than b, we do not have an overflow. However, anticipating the hardware, where it is the custom to enter the end-around carry prematurely (enter it in all cases), we write

$$A - B \simeq 1 - [a + (1 - b - e)] - e \qquad (2.6.10)$$

$$\simeq 1 - a - 1 + b + e - e \qquad (2.6.11)$$

$$\simeq b - a \qquad a \leq b \quad A, B < 0 \qquad (2.6.12)$$

An example of this appears as Figure 2.6.3.
When the numbers are positive and a is smaller than b,

$$A - B = 1 + [1 - \{a + (1 - b - e)\} - e] \qquad (2.6.13)$$

$$= 1 + (1 - a - 1 + b + e - e) \qquad (2.6.14)$$

$$= 1 + b - a \qquad a < b \quad A, B > 0 \qquad (2.6.15)$$

which is shown by the example in Figure 2.6.3.

2.7 COMPLEMENT NOTATION SUBTRACTION

1's Complement Subtraction

Subtraction of binary numbers in 1's complement notation is always performed in the following manner: The complete 1's complement of the subtrahend (this includes the complementing of the sign bit) is added to the minuend. Whenever a *carry occurs* out of the *sign* bit, a 1 is added to the least significant bit of the result; when *no carry occurs* from the *sign* bit, this result is left intact.

Notes

```
   +13:  0.01101          −13:  1.10010
−(−11):  1.10100       −(+11):  0.01011

         0.01101                1.10010
         0.01011                1.10100
        _____               _____

   +24:  0.11000               1.00110
                                      1
                              _____
                        −24:  1.00111
```

In all cases, add the 1's complement of the subtrahend; for a carryout of the sign position *only*, add *e* to the sum. The sign is then correct.

```
   +13:  0.01101          −13:  1.10010
−(+11):  0.01011       −(−11):  1.10100

         0.01101                1.10010
         1.10100                0.01011
        _____               _____

         0.00001          −2:  1.11101
                1
        _____
    +2:  0.00010
```

```
   +11:  0.01011          −11:  1.10100
−(+13):  0.01101       −(−13):  1.10010

         0.01011                1.10100
         1.10010                0.01101
        _____               _____

    −2:  1.11101                0.00001
                                      1
                              _____
                         +2:  0.00010
```

FIGURE 2.7.1. Subtraction of binary numbers in 1's complement notation

TABLE 2.7   Subtraction in All Representations

Entry	Minuend A	Subtrahend B	Larger	Result represented by	What is happening	Restriction	Notation
1	+	−	Either	$a + b$	$a + b$	$a + b < 1$	Sign and magnitude
2	−	+	Either	$1 + a + b$	$1 + a + b$	$a + b < 1$	
3	+	+	a	$a - b$	$[a + (1 - b - e) + e] \pmod 1$		
4	+	+	b	$1 + (b - a)$	$1 + [1 - \{a + (1 - b - e)\} - e] \pmod 1$		
5	−	−	a	$1 + (a - b)$	$1 + [a + (1 - b - e) + e] \pmod 1$		
6	−	−	b	$b - a$	$1 - [a + (1 - b - e)] - e$		$-a \cong 1 + a$
7	+	−	Either	$a + b$	$a + b$	$a + b < 1$	
8	−	+	Either	$2 - (a + b) - e$	$[(2 - a - e) + (2 - b - e) + e] \pmod 2$	$a + b < 1$	1's complements
9	+	+	a	$a - b$	$[a + (2 - b - e) + e] \pmod 2$		
10	+	+	b	$2 - (b - a) - e$	$a + (2 - b - e)$		
11	−	−	a	$2 - (a - b) - e$	$(2 - a - e) + b$		
12	−	−	b	$b - a$	$[(2 - a - e) + b + e] \pmod 2$		$-a \cong 2 - a - e$
13	+	−	Either	$a + b$	$a + b$	$a + b < 1$	
14	−	+	Either	$2 - (a + b)$	$[(2 - a) + (2 - b - e) + e] \pmod 2$	$a + b < 1$	2's complements
15	+	+	a	$a - b$	$[a + (2 - b - e) + e] \pmod 2$		
16	+	+	b	$2 - (b - a)$	$a + (2 - b - e) + e$		
17	−	−	a	$2 - (a - b)$	$(2 - a) + [2 - (2 - b) - e] + e$		
18	−	−	b	$b - a$	$[(2 - a) + \{2 - (2 - b) - e\} + e] \pmod 2$		$-a \cong 2 - a$

Mod 1 means neglect carries into sign position
Mod 2 means neglect carries out of sign position

Examples for each sign and size combination of minuend and subtrahend are found in Figure 2.7.1. The equations are presented in Table 2.7; their reduction is left to the reader as an exercise.

2's Complement Subtraction

Numbers in 2's complement notation are always subtracted in the following manner. The 1's complement of the subtrahend, including the sign bit, is added to the minuend. At the same time, a 1 (*e*) is added into the least significant bit *regardless* of the signs of the numbers or their relative magnitude. It *always* occurs.

Examples are found illustrating the procedure in Figure 2.7.2. The equations are found in Table 2.7 with the justification left for the reader.

Notes

```
   +13:  0.01101          −13:  1.10011
−(−11):  1.10101       −(−11):  0.01011

         0.01101                1.10011
         0.01010                1.10100
              1                      1
        _____               _____

   +24:  0.11000          −24:  1.01000
```

```
   +13:  0.01101          −13:  1.10011
−(+11):  0.01011       −(−11):  1.10101

         0.01101                1.10011
         1.10100                0.01010
              1                      1
        _____               _____

    +2:  0.00010           −2:  1.11110
```

In all cases add the 1's complement of the subtrahend to the minuend and add a carry into the least significant bit; ignore carry out of sign bit.

```
   +11:  0.01011          −11:  1.10101
−(+13):  0.01101       −(−13):  1.10011

         0.01011                1.10101
         1.10010                0.01100
              1                      1
        _____               _____

    −2:  1.11110           +2:  0.00010
```

FIGURE 2.7.2 Subtraction of binary numbers in 2's complement notation

Summary

A summary of the equations for subtraction of signed binary numbers in all three representations is found in Table 2.7. It is organized in the same fashion as Table 2.5 which was discussed previously.

Error or Overflow Detection

There is a problem which arises and is treated differently in the three notations: addition or subtraction may produce a result which exceeds the word size of the computer. In using the sign and magnitude notation, the magnitudes of numbers are added together regardless of whether we are performing addition or subtraction. Hence, an error is detected by examining whether a carry is produced in the most significant bit of the sum. In both forms of complement notation, the addition of two negatively signed numbers should produce an overflow from the most significant bit of the sum. If such an overflow does not appear, then an error has taken place.

Subtraction of oppositely signed numbers can also produce a number exceeding the word size of the computer. Hence, we monitor the most significant bit for all notations.

Recovery from errors or overflow is always left to the programmer. He can have the computer stop until the operator intervenes. If this kind of fault is less important, he can have the error recorded in memory for reference when the results are printed out. He may also provide a long error procedure to check through the data for possible contamination. This is up to the user and programmer.

2.8   RECAPITULATION, ADDITION AND SUBTRACTION

Composite Rules

Of most benefit in determining the ease of implementation is to examine a complete rule for combined addition and subtraction. Such is now done, starting with the simplest case.

2's complement representation

We wish to combine the rules of Figure 2.5 and Figure 2.7.2. This is easy. For addition (subtraction) the addend (1's complement of the subtrahend) is added to the augend (minuend) with no carry (a carry) entered in the least significant position. All bits are added including the sign bit and any carry from the sign bit is ignored.

1's complement representation

For this representation the rules in Figures 2.4 and 2.7.1 are combined. For addition (subtraction) the addend (1's complement of the subtrahend) is added to the augend (minuend). All bits including the sign bit are added. An e is added to the least significant position only when a carry occurs from the sign position.

sign and magnitude

Combine Figures 2.3 and 2.6. Change the sign of the subtrahend only for subtraction. When the operands have the same sign, add their magnitudes and give the result that sign. When the signs differ, add the 1's complement of the addend (subtrahend), adding all except the sign bit. If a carry is produced at the most significant position, add 1 to the least significant bit and give the result the sign of the augend (minuend). If no carry is produced, complement the sum, appending the sign of the addend (opposite from the original subtrahend).

Comparison

Exactly one cycle is required for addition or subtraction of *any* two 2's complement numbers. Additional operations are sometimes required for the representations. This would seem to give a definite advantage to 2's complement representation. However, we will see that extra hardware is required for multiplication and an extra quotient correction cycle is *always* required for 2's complement division. Hence the selection of machine representation is not cut and dried and depends upon the trade-offs. The reader can draw his own conclusions after reading about multiplication and division.

Assuming that the sign of the operands is random (a questionable assumption), oppositely signed numbers are added half the time. In half of these cases, for sign and magnitude notation, the wrong number is subtracted and the result must be complemented. Hence we can say that 25 per cent of the time an extra cycle is required for complementation. This must be contrasted with the straightforward manner in which multiplication and division are done in this notation.

By a similar reasoning and an examination of Figure 2.4, it can be seen that 1's complement representation requires that a 1 is added into the right side of the sum 25 per cent of the time. This may require a partial or complete add cycle.

PROBLEMS

In problems 2.1 thru 2.4 below use binary numbers of the form *s.bbb bbb bbbb*. In other words, ten-bit binary numbers with one additional bit at the left reserved for the sign. The binary point follow the sign bit.

Thus the magnitude of all representable numbers is less than 1 or in certain exception, exactly 1. All such numbers can be considered as fractions with decimal denominators 1024 and integral decimal numerators.

In the following problems the numbers used are the decimal numerators of fractions with the decimal denominator 1024.

2.1 In sign and magnitude notation do the following additions:

a.	633	b.	407	c.	−633	d.	−407
	407		211		−211		−633

e.	−407	f.	+633	g.	−211	h.	+407
	+211		−407		+407		−633

2.2 In 1's complement notation repeat Problems 2.1a thru 2.1h.

2.3 In 2's complement notation repeat Problems 2.1a thru 2.1h.

2.4 Perform *subtraction* for Problem 2.1a thru 2.1h,
   a. For sign-and-magnitude notation.
   b. For 1's complement notation.
   c. For 2's complement notation.

2.5 a. What difficulties would be encountered in conceiving an integral rather than fractional notation as far as addition and subtraction are concerned?
   b. How would you indicate sign in each of the three notations?
   c. Would you anticipate any complications for multiplication and division? Why? For any representation?

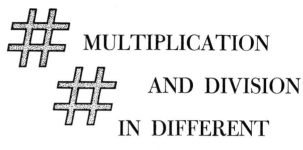

3

MULTIPLICATION
AND DIVISION
IN DIFFERENT
BINARY REPRESENTATIONS

3.1 MULTIPLYING POSITIVE NUMBERS

Multiplication

The general principles by which the computer performs multiplication are very simple-minded. Multiplication is carried out by sequences of additions and shifts or shifts alone; the number of each and their order is determined by the multiplier digits. For binary numbers, additions take place only one at a time and not in multiples. The multiplier is examined from one end to the other, bit by bit; if a bit is a 1, addition and shifting is called for; if the bit is a 0, only shifting is performed.

Theoretically, the multiplier may be examined from either end. When dealing with negative multipliers in 2's complement notation, it is almost mandatory to scan from right to left and complement at the same time because of the form of the complement rule. The preference for scan direction is thus determined, first by the representation used, then by the hardware design of the computer. If the scan is from left to right, then the partial product is shifted to the left after each new bit is examined and after an addition of the multiplicand to the partial product has taken place—if required. When new additions of the multiplicand are made to the partial product, the carry must be permitted to ripple all the way

44

to the left end of the register. This may happen at the last possible addition of the multiplicand to the partial product. At that time, the product occupies two full registers. Hence, a double-length adder *must* be provided to furnish *a possible two-word* carry propagation for left-to-right multiplier bit examination.

For right-to-left examination, each time a multiplicand addition is called for, it is performed to the more significant portion of the partial product double word. A carry cannot affect the less significant portion. It can propagate left as far as required as long as a single-word adder is provided.

In most of this volume the discussion of multiplication is confined to a right-to-left examination of the multiplier bits because,

1. No known machine does otherwise.

2. Only a single-word adder is needed.

3. A 2's complement representation complementing rule is practicable.

In the descriptions that follow, capital letters again stand for signed numbers and small letters for the magnitude of these numbers, e for 2^{-N} and e^2 for 2^{-2N}. We encounter the latter symbols since there are n numerical bits in the multiplier and multiplicand and $2n$ bits in the product. A line number in a figure is preceded by L.

Multiplication of Positive Numbers

Figure 3.1 illustrates the multiplication of two positive binary numbers. The lines of the numerical multiplication are labeled L1, L2, etc., for easy reference. The bits of the multiplier, L2, are scanned from right to left. Since the right-most bit of the multiplier, b_5, is 1, the multiplicand is entered on L3. Since b_4 is 0, the multiplicand shifted left once appears as L4. L3 and L4 are added together, the sum appearing as L5. Another shift of the multiplicand is performed for the third bit of the multiplier, b_3. Since b_3 is 0, when it multiplies $2^{-3}a$ it produces all 0's, L6. The multiplicand shifted to the right three times, appears as L7, corresponding to the left-most 1 in the multiplier, b_2. L7 is added to L5 (with L6) to give L8. Bit one, b_1, is 0; hence, L9 is all 0's, and when added to L8, gives the final product which is the same found in L8 and L10.

	Notes	Expression	Line
.01101	Multiplicand	$A = a$	L1
.01011	Multiplier	$B = b$	L2
0.0000001101	Enter right bit times multiplicand	$b_5(2^{-5}a)$	L3
0.0000011010	Next bit times multiplicand, shift	$b_4(2^{-4}a)$	L4
0.0000100111	Add	L3 + L4	L5
0.0000000000	Next bit times multiplicand, shift	$b_3(2^{-3}a)$	L6
0.0001101000	Next bit times multiplicand, shift	$b_2(2^{-2}a)$	L7
0.0010001111	Add	L5 + L6 + L7	L8
0.0000000000	Next bit times multiplicand, shift	$b_1(2^{-1}a)$	L9
0.0010001111	Add	L8 + L9 (result)	L10

FIGURE 3.1 $(+11 \times 2^{-5})(+13 \times 2^{-5}) = +143 \times 2^{-10}$ performed for all representations

Sign and Magnitude Multiplication

To multiply numbers in the sign and magnitude notation, the magnitudes of the numbers are multiplied as in Figure 3.1. The sign of the product is determined by the well-known sign rule for multiplication, "Like signs produce a positive product, etc."

3.2   1's COMPLEMENT MULTIPLICATION

Find $B \times A$ for $B = +b$, $A = -a$

In this case, we have a positive multiplier, $+b$, but a negative multiplicand, $-a$. Let us see what happens when we try to multiply the numbers directly. We will have

$$b(2 - a - e) = 2b - ab - eb \tag{3.2.1}$$

$$= -ab + 2b - eb \tag{3.2.2}$$

However, the desired result AB has the representation

$$AB \simeq 2 - ab - e^2 \tag{3.2.3}$$

The difference, d, between the desired result and that found by direct multiplication of the quantities is given by

$$d = AB - (-ab + 2b - eb) = 2 - ab - e^2 + ab - 2b + eb \qquad (3.2.4)$$

$$= 2 - b(2 - e) - e^2 \qquad (3.2.5)$$

One way to calculate AB is to multiply the numbers directly, and then add the correction d.

$$AB \simeq A \cdot B + d = b(2 - a - e) + \{2 - b(2 - e) - e^2\} \, (3.2.6)$$

This method is actually incorporated into some computers. The numbers are multiplied together directly, and then the correction is added automatically to produce the correct product.

1.10010	Multiplicand $(2 - a - e)$	L1
0.01011	Multiplier (b)	L2
1.1111110010	$b_5(2 - 2^{-5}a - e^2)$	L3
1.1111100101	$b_4(2 - 2^{-4}a - e^2)$	L4
1.1111010111	L3 + L4	L5
1	e^2	L6
1.1111011000	L5 + L6	L7
1.1110010111	$b_2(2 - 2a^{-2} - e^2)$	L8
1.1101101111	L7 + L8	L9
1	e^2	L10
1.1101110000	L9 + L10	L11

FIGURE 3.2.1 $(+11 \times 2^{-5})(-13 \times 2^{-5}) = -143 \times 2^{-10}$ using 1's complement notation

A better way to perform multiplication (one which does not need a correction) is illustrated in Figure 3.2.1. Note that each time a 0 appears as a multiplier bit, no addition of the multiplicand to the partial product is performed. In the figure (and those that follow) the line containing b_i is omitted when $b_i = 0$, since this detail has been illustrated already. For each 1 appearing in the multiplier, we add the properly shifted multiplicand. This multiplicand shifting is done in a peculiar way. As we shift it to the left, we enter 1's at the right instead of 0's. Note also that, since the computer's adding negative numbers, an end-around carry *always* occurs.

This is because they are represented as $\geq 1.0\cdots 0$ and the sum of the two of them is greater than $1.1\cdots 1$ or $1 + W$. Therefore, the word-length of the register is exceeded and an overflow occurs. The end-around carry is *always* added into the least significant bit position of the product (the e^2 position). Follow along with the processing illustrated in Figure 3.2.1 and note that no correction is required in the resulting product.

To justify the above-mentioned processing, let us examine what quantity is added to the partial product for each multiplier bit which is a 1. Call the increment I_i corresponding to the ith multiplier bit, where $b_i = 1$. Then,

$$I_i = [2 - 2^{-i}(a + e)] + (2^{-i-1} + 2^{-i-2} + \cdots + 2^{-N})e + 2^{-N}e \quad (3.2.7)$$

where the brackets enclose the 1's complement of the multiplicand after having been shifted i places; the second term is for the final string of 1's; and the last term is the carry into the $2N$th bit. Now,

$$(2^{-i-1} + 2^{-i-2} + \cdots + 2^{-N}) + 2^{-N} = (2^{-i} - 2^{-N}) + 2^{-N} = 2^{-i} \quad (3.2.8)$$

Therefore we have the following simplification:

$$I_i = 2 - 2^{-i}(a + e) + 2^{-i}e = 2 - 2^{-i}a \quad (3.2.9)$$

When each of these terms is added together, we find that the sum is the product desired, as shown below:

$$AB \simeq \left[\sum_i b_i \{ (I_i - e^2) + e^2 \} - e^2 \right] \pmod 2 \quad (3.2.10)$$

$$\simeq \left[\sum b_i (2 - 2^{-i}a) - e^2 \right] \pmod 2 \quad (3.2.11)$$

$$\simeq \left[2 \sum b_i - a \sum b_i 2^{-i} - e^2 \right] \pmod 2 \quad (3.2.12)$$

$$\simeq (2b_i - ab - e^2) \pmod 2 \quad (3.2.13)$$

$$\simeq 2 - ab - e^2 \quad (3.2.14)$$

In (3.2.10), the contents of the parentheses represents the properly shifted multiplicand; the term e^2 added to this, within the braces, represents the end-around carry. We have recorded an end-around carry for each multiplier bit which was 1. This is one too many; actually *one less* addition is performed than there are multiplier bits which is the reason for the right hand $-e^2$; it cancels out that one extra end-around carry.

Find $B \times A$ for $B = -b$, $A = +a$

Although there are alternate methods for performing multiplication with a negative multiplier, $-b$, and a positive multiplicand, $+a$, we will discuss only one that is fairly common. This example is illustrated in Figure 3.2.2. First, the 1's complement of the multiplier is taken automatically in the computer. Now, for each 1 in the complemented multiplier, the computer adds in the complement of the multiplicand. This is a

0.01101	Multiplicand (a)	L1
1.10100	Multiplier ($2 - b - e$)	L2
0.01011	$2 - $ L2 $- e$ (b)	L3
1.1111110010	$b_5(2 - 2^{-5}a - e^2)$	L4
1.1111100101	$b_4(2 - 2^{-4}a - e^2)$	L5
1.1111010111	L4 + L5	L6
1	e^2	L7
1.1111011000	L6 + L7	L8
1.1110010111	$b_2(2 - 2^{-2}a - e^2)$	L9
1.1101101111	L8 + L9	L10
1	e^2	L11
1.1101110000	L10 + L11	L12

FIGURE 3.2.2 $(-11 \times 2^{-5})(+13 \times 2^{-5}) = -143 \times 2^{-10}$ using 1's complement notation

complement of a positive number, and so will be a negative number which is shifted to the left a number of positions corresponding to the position of *this* 1 in the complemented multiplier. As the multiplicand complement is shifted to the left, 1's enter at the right.

Each addition of the multiplicand complement produces an end-around carry which, in turn, is added to a 1 to the least significant bit position. The result of this series of additions is a product which requires no correction.

Compare Figures 3.2.2 and 3.2.1 to see that the effect of complementing both the multiplier and the multiplicand produces the same result for $(-b)(+a)$ as for $(+b)(-a)$, as would be expected.

Since the two methods just discussed are so similar, it might seem that no justification is required for this method. However, as shown below, the complement of the negative number results in the magnitude of that number.

$$2 - (2 - b - e) - e = 2 - 2 + b + e - e \qquad (3.2.15)$$

$$= +b \qquad (3.2.16)$$

The full equations for this method are then

$$AB \simeq \left[\sum_i b_i \{ (2 - 2^{-i}a - e^2) + e^2 \} - e^2 \right] \pmod 2 \qquad (3.2.17)$$

$$\simeq 2 - ab - e^2 \qquad (3.2.18)$$

Find $B \times A$ for $B = -b$, $A = -a$

When both numbers are negative, $-b$ and $-a$, we expect a positive product. We find the complement of the multiplier as shown in Figure 3.2.3. For each bit of the *multiplier complement* which is a 1 (or for each

1.10010	Multiplicand $(2 - a - e)$	L1
1.10100	Multiplier $(2 - b - e)$	L2
0.01011	$2 - L2 - e$ (b)	L3
0.0000001101	$b_5(2^{-5}a)$	L4
0.0000011010	$b_4(2^{-4}a)$	L5
0.0000100111	L4 + L5	L6
0.0001101000	$b_2(2^{-2}a)$	L7
0.0010001111	L6 + L7	L8

FIGURE 3.2.3 $(-11 \times 2^{-5})(-13 \times 2^{-5}) = +143 \times 2^{-10}$ using 1's complement notation

bit of the multiplier which is 0), we add the complement of the multiplicand to the partial product. Since the numbers we are adding represent positive numbers, there should be no end-around carry and addition should produce a positive result. As we shift the number we are adding to the left, we enter 0's to the right. The result requires no correction.

We can justify this process without resorting to any formulas. After all, the complement of B is b and the complement of A is a, so that the product of these two is undoubtedly ab.

3.3 2's COMPLEMENT
MULTIPLICATION

**Find $B \times A$ for $B = +b$,
$A = -a$**

Recall that the 2's complement is formed by reversing the 0's and 1's in a word and *then adding a 1 to the right-hand bit*.

The multiplication of a positive multiplier, $+b$, with a negative multiplicand, $-a$, is illustrated in Figure 3.3.1. Each 1 in the multiplier requests

1.10011	Multiplicand $(2 - a)$	L1
0.01011	Multiplier (b)	L2
1.1111110011	$b_5(2 - 2^{-5}a)$	L3
1.1111100110	$b_4(2 - 2^{-4}a)$	L4
1.1111011001	L3 + L4	L5
1.1110011000	$b_2(2 - 2^{-2}a)$	L6
1.1101110001	L5 + L6	L7

FIGURE 3.3.1 $(+11 \times 2^{-5})(-13 \times 2^{-5}) = -143 \times 2^{-10}$ using 2's complement notation

the addition of the multiplicand appropriately shifted to the left. However, for 2's complement multiplication, when shifting the multiplicand to the left, we enter 0's at the right which produces the correct product without further manipulation. The following equations represent the justification for these conclusions.

$$BA \simeq \left[\sum_i b_i(2 - a2^{-i})\right] \text{(mod 2)} \tag{3.3.1}$$

$$\simeq \left[2 \sum b_i - a \sum b_i 2^{-i}\right] \text{(mod 2)} \tag{3.3.2}$$

$$\simeq \left[2 \sum b_i - ab\right] \text{(mod 2)} \tag{3.3.3}$$

$$\simeq 2 - ab \tag{3.3.4}$$

Observe that 2's are added into the product for each 1-bit in the multiplier. These excess numbers are automatically removed because of the word size of the register which performs addition "modulo 2."

Thus we can say multiplication with a positive multiplier is done directly and with no correction.

Find $B \times A$ for $B = -b$, $A = +a$, Method 1

Direct multiplication of two numbers of opposite sign, the multiplier being negative, in 2's complement notation does not result in a proper product. We may perform multiplication as suggested in connection with the 1's complement notation. That is, we may perform the direct multiplication of the quantities and then make a correction. This is called Method 1 and is illustrated in Figure 3.3.2. The multiplicand, shifted to

0.01101	Multiplicand (a)	L1
1.10101	Multiplier ($2 - b$)	L2
0.0000001101	$(2 - b)_5 (2^{-5}a)$	L3
0.0000110100	$(2 - b)_3 (2^{-3}a)$	L4
0.0001000001	L3 + L4	L5
0.0011010000	$(2 - b)_1 (2^{-1}a)$	L6
0.0100010001	L5 + L6	L7
1.10010	$2 - a - e$	L8
1	e	L9
1.1101110001	L7 + L8 + L9	L10

FIGURE 3.3.2 $(-11 \times 2^{-5})(+13 \times 2^{-5}) = -143 \times 2^{-10}$ using 2's complement notation, Method 1

the left a proper number of times, is added to the partial product for each 1 that appears in the multiplier, except the sign bit. For the shift of the multiplicand to the left, 0's are entered at the right. When the calculation is complete, the full 1's complement of the multiplicand, including the sign bit, is added to this result. Also, a 1 is added to the Nth position of the product. The result should now be correct. The justification is as follows:

$$BA \simeq (1 - b)a + (2 - a - e) + e \qquad (3.3.5)$$

$$\simeq a - ab + 2 - a - e + e \qquad (3.3.6)$$

$$\simeq 2 - ab \qquad (3.3.7)$$

In (3.3.5) the first term represents the uncorrected product, the second term is the 1's complement of the multiplicand, and the third term is the 1 added to the Nth position of the product.

Find $B \times A$ for $B = -b$, $A = -a$, Method 1

The multiplication of two negative numbers by Method 1 is illustrated in Figure 3.3.3. As in the last subsection, multiplication is performed by adding the multiplicand, appropriately shifted, to the partial product for each 1 in the multiplier, except the sign bit. The shift of the multiplicand

1.10011	Multiplicand $(2 - a)$	L1
1.10101	Multiplier $(2 - b)$	L2
1.1111110011	$(2 - b)_5(2 - 2^{-5}a)$	L3
1.1111001100	$(2 - b)_3(2 - 2^{-3}a)$	L4
1.1110111111	L3 + L4	L5
1.1100110000	$(2 - b)_1(2 - 2^{-1}a)$	L6
1.1011101111	L5 + L6	L7
0.01100	$2 - (2 - a) - e = a - e$	L8
1	e	L9
0.0010001111	L7 + L8 + L9	L10

FIGURE 3.3.3 $(-11 \times 2^{-5})(-13 \times 2^{-5}) = +143 \times 2^{-10}$ using 2's complement notation, Method 1

to the left enters 0's into the right-hand side. After the product is formed, it is corrected: we add the full 1's complement of the multiplicand, we also add a 1 to the Nth position to the right of the product. The justification for this procedure is found in the following equations:

$$BA \simeq \left[\sum (1 - b)_i (2 - a2^{-i}) + (2 - (2 - a) - e) + e\right] \pmod 2$$
$$(3.3.8)$$

$$\simeq \left[2 \sum (1 - b)_i - \sum (1 - b)_i a2^{-i} + 2 - 2 + a - e + e\right]$$
$$\pmod 2 \quad (3.3.9)$$

$$\simeq \left[2 \sum (1 - b)_i - a \sum 2^{-i} + a \sum b_i 2^{-i} + a\right] \pmod 2 \quad (3.3.10)$$

$$\simeq -a + ab + a = ab \quad (3.3.11)$$

The first term in (3.3.8) is a direct product of the multiplier and the multiplicand; $(1 - b)_i$ is the ith bit in the numerical portion of the negative multiplier. The second term is the 1's complement of the negative multiplicand. The last term is that extra 1 added to the nth position of the product.

Find $B \times A$ for $B = -b$, $A = +a$, Method 2

A better method, Method 2, of doing 2's complement multiplication with a negative multiplier is illustrated in Figure 3.3.4. Method 2 requires no correction; it does require, however, that we take the 2's complement

0.01101	Multiplicand (a)	L1
1.10101	Multiplier $(2 - b)$	L2
01011	$2 - (2 - b)$ (b)	L3
1.1111110010	$b_5[2 - 2^{-5}(a + e)]$	L4
1	$2^{-5}e$	L5
1.1111110011	L4 + L5	L6
1.1111110100	$b_4[2 - 2^{-4}(a + e)]$	L7
10	$2^{-4}e$	L8
1.1111011001	L6 + L7 + L8	L9
1.1110010000	$b_2[2 - 2^{-2}(a + e)]$	L10
1000	$2^{-2}e$	L11
1.1101110001	L9 + L10 + L11	L12

FIGURE 3.3.4 $(-11 \times 2^{-5})(+13 \times 2^{-5}) = -143 \times 2^{-10}$ using 2's complement notation, Method 2

of the multiplier. The 2's complement is always more difficult to form than the 1's complement; to obtain it we use the following rule:

Starting from the right, for each 0 in the number we are complementing, we place a 0 in the complement; the first time we encounter a 1 in the original number we place a 1 in the complement: thereafter, every 0 we encounter is replaced by a 1 and every 1 by a 0.

Thus the 2's complement of 0.110100 is 1.001100.

For each 1 that appears in the multiplier complement $[2 - (2 - b)]$, we add the 1's complement of the multiplicand, properly shifted $[2 - 2^i(a + e)]$. At the same time, we add a 1 shifted to the left a number of times corresponding to the multiplier digit under consideration, $2^i e$. When this is totaled, it should equal the product we desire. The justification is as follows:

$$BA \simeq \left[\sum \{2 - (2 - b)\}_i\{2 - 2^{-i}(a + e) + 2^{-i}e\}\right] \text{ (mod 2)} \quad (3.3.12)$$

$$= \left[\sum b_i(2 - 2^{-i}a)\right] \text{ (mod 2)} \quad (3.3.13)$$

$$= \left[2 \sum b_i - a \sum b_i 2^{-i}\right] \text{ (mod 2)} \quad (3.3.14)$$

$$= \left[2 \sum b_i - ab\right] \text{ (mod 2)} \quad (3.3.15)$$

$$= 2 - ab$$

The first factor in braces in (3.3.12) is the ith bit of 2's complement of the multiplier. To obtain the second factor (in braces), we subtract the multiplicand, shifted right i places, from 2 to get its 1's complement. We then subtract e, similarly shifted. Hence, the second factor is the 2's complement of the shifted multiplicand. The terms are added mod 2 to yield the negative product in 2's complement notation.

Find $B \times A$ for $B = -b$, $A = -a$, 2's Complement Notation, Method 2

Multiplication of two negative numbers by Method 2 is illustrated in Figure 3.3.5. Again, we take the 2's complement of the multiplier according to the rules. We add the 1's complement of the multiplicand, properly shifted, to the partial product. For each place shifted to the left, we enter

1.10011	Multiplicand $(2 - a)$	L1
1.10101	Multiplier $(2 - b)$	L2
01011	$2 - (2 - b)$ (b)	L3
0.0000001100	$b_5 2^{-5}[2 - (2 - a) - e]$	L4
0.0000000001	$2^{-5}e$	L5
0.0000001101	L4 + L5	L6
0.000001100	$b_4 2^{-4}[2 - (2 - a) - e]$	L7
0.000000001	$2^{-4}e$	L8
0.0000100111	L6 + L7 + L8	L9
0.0001100	$b_2 2^{-2}[2 - (2 - a) - e]$	L10
0.0000001	$2^{-2}e$	L11
0.0010001111	L9 + L10 + L11	L12

FIGURE 3.3.5 $(-11 \times 2^{-5})(-13 \times 2^{-5}) = +143 \times 2^{-10}$ using 2's complement notation, Method 2

TABLE 3.3 Equations for Multiplication of Signed Binary Numbers in All Three Representations

Entry	$a = \lvert A \rvert$ Multiplicand	$b = \lvert B \rvert$ Multiplier	Desired result	Method	Representation
1	$+$	$+$	ab	ab	Sign
2	$-$	$+$	$1 + ab$	$1 + ab$	and
3	$+$	$-$	$-ab$	$1 + ab$	magnitude
4	$-$	$-$	ab	ab	
5	$+$	$+$	ab	ab	
6	$-$	$+$	$2 - ab - e^2$	$\{\Sigma\, b_i[(2 - 2^{-i}a - e^2) + e^2] - e^2\}\ (\text{mod } 2)$	1's
7	$+$	$-$	$2 - ab - e^2$	$2 - (2 - b - e) - e) = b$ $\{\Sigma\, b_i[(2 - 2^{-i}a - e^2) + e^2] - e^2\}\ (\text{mod } 2)$	complement
8	$-$	$-$	ab	$[2 - (2 - b - e) - e][2 - (2 - e - e) - e]$	
9	$+$	$+$	ab	ab	2's
10	$-$	$+$	$2 - ab$	$[\Sigma\, b_i(2 - a2^{-i})](\text{mod } 2)$	complement
11	$+$	$-$	$2 - ab$	$(1 - b)a + (2 - a - e) + e$	method 1
12	$-$	$-$	ab	$\{\Sigma\,(1 - b)_i(2 - a2^{-i}) + [2 - (2 - a) - e + e]\}$ $(\text{mod } 2)$	

TABLE 3.3   (*Continued*)

			ab	ab	2's complement method 2
13	+	+	ab	$\Sigma\, b_i(2 - a2^{-i})$	
14	−	+	$2 - ab$		
15	+	−	$2 - ab$	$\{\Sigma[2 - (2 - b)]_i[2 - 2^{i}(a + e) + 2^{-i}e]\}\,(\bmod\ 2)$	
16	−	−	ab	$2 - (2 - b) = b$ $b[2 - (2 - a) - e + e] = ab$	

a 0 into the right-hand side of the multiplicand. When we add in the shifted multiplicand, we also add 1 in the proper position so that we will obtain the 2's complement of the multiplicand. The final result should be the product of the numbers without any correction required, as follows:

$$BA \simeq [2 - (2 - b)][2 - (2 - a) - e + e] \qquad (3.3.17)$$

$$\simeq ba \qquad\qquad\qquad\qquad\qquad\qquad\qquad (3.3.18)$$

Each one of the factors in (3.3.17) simplifies respectively into b and a.

Summary

The equations associated with sign multiplication of binary numbers are summarized in Table 3.3. For each combination of multiplier and multiplicand, the desired result is listed, together with the equation for obtaining this result.

The choice of methods for performing multiplication, as usual, is left to the designer. He views the arithmetic unit as a whole and weighs cost against speed for each detail: the first method of multiplication with negative multipliers requires an extra correction cycle at the end, whereas the second method although it does not require this cycle, uses a more costly technique to decode the multiplier.

3.4   INTRODUCTION TO DIVISION

This section covers *signed* division in the various binary number representations. Division is always performed by repeated subtraction and shifts. A subtraction is done only when it produces a partial remainder with the same sign as the last previous partial remainder; subtraction is otherwise inhibited.

The manipulation of the operands and the intermediate results completely depends on the representation used. The comprehension of these manipulations will enable us to investigate the use of these representations in implementing the rapid algorithms used in fast division (Chapters 12–14).

Quotient of Positive Numbers, Any Representation

In discussing division we will use the following symbols: A is the dividend, which is usually stored in the accumulator (A) register, and its magnitude is denoted by a; D is the divisor and its magnitude is d; Q

is the quotient which we are looking for and its magnitude is q; R is the remainder and its magnitude is r. The sign of the participants is directly available from A and D.

0.01011	Quotient Q	L1
0.01101/0.0010010001	Dividend A	L2
1.1110010000	$2 - 2^{-2}(D + e)$	L3
$\overline{}$		
⌐0.0000100001	L2 + L3	L4
└────────►1	$2^{-2}e$	L5
$\overline{}$		
0.0000101001	L4 + L5	L6
1.1111100100	$2 - 2^{-4}(D + e)$	L7
$\overline{}$		
⌐0.0000001101	L6 + L7	L8
└────────►1	$2^{-4}e$	L9
$\overline{}$		
0.0000001111	L8 + L9	L10
1.1111110010	$2 - 2^{-5}(D + e)$	L11
$\overline{}$		
⌐0.0000000001	L10 + L11	L12
└────────►1	$2^{-5}e$	L13
$\overline{}$		
0.0000000010	R = L12 + L13	L14

FIGURE 3.4 $(+145 \times 2^{-10})/(+13 \times 2^{-5}) = +11 \times 2^{-5} + 2 \times 2^{-10}$
as performed in all binary representations

Division is performed by subtraction, as illustrated in Figure 3.4. For positive numbers, although not apparent in this figure, the computer performs subtraction by complement addition. For each digit that we generate in the quotient, we perform either a subtraction (complement addition) and a shift, or only a shift.

In the example illustrated, we wish to subtract the divisor from the dividend. By convention, the divisor is initially larger than the dividend and the first subtraction cannot be performed without having the sign of the result differ from that of the original dividend. Therefore, if we align the numbers according to the binary point, a successful subtraction cannot be performed. 0 is entered after the binary point of the quotient, L1, and the divisor complement is shifted one place to the right, L3. We try another subtraction by complementing the divisor (now shifted) and adding it to the dividend. This does not cause a sign change and, therefore, we perform it.

Since we are adding the 1's complement of the divisor, the result will not be correct. To correct the result, add a 1 to the result in the position corresponding to the least significant bit of the shifted divisor. Incidentally, the 1 coming out as a carry from the sign position of the result not only indicates that the subtraction is successful, but can also be used as the end-around carry to cause correction after subtraction.

The foregoing process is continued. For each unsuccessful subtraction, a 0 is placed in the quotient and the divisor is shifted one more position to the right. When successful subtraction is performed, a 1 is entered into the quotient and the divisor is again shifted to the right. After sufficient quotient bits have been generated, we may stop because we perform division much like the "paper and pencil" method where the remainder is maintained correct in both sign and magnitude.

To justify this procedure, let us see if we can determine the equations which state mathematically what is occurring. For each subtraction we perform we add the quantity symbolized by I_i to the partial remainder.

$$I_i = -q_i 2^{-i} D \tag{3.4.1}$$

As this quantity is being added to the partial remainder, it appears as

$$I_i = q_i [\{2 - 2^{-i}(d + e)\} + 2^{-i}e] \tag{3.4.2}$$

$$= q_i(2 - 2^{-i}d) \tag{3.4.3}$$

The term within the braces of (3.4.2) is the 1's complement of the shifted divisor—the shifting is indicated by the factor 2^{-i}. The correction factor, the shifted end-around carry, is the right-hand term within the brackets of that equation. The remainder, after we have generated all the quotient digits, is given by

$$R = [A + \sum q_i(2 - 2^{-i}d)] \ (\text{mod } 2) \tag{3.4.4}$$

$$= (a + 2 \sum q_i - d \sum q_i 2^{-i}) \ (\text{mod } 2) \tag{3.4.5}$$

$$= a - qd \tag{3.4.6}$$

Notice that in (3.4.5) we have a number of 2's included in the equation. These result from the repeated addition of the 1's complement of a positive number. Since the register size is fixed, these 2's are discarded, which is indicated in the equations by the factor "(mod 2)." Notice that the right-hand summation within the first set of parentheses reduces to the product of the quotient and the divisor indicated in (3.4.6) as qd.

Sign and Magnitude Division

To divide numbers which are in sign and magnitude form, we simply divide the magnitudes, as discussed in the previous subsection, and attach the appropriate sign as determined by the grammar-school rule.

$$r = a - qd \tag{3.4.7}$$

Thus, the magnitude of the remainder and quotient are determined. The determination of the sign is summarized in Table 3.6.

3.5 1's COMPLEMENT DIVISION

Division for $A = -a$, $D = +d$

An example of division of a positive divisor into a negative dividend is shown in Figure 3.5.1. We *add* the divisor, $+d$, to the dividend, $-a$, (and then shift right) whenever a sign change is not produced. Since we

1.10100	Quotient Q	L1
0.01101/$\overline{1.1101101110}$	Divisor A	L2
0.0001101	$2^{-2}D$	L3
———————		
1.1111010110	L2 + L3	L4
0.000001101	$2^{-4}D$	L5
———————		
1.1111110000	L4 + L5	L6
0.0000001101	$2^{-5}D$	L7
———————		
1.1111111101	L6 + L7	L8

FIGURE 3.5.1 Performing $(-145 \times 2^{-10})/(+13 \times 2^{-5}) = (-11 \times 2^{-5}) + (-2 \times 2^{-10})$ using 1's complements

are adding a positive number to a negative number, no carry is produced from the sign position as long as the result is negative. This also means that no correction is necessary in the partial remainder. The sign digit of the quotient is made 1, and the divisor is shifted one position to the right before we start. We place a 1 in the quotient whenever addition is *not* performed and a 0 when addition is performed. Of course, even when no addition occurs the divisor is still shifted one position to the right. After generating sufficient quotient bits, the remainder will be correct, since it is maintained with the proper sign and magnitude.

To repeat, the lack of an end-around carry indicates successful addition and no carry correction is required.

The increment that is being added to the partial remainder is

$$I_i = \bar{Q}_i 2^{-i} d \tag{3.5.1}$$

The remainder, R, is

$$R = A + \sum \bar{Q}_i 2^{-i} d \tag{3.5.2}$$

$$= (2 - a) + \bar{q}d \tag{3.5.3}$$

$$= (2 - a - qd) \tag{3.5.4}$$

where $\bar{Q}_i$ indicates the complement of the quotient bit, Q_i.

Division with $A = +a$, $D = -d$

For division with a negative divisor, $-d$, and a positive dividend, $+a$, illustrated in Figure 3.5.2, we *add* the divisor to the partial remainder every time that this addition does not produce a sign change in the partial remainder; then we shift the divisor one position to the right. For an unsuccessful addition the divisor also is shifted right.

1.10100	Quotient Q	L1
1.10010/0.0010010001	Dividend A	L2
1.1110010	$2 - 2^{-2}(d + e)$	L3
0.0000100001 ⤵	L2 + L3	L4
⟶1	$2^{-2}e$	L5
0.0000101001	L4 + L5	L6
1.111110010	$2 - 2^{-4}(d + e)$	L7
0.0000001101 ⤵	L6 + L7	L8
⟶1	$2^{-4}e$	L9
0.0000001111	L8 + L9	L10
1.1111110010	$2 - 2^{-5}(d + e)$	L11
0.0000000001 ⤵	L10 + L11	L12
⟶1	$2^{-5}e$	L13
0.0000000010	L12 + L13	L14

FIGURE 3.5.2 Performing $(+145 \times 2^{-10})/(-13 \times 2^{-5}) = (-11 \times 2^{-5}) + (+2 \times 2^{-10})$ using 1's complement notation

Since we are adding a negative number to a positive one, the result will be positive only when an end-around carry occurs. Also, to keep our result positive, since we are using 1's complement notation, we must correct the result by adding the end-around carry into the least significant bit position of the shifted divisor. As we start the division, we enter a 1 into the sign position of the quotient and shift the divisor one position to the right. We enter a 0 for each successful addition and a 1 when only a shift of the divisor is performed. After developing the proper number of quotient bits, the remainder is correct in both sign and magnitude.

The increment which is being added to the partial remainder is

$$I_i = \bar{Q}_i 2 - 2^{-i}(d + e) \tag{3.5.5}$$

The remainder takes the form

$$R = A + \sum \bar{Q}_i [2 - 2^{-i}(d + e) + 2^{-i}e] \tag{3.5.6}$$

When this equation is simplified, the result will be the proper remainder, as shown in Table 3.6.

Division with $A = -a$, $D = -d$

The division of negative numbers is illustrated in Figure 3.5.3. We complement the divisor and add it to the partial remainder as long as this partial remainder remains negative after the addition. A 0 is entered into the sign bit of the quotient and the divisor is shifted one place to the right

$\overline{0.01011}$	Quotient Q	L1
$1.10010/1.1101101110$	Dividend A	L2
0.0001101000	$2^{-2}(2 - D - e)$	L3
$\overline{}$		
1.1111010110	L2 + L3	L4
0.0000011010	$2^{-4}(2 - D - e)$	L5
$\overline{}$		
1.1111110000	L4 + L5	L6
0.0000001101	$2^{-5}(2 - D - e)$	L7
$\overline{}$		
1.1111111101	L7 + L8	L8

NOTE: $D = 2 - d - e$
$(2 - D - e) = 2 - (2 - d - e) - e = d$

FIGURE 3.5.3 Performing $(-145 \times 2^{-10})/(-13 \times 2^{-5}) = (+11 \times 2^{-5}) + (-2 \times 2^{-10})$ using 1's complement notation

before we start. For each successful addition, a 1 is entered into the corresponding quotient position and a 0 is entered whenever an addition cannot be successfully performed. The divisor is shifted to the right after each trial, successful or unsuccessful.

The justification for this procedure requires that we examine the increment, which is

$$I_i = Q_i 2^{-i}(2 - d - e) \qquad (3.5.7)$$

$$= Q_i 2^{-i}[2 - (2 - D - e) - e] \qquad (3.5.8)$$

$$= Q_i 2^{-i}d \qquad (3.5.9)$$

From (3.5.9), we see that the increment is a positive number which we add to the negative number as long as the latter does not become positive. This means that no end-around carry is generated when a correct addition is performed and, hence, no correction is required. The remainder is

$$R = A + \sum Q_i 2^i d \qquad (3.5.10)$$

which will be correct (negative) after the proper number of quotient digits is produced.

3.6 2's COMPLEMENT DIVISION

**Division for $A = -a$,
$D = +d$**

Positive numbers in 2's complement notation are divided as sign and magnitude numbers. In Figure 3.6.1, we see a negative number divided by a positive number. We first enter a 1 into the sign position of the quo-

$$
\begin{array}{lll}
\underline{1.10100} \quad +e = 1.10101 & & \\
0.01101/\overline{1.1101101100} & \text{Dividend } A & \text{L1} \\
0.0001101 & 2^{-2}\,D & \text{L2} \\
\hline
1.1111010110 & \text{L1} + \text{L2} & \text{L3} \\
1101 & 2^{-4}\,D & \text{L4} \\
\hline
1.1111101110 & \text{L3} + \text{L4} & \text{L5} \\
1101 & 2^{-5}\,D & \text{L6} \\
\hline
1.1111111011 & \text{L5} + \text{L6} & \text{L7} \\
\end{array}
$$

FIGURE 3.6.1   Performing $(-148 \times 2^{-10})/(+13 \times 2^{-5}) = (-11 \times 2^{-5}) + (-5 \times 2^{-10})$ using 2's complements

tient and shift the divisor one place to the right. We then try to add the
shifted divisor directly to the partial remainder. We are adding a positive
number to a negative one and wish the result to remain negative. Hence,
successful addition will not produce an end-around carry and correction is
unnecessary. After each trial, the divisor is shifted one position to the
right. For each successful addition, a 0 is entered in the quotient bit;
whereas a 1 is entered if addition is not performed.

After the proper number of quotient bits is generated, the remainder
will be correct in both magnitude and sign; however, the quotient will not
be correct—it will be in 1's complement notation. Since we want the result
in 2's complement form, we must correct the quotient by adding a 1 on its
least significant bit position. This correction is indicated in the top line of
Figure 3.6.1 by the addition of e to the quotient generated earlier.

To justify this, we note that the increment we are using is

$$I_i = (1 - Q + e)_i 2^{-i} d \tag{3.6.1}$$

where $(1 - Q - e)_i$ indicates the complement of the ith bit of the uncorrected quotient (the 1's complement of this quotient bit). The second
factor, $2^{-i}d$, of (3.6.1) is the shifted divisor. The remainder is obtained by
summing the increments and adding them to the dividend.

$$R = A + \sum (1 - Q - e)_i 2^{-i} d \tag{3.6.2}$$

This expression can be simplified to obtain the result listed in Table 3.6.

Division for $A = +a$, $D = -d$

The procedure for dividing a positive dividend by a negative divisor is
very similar to that of the previous subsection and is illustrated in Figure
3.6.2. Again, we add the divisor directly to the partial remainder when a
carry will result. We ignore the carry and shift one position to the right
for each trial. At the start of the process, a 1 is entered into the sign position of the quotient and the divisor is shifted one position to the right.
A 0 is entered in the corresponding bit position for each successful addition;
a 1 is entered when addition is not performed. Again, the remainder will be
correct although this time it is positive. The quotient must be corrected by
adding a 1 in the least significant position in order to convert from 1's
complement notation to 2's complement notation, which is shown in the
top of the figure.

$$
\begin{array}{lll}
\underline{1.10100} \;\; + e = 1.10101 & & \\
1.10011/\overline{0.0010010100} & \text{Dividend } A & \text{L1} \\
1.1110011 & 2 - 2^{-2}d & \text{L2} \\
\hline
0.0000101100 & \text{L1 + L2} & \text{L3} \\
1.111110011 & 2 - 2^{-4}d & \text{L4} \\
\hline
0.0000010010 & \text{L3 + L4} & \text{L5} \\
1.1111110011 & 2 - 2^{-5}d & \text{L6} \\
\hline
0.0000000101 & \text{L5 + L6} & \text{L7} \\
& & \text{L}
\end{array}
$$

FIGURE 3.6.2 Performing $(+148 \times 2^{-10})/(-13 \times 2^{-5}) = (-11 \times 2^{-5}) +$ $(+5 \times 2^{-5})$ using 2's complements

The increment we are using is

$$
I_i = (1 - Q - e)_i(2 - 2^{-i}d) \tag{3.6.3}
$$

where the second factor is the divisor appropriately shifted to the right. Then the remainder is

$$
R = A + \sum (1 - Q - e)_i(2 - 2^{-i}d) \tag{3.6.4}
$$

which simplifies to the proper entry in Table 3.6.

Division for $A = -a$, $D = -d$

Division of negative numbers is shown in Figure 3.6.3. We will try to add the 1's complement of the divisor to the partial remainder and simultaneously enter a 1 into the least significant bit of the shifted divisor. This is shown on lines 3 and 4, for instance, of Figure 3.6.3. Successful addition will not produce an end-around carry. However, the fact that we were dealing with a negative number in 2's complement form was compensated for during addition by entering the extra 1 in the least significant bit position. This is easy to implement hardware-wise.

The sign bit of the quotient is made 0, and a one-position shift is performed upon the divisor when we start. 1's are entered in the corresponding bits of the quotient for each successful addition; 0's are entered when addition is not performed. The divisor is shifted one position to the right whether addition is performed or not. The note in Figure 3.6.3 shows

TABLE 3.6   Equations for Division of Signed Binary Numbers, All Representations

Entry	$d = \lvert D \rvert$ Divisor	$a = \lvert A \rvert$ Dividend	$q = \lvert Q \rvert$ Quotient	$r = \lvert R \rvert$ Remainder	Method	Representation
1	+	+	$Q = q$	$R = r$	$R = a + \Sigma q_i[2 - 2^{-i}(d + e) + 2^{-i}e]$	Sign and magnitude
2	+	−	$Q = 1 + q$	$R = r$	$R = 1 + a + \Sigma q_i[2 - 2^{-i}(d + e) + 2^{-i}e]$	
3	−	+	$Q = 1 + q$	$R = 1 + r$	$R = a + \Sigma q_i[2 - 2^{-i}(d + e) + 2^{-i}e]$	
4	−	−	$Q = q$	$R = 1 + r$	$R = 1 + a + \Sigma q_i[2 - 2^{-i}(d + e) + 2^{-i}e]$	
5	+	+	$Q = q$	$R = r$	$R = A + \Sigma q_i[2 - 2^{-i}(D + e) + 2^{-i}e]$	1's complement
6	+	−	$Q = 2 - q - e$	$R = r$	$R = A + \Sigma Q_i 2^{-i}D$	
7	−	+	$Q = 2 - q - e$	$R = 2 - r - e$	$R = A + \Sigma Q_i[2 - 2^{-i}(d + e) + 2^{-i}e]$	
8	−	−	$Q = q$	$R = 2 - r - e$	$R = A + \Sigma q_i 2^{-i}(2 - D - e)$	
9	+	+	$Q = q$	$R = r$	$R = A + \Sigma q_i[2 - 2^{-i}(D + e) + 2^{-i}e]$	2's complement
10	+	−	$Q = 2 - q$	$R = r$	$R = A + \Sigma(1 - Q + e)_i 2^{-i}D$	
11	−	+	$Q = 2 - q$	$R = 2 - r$	$R = A + \Sigma(1 - Q + e)_i(2 - 2^{-i}d)$	
12	−	−	$Q = q$	$R = 2 - r$	$R = A + \Sigma q_i[2 - 2^{-i}(D + e) + 2^{-i}e]$	

$$
\begin{array}{lll}
\underline{0.01011} & \text{Quotient } Q & \text{L1} \\
1.10011/\overline{1.1101101100} & \text{Dividend } A & \text{L2} \\
0.0001100 & 2^{-2}(2 - D - e) & \text{L3} \\
1 & 2^{-2}e & \text{L4} \\
\hline
1.1111010100 & \text{L2 + L3 + L4} & \text{L5} \\
0.000001100 & 2^{-4}(2 - D - e) & \text{L6} \\
1 & 2^{-4}e & \text{L7} \\
\hline
1.1111101110 & \text{L5 + L6 + L7} & \text{L8} \\
0.0000001100 & 2^{-5}(2 - D - e) & \text{L9} \\
1 & 2^{-5}e & \text{L10} \\
\hline
1.1111111011 & \text{L8 + L9 + L10} & \text{L11}
\end{array}
$$

NOTE: $D = 2 - d$

$$2 - D - e = 2 - (2 - d) - e = d - e$$

FIGURE 3.6.3   Performing $(-148 \times 2^{-10})/(-13 \times 2^{-5}) = (+11 \times 2^{-5}) + (-5 \times 2^{-10})$ using 2's complements

that when we take the 1's complement of the negative divisor, we will get the magnitude of the divisor less e. Since we want the magnitude of the divisor, we must correct this quantity by adding in e.

The increment which we are applying is

$$I_i = q_i\{2 - [2 - 2^{-i}(d + e)] + 2^{-i}e\} \tag{3.6.5}$$

which reduces to

$$I_i = q_i(2^{-i}d) \tag{3.6.6}$$

which is the shifted magnitude of the divisor. When these increments are summed and added to the dividend, we have

$$R = A + \sum q_i 2^{-i}d \tag{3.6.7}$$

Summary

The proper form of the quotient and remainder for division in each representation is summarized in Table 3.6 where the method for obtaining this result in equation form is also listed.

PROBLEMS

In the following problems the numbers used are the decimal numerators of fractions with the denominator assumed to be 10^3.

3.1 Using 2's complement notation show how the computer would perform the indicated multiplication using the second method described in the text when a choice exists.

a. $+633$ b. -211 c. -407 d. -407
$\times +407$ $\times +407$ $\times +633$ $\times -211$

3.2 Show the multiplications of 3.1 using 1's complement notation.

3.3 Show the multiplications of 3.1 using sign and magnitude notation.

3.4 Using 2's complement notation show how the computer would perform the indicated *divisions* using the second method of the text where a choice obtains

a. $+407$ b. -24 c. $+407$ d. -211
$+633$ $+407$ -633 -633

3.5 Show the performance of the division of 3.4 using 1's complement notation.

3.6 Show the performance of the division of 3.4 using sign and magnitude notation.

3.7 Examine multiplication and division using integer notation.
   a. What problems present themselves?
   b. What methodological rules do you propose?
   c. Outline a complete integer representation.

3.8 Repeat 3.1 for sign and magnitude notation, this time examining the multiplier from *left to right*.

4

FAST ADDERS

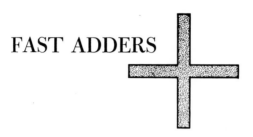

4.1 INTRODUCTION

Parallel Register Symbols

To facilitate the discussion of the hardware required to implement addition, an appropriate simplification of the symbols will be used. In parallel adders especially, there is a great deal of duplication of the logic that interconnects basic functional units. For instance, Figure 4.1.1 shows two registers labeled A and B, connected together by a number of gates and mixers. The particular arrangement portrayed in this figure allows us these four transfers: A to B directly; the complement of A to B; A, shifted one position to the right, to B; the complement of A, shifted one position to the right, to B.

The arrangement of the figure can be readily followed from the symbols used: for instance, &1 gates the true output of the first bit of A, whereas &'2 gates the complement of the first bit of A. ∨3 mixes these two outputs. The unshifted output passes from ∨3 through &4 into the first bit of B. For a right shift, the output of ∨3 passes through &5 and ∨6 into the second bit of B. This logic is repeated for each bit in the register. Typical computers use registers of 24 to 60 bits.

To portray the entire register in this fashion is unnecessary and tiresome. One alternative is to use the pipeline notation in which a set of signals is represented by a pipeline (a pair of parallel lines). However, although

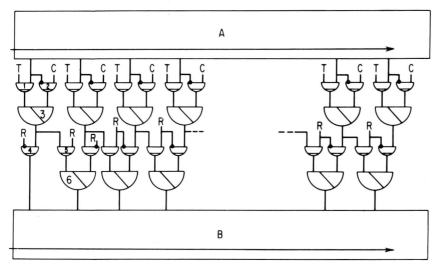

FIGURE 4.1.1 Typical interconnections of two systems

satisfactory for the intermediate stages, separate indications would be required for the extreme right- and left-hand stages.

A more workable simplification for the whole mess of Figure 4.1.1 is shown in Figure 4.1.2. The double vertical line connecting A and B indicates a direct transfer of A to B. The T next to this double line indicates that this path is used when a "true" signal is present. The solid double vertical line connecting A and B with a C next to it indicates that the output of A is inverted before it is entered into B and that this takes place when

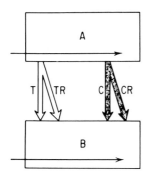

FIGURE 4.1.2 Another version of Figure 4.1.1 using the simplified symbols

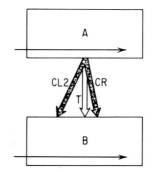

FIGURE 4.1.3 Simplified symbols used to portray another interconnection of registers A and B

a "complement" signal is present. The double slanted line from A to B indicates that the output of A is shifted to the right as it is entered into B when the "true right" signal is present. The slanted solid line from A to B indicates that the inverted output of A is entered into B when the "complement right" signal is present.

Another example of this type of symbol is found in Figure 4.1.3. A is entered directly into B for the T signal; A is complemented and shifted right one position for the CR signal; A is complemented and shifted two places to the left for the CL2 signal.

Register Arrangement for Addition

There are several arrangements of the registers which can be used for parallel addition. Figure 4.1.4 indicates an arrangement that is called a **single-rank accumulator**. The augend and the addend are entered, from memory, into the B and A registers respectively. The addend may be present from a previous calculation and, therefore, a transfer from memory may not be required for it. At any rate, assume the two numbers to be added are in A and B.

The adder receives the numbers to be added from their respective registers and produces a sum output. Present circuitry is so fast that the sum can be entered from the adder into the A register before the change in the

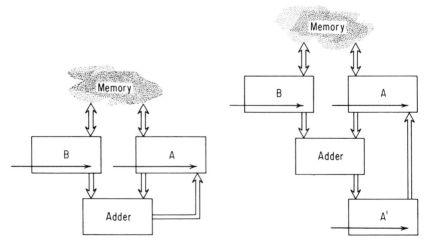

FIGURE 4.1.4 The single-rank accumulator

FIGURE 4.1.5 The double-rank accumulator

A register is reflected in a change in the sum from the adder. In other words, there is a minimum time required from the application of the signals to the adder until the adder produces a usable sum output. Further time is required to pass this sum signal to the receiving register.

What happens if we make one of the source registers, say A, also the receiving register? Let us call the minimum transit time T_m. At time T_m, some signal, probably not the correct one, will appear and try to set A. Suppose that by time T_d the sum output is known to be definitely correct, as long as the original inputs are present. While the setting time of A, T_s, is small compared with T_m, we are safe with this method.

Some time T after T_m, strobe the output and start to set A. Some bits of A set before others; but all will be set by T_s. Since T_s is less than T_m, the sum output does not change during this interval. At $T + T_s$, the strobe is removed; the output of the adder is the same as at T until $T + T_m$. When the adder has altered at $T + T_m$, it is too late to affect A because the entry from the adder is blocked.

Figure 4.1.5 illustrates the **double rank accumulator** which gets around the timing problem by avoiding it. Here the output of the adder is entered into a different register labeled A′. In a second operation, the contents of A′ are returned to A. This addition is a two-step operation. Once the sum is stored in A′, the adder is no longer used. Timing problems in this method are not complicated.

4.2 THE ADDER STAGE

The full adder is developed in most introductory texts on computer logic, together with the equations for such a unit. A simple block of an adder unit is shown in Figure 4.2.1. Here the addend and augend bit inputs for a given stage appear as A and B and the carry into the stage from the previous stage is furnished by C'; the unit produces a sum output S and a carry output C. The equations for these functions are

$$C = AB + BC' + AC' \tag{4.2.1}$$

$$S = A\bar{B}\bar{C'} + \bar{A}B\bar{C'} + \bar{A}\bar{B}C' + ABC' \tag{4.2.2}$$

A Simple Adder

Equations (4.2.1) and (4.2.2) are implemented most simply by the logic of Figure 4.2.2. Besides its simplicity, notice that this logic takes only one pair of stages, one & and one ∨, for a signal to reach either output.

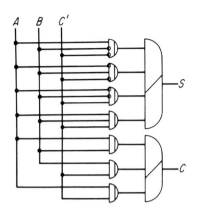

FIGURE 4.2.1 The
parallel adder block

FIGURE 4.2.2 Simple logic
for an adder block

A More Complex Adder

Figure 4.2.3 shows an adder that does not appear to be more efficient. However, note that there are just eight blocks and they are all *two-input* blocks. Finally, there is just one denial or invertor called for.

The carry function C is

$$C = C'(X + Y) + XY \qquad (4.2.3)$$

Upon expansion this is seen to be identical with (4.2.1).

The sum is

$$S = \bar{C}(A + B + C') + ABC' \qquad (4.2.4)$$

which seems reasonable, since it requires a sum output if there is *no* carry out and *any* input or else *all* inputs. If there is a carry, we know there are at

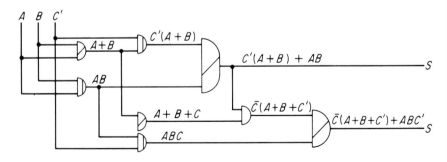

FIGURE 4.2.3 An adder using eight two-input D blocks

least two inputs. Hence, denying a carry indicates, at most, one input. Thus, $C(A + B + C)$ means *exactly one* input and ABC' means *exactly three* inputs. Together, these are the conditions for the sum.

The same reasoning can be put into the more rigorous Boolean form very simply. From (4.2.1) and the definition of the complement as the universal class (I) less the given term(s) we have

$$\bar{C} = I - C = \bar{A}\bar{B}\bar{C}' + \bar{A}BC' + A\bar{B}C' + AB\bar{C}' \qquad (4.2.5)$$

This is applied to the first term of (4.2.4).

$$\bar{C}(A + B + C') = (\bar{A}\bar{B}\bar{C}' + \bar{A}BC' + A\bar{B}C' + AB\bar{C}')\,(A + B + C)$$

$$(4.2.6)$$

However,

$$\bar{A}\bar{B}\bar{C}'(A + B + C') = \wedge \qquad \text{(the null element)} \qquad (4.2.7)$$

$$\bar{A}BC'(A + B + C') = \bar{A}BC' \qquad (4.2.8)$$

$$A\bar{B}C'(A + B + C') = A\bar{B}C' \qquad (4.2.9)$$

$$AB\bar{C}'(A + B + C') = AB\bar{C}' \qquad (4.2.10)$$

Hence,

$$\bar{C}(A + B + C') = \bar{A}BC' + A\bar{B}C' + AB\bar{C}' \qquad (4.2.11)$$

Finally,

$$S = \bar{A}BC' + A\bar{B}C' + AB\bar{C}' + ABC' \qquad (4.2.12)$$

which is the same as (4.2.2).

Adding Into a Register

Another method of addition is found in Figure 4.2.4: the adder augments the accumulator, A, according to the contents of the addend register, B. The trouble with this method is that the adder and accumulator are so closely associated together that it is impossible to add into anything but the accumulator, unless that register also has the adder logic associated with it.

One logic for adding into a register is illustrated by Figure 4.2.5. Let us examine the sum operation first. If there is a B input, the A bit storage is triggered once. If there is a carry from the previous stage, C', A is triggered a little later regardless of whether it was triggered before or not. The final condition of A is 1 in any of the following conditions: $A\bar{B}\bar{C}'$; $\bar{A}B\bar{C}'$;

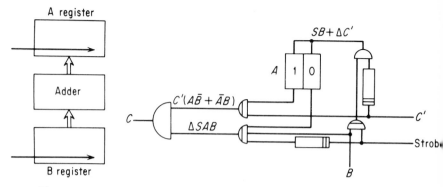

FIGURE 4.2.4
Adding into a register

FIGURE 4.2.5 Logic for adding
into a register

$\bar{A}\bar{B}C'$; the double trigger condition which is ABC'. Hence A', the final condition of A, is given by S in (4.2.2).

A carryout is checked after A has had time to be set by the strobe pulse for the case where the B input is present. For AB, the delayed strobe ΔS passes out of the carry mixer. For the case AB, when the carry-in pulse C' comes along, it finds an A condition and cannot pass out. This is as it should be, for carry information has already been passed over to the next stage as ΔSAB. Should the carry-in pulse find an A condition, it could only arise from $A\bar{B}$ or $\bar{A}B$; hence, C' is passed up to the next stage. Then we have

$$C = AB + C'(A\bar{B} + \bar{A}B) \qquad (4.2.13)$$

which obviously reduces to (4.2.1).

4.3 ADDER TIMING

To facilitate our discussions, we define three new symbols:

$$^1G = AB \qquad (4.3.1)$$

$$^0G = \bar{A}\bar{B} \qquad (4.3.2)$$

$$P = A\bar{B} + \bar{A}B \qquad (4.3.3)$$

^1G is the symbol for a 1-carry generation and is produced only when there is an input on both A and B lines. ^0G is the nongenerate or 0-carry generation, symbol. Such a signal occurs only when both input signals are *absent*. P is the symbol for propagate, which indicates that a carry will be produced if there is an input on the A or the B lines and a carry is present from the previous stage. A 1-carry will exist under the condition

$$^1C = {}^1G + P\,{}^1C' \qquad (4.3.4)$$

where $^1C'$ is a 1-carry from the previous stage.

Carry Configurations and Timing

The problem which presents itself in treating the carry time is due to the propagate stages. With a series of propagate stages, each stage must wait until its predecessor has determined its carry output. To illustrate this point, the symbols in Figure 4.3.1 are used. An empty box indicates a stage

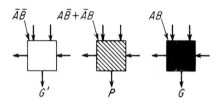

FIGURE 4.3.1 Symbols to distinguish an adder which is in, respective to a 0-generate, a propagate, and a 1-generate state

which *generates* a *no-carry*; we consider both *carry* and *no-carry* outputs, since one of these must be present in order for the stage to be *committed*. A solid box indicates a stage which *generates* a *carry*; such a stage is *committed*, since it immediately has a definite output. A sectioned stage is a propagate stage; it is *not committed* and has no output until a suitable input is provided.

Figure 4.3.2 shows a typical arrangement of carries which might occur in a string of adder stages. Carry outputs from stages F1, F2, F3, F8, and F12 occur immediately. The other stages await the decision of their predecessors. Thus, the carry output from F4 will be 1 when that stage receives the carry input from F3. Continuing down the line, F7 will not produce a 1 output until it receives the 1 input from F6, which in turn waits for F5 which is waiting for F4 which must be actuated by F3. As you can see, the worse case is as bad as that shown in Figure 4.3.3, where all stages between the first and the last are propagate stages. The last stage cannot respond until the first stage has sent its signal all the way down the line.

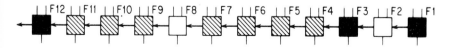

FIGURE 4.3.2 A typical carry state representation for a set of parallel adders

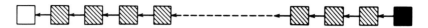

FIGURE 4.3.3   The worst carry state representation for a set of
parallel adders

Solutions for the Timing Problem

The first solution to the problem presented above is to allow the adder stages to function as described without interference and to provide sufficient time for the worst case to be completed. The time required for the case of Figure 4.3.3 is calculated or measured. After the addition process is started, this maximum time is waited out. Then the output of the adder is entered into its destination register. This adder is called **synchronous**. It produces a usable sum in *a fixed length of time regardless of the numbers being added*. Synchronous adders are covered in Section 4.4.

The second solution provides a means for reporting when each stage has completed its task of carry generation or propagation and of sum-bit generation. The **full word adder** indicates that the addition process is complete when all stages have reported that their task is complete. Now, since some stages produce no carry, they must also be able to report when 0-carry (another name for no carry) is the proper output for a stage. In other words, when a stage has settled down, it either produces a 1-carry or a 0-carry output that it can report. Before then it has *no* carry output. Full word adders are self-timing; their operating time depends upon the size and character of the numbers being added (see Section 4.5).

Another solution is to examine the inputs to a number of stages and, somehow, simultaneously predict the carry outputs for this group of stages. This is called the **carry lookahead**. (For detailed discussion, see Chapter 5.)

The last method to be considered is called the **conditional sum method** in which we produce double-sum and carry outputs from each stage on the two assumptions of a 0 carryin or a 1 carryin. In successive stages, we determine which of these assumptions is true for groups of carry blocks (see Chapter 6).

4.4 THE SYNCHRONOUS ADDER

The arrangement of units to perform addition which results in the most time-consuming parallel method is called the synchronous adder, Figure

4.4.1. The A register contains the augend which has been placed there during a previous operation. To start addition, we transfer the addend from memory to the B register. After that register has had time to settle down, it may be used by the adder. The signal which enters the augend, delayed by a delay unit, can also signal the adder to perform addition.

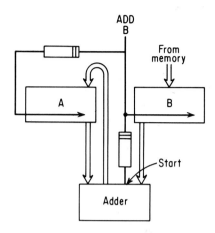

FIGURE 4.4.1   The synchronous adder

A set of full adders are arrayed together to yield the combination of Figure 4.4.1, as in Figure 4.4.2. Each of the boxes contains the logic of a full adder, such as that of Figure 4.2.2, Figure 4.2.3, or even Figure 4.2.5, the register and adder are integral.

The adder examines the true quantity emanating from the A and B registers and performs addition. As discussed in the previous section, the time required for the carry to ripple from one end of the adder to the other is a variable. Therefore, we must allow for the worst case. The ADD B signal, delayed by a time dictated by the worse case, is used to enter the sum produced by the adder into the A register.

The entry of the sum into the A register corrupts the input to the adder; but as long as the sum is transferred intact, we do not care what happens to the augend and we can inhibit further output from the adder.

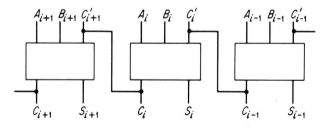

FIGURE 4.4.2

4.5 SELF-TIMING ADDER

In order to make the adder self-timing, each adding unit must have facilities for reporting a 1-carry and a 0-carry. The adder stage can report either a 1-carry, a 0-carry, or neither, but not both. Neither carry would be reported when the carry from *this* stage depends upon the carry from a previous stage which has not reported in yet—the propagate case.

Equations

We have distinguished two cases of carry generation: the generation of a 1-carry indicated by the symbol ^1G, defined in (4.3.1); a 0-carry which is defined when both A and B inputs are absent, defined by (4.3.2). The propagate indicated by P, was defined by (4.3.3).

A 1-carry is produced from *this stage*, if there is a 1-generate from this stage or if there is a propagate in this stage and there was a 1-carry from the previous stage. This relation is

$$^1C = {}^1G + {}^1C'P \qquad (4.5.1)$$

where $^1C'$ is the 1-carry from the previous stage. The similar condition that this stage will issue a 0-carry is

$$^0C = {}^0G + {}^0C'P \qquad (4.5.2)$$

where, similarly, $^0C'$ is a 0-carry from the previous stage.

Block Arrangement

The arrangement of the stages of the self-timing, or **asynchronous** adder, is illustrated in Figure 4.5.1. Each stage has two carry inputs (0 and 1) and two carry outputs (0 and 1). Remember that, for any stage, an output signal may be present on either carry line or on neither, but not on both. For each pair of output lines in Figure 4.5.1, you will note a $\vee$-mixer. Its output

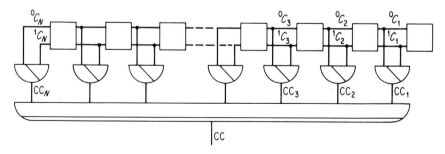

FIGURE 4.5.1   Carry-complete logic for the asynchronous adder

indicates whether a signal has appeared on either one of these lines. One large &-gate monitors all the mixers and produces an output only when every stage has reported in.

Logic

In Figure 4.5.2, we see the logic for the carry production of a single stage. &1 produces a 0-carry propagate signal, &2 produces a 1-carry propagate signal. $\vee 3$ produces a 0-carry signal, if a 0-carry generate or 0-carry propagate signal occur; $\vee 4$ produces a 1-carry signal, if either a 1-

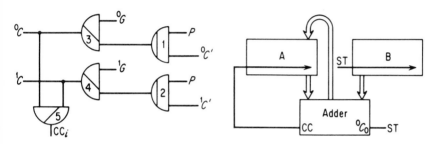

FIGURE 4.5.2   Carry logic, asynchronous   FIGURE 4.5.3   Full asynchronous
                       adder   accumulator

carry generate or a 1-carry propagate signal are present. $\vee 5$ monitors the two carry output lines and produces a signal, CC_i, when one of the carry lines bears a signal. There is a carry-complete mixer for each stage. They report to the add-complete gate of Figure 4.5.1. When all of them have reported in, *then* addition is nominally complete.

Accumulator Block Diagram

In Figure 4.5.3, we see the system layout for the asynchronous single-rank accumulator. The augend is entered into the B register from memory by the start signal ST. This signal is also entered into the input of the first adder stage as a 0-carry input for addition. Each stage of the adder then begins to function, and, when all stages have produced a carry signal of one sort or another, the adder will produce a carry-complete signal, CC. This indicates that a sum has been produced by the adder and now can be transferred to its destination. The carry-complete signal provides the means of entering the sum from the adder into the A register.

This method of performing addition achieves a high efficiency factor as opposed to the synchronous method. Statistical analysis and the theory of runs has shown that, on the average, the time required for addition by this method is approximately the transit time for seven stages for a 48-bit adder. The completion time for the synchronous adder of 48 stages would, naturally, be 48 stages of transit time.

Why would one choose a synchronous adder when, for only a small additional cost in the total computer, a much faster adder could be furnished? When the overall computer speed is limited by some other unit than the processor (the memory, perhaps), increasing the processor's speed *does not* produce an increase in computational speed and is *not* worth the adder cost. Further, asynchronous operation requires more complicated logic for handling multiplication and division, thereby causing the cost to rise again. Thus, for some computers the decreased *cost* and *speed* may be desirable.

More detail is presented on the matter of the time required for addition in Section 6.8 where other methods of doing fast addition are compared and contrasted.

PROBLEMS

4.1 The asynchronous adder requires a carry-complete gate N bits wide. How may this be achieved in practice?

4.2 Convert the asynchronous adder to NOR logic; include the N-wide gate.

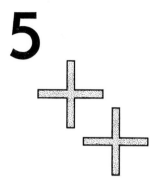

5

THE CARRY LOOKAHEAD ADDER

5.1 THE PRINCIPLE

The principle of carry lookahead is to examine a number of stages of inputs to the adder and, simultaneously, to produce the proper carries for each of these stages. These carries are then applied to the adder block for each stage which then produces the proper sum bit.

In its simplest form, the carry lookahead would be incorporated into a system as shown in Figure 5.1. Notice that a group of A inputs and B inputs is applied to a carry unit, together with the initial carry input. The carry into the least significant bit (zero in the case of normal addition) is automatically entered. The carry unit produces all the carries required for this group of inputs; the sum block then produces the sum outputs. Notice that there are other levels incorporated in this scheme. Although it is conceivable that all the carries and sums for a complete register could be calculated in two steps, this would require gates and mixers with a large number of inputs. Present circuit designs make this method prohibitive.

Let us examine an adder which performs the carry function with a lookahead on several levels. At the bottom level, the zero level, we find the carry outputs for a number of stages, say five. The carry output of the fifth stage is then applied to another carry unit at the next or first level, producing the carries for the sixth to tenth stages. This unit requires the carryout of the fifth stage as one input and so must wait for the completion of the zero-

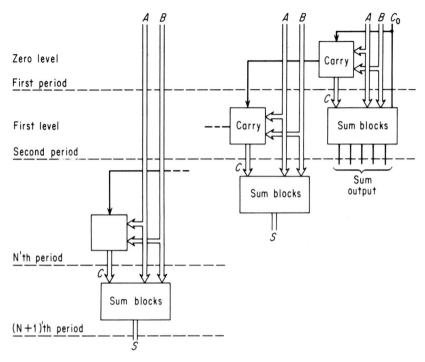

FIGURE 5.1   The simplest carry lookahead adder system

level carry unit. In this fashion we may produce all the carries for the adder in a number of time periods proportional to the number of levels. These are then applied to sum blocks which produce the sum bits in a single period.

Carry lookahead may be done using only simple lookahead units which determine a set of carries for a set of pairs of bits to be added. These units can operate only when *the carry into the set under consideration* is available. This zero-level unit is discussed in Section 5.2. The unit to produce the sum from this set of carries and the bit pairs is discussed in Section 5.3.

To make the lookahead more effective, it is possible to perform sets of logical operations at different time periods so that in the last time period all sums and carries are available in a shorter total elapsed time. This requires the preparation, in sequence, of intermediate logical quantities to be used to prepare the final logical variables.

In fact, in the most efficient, large-word, lookahead systems, the auxiliary logical expressions are used to form *further auxiliary logical expressions.* Only in the final step are they used to obtain the result, the sum bits. Sections 5.4, 5.5, and 5.6 explore the use of auxiliary functions for carry lookahead addition.

5.2 ZERO-LEVEL CARRY LOOKAHEAD UNIT

Equations

We will use the definition for 1-carry generate and 1-carry propagate presented in the previous sections; that is,

$$G_i = A_i B_i \qquad (5.2.1)$$

$$P_i = A_i \bar{B}_i + \bar{A}_i B_i \qquad (5.2.2)$$

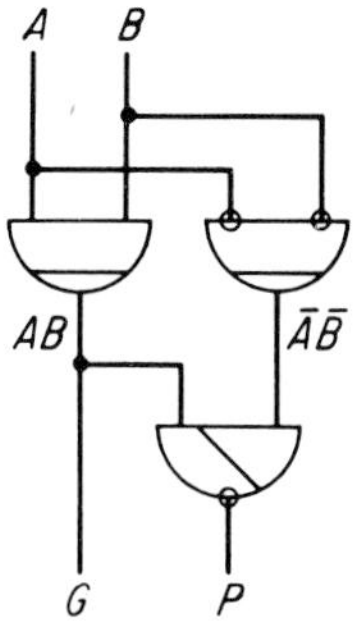

Since we are only concerned with 1-carries, we have dropped the left superscript. The 1-carry output, C_k, for the kth stage in terms of the carry output of the previous stage, C_{k-1}, is

$$C_k = G_k + P_k C_{k-1} \qquad (5.2.3)$$

We can now define the carryout of this stage in terms of the carry in the two previous stages in an iterative equation. Thus,

$$C_k = G_k + P_k(G_{k-1} + P_{k-1}C_{k-2}) \qquad (5.2.4)$$

$$= G_k + P_k G_{k-1} + P_k P_{k-1} C_{k-2} \qquad (5.2.5)$$

FIGURE 5.2.1 Logic of the block which forms G and P

Continuing in this fashion, we can define the carry output of this stage in terms of the carry input to the adder as

$$C_k = G_k + P_k G_{k-1} + P_k P_{k-1} G_{k-2} + \cdots + P_k P_{k-1} P_{k-2} \cdots P_1 C_0 \qquad (5.2.6)$$

Let us add the following definition:

$$G_0 = C_0 \qquad (5.2.7)$$

Then we can write

$$C_k = G_k + \left(\prod_{i=k}^{k} P_i\right)G_{k-3} + \left(\prod_{i=k-1}^{k} P_i\right)G_{k-2} + \left(\prod_{i=k-2}^{k} P_i\right)G_{k-3}$$

$$+ \cdots + \left(\prod_{i=1}^{k} P_i\right)G_0 \qquad (5.2.8)$$

Examining the terms of (5.2.8) one at a time, we see that each one consists of a *generate term* and the *product of a number of propagate terms*. Thus, the equation above says, "We have a carry if this stage generates it, or if the previous stage generates it and this stage can propagate it, or if the next previous stage generates it and it is propagated by this stage and the previous stage, etc." The final term says, "We get a carry from this stage if there is an initial carry and all the intervening stages propagate it."

Equation (5.2.8) can be written in more compact form, as follows:

$$C_k = \sum_{j=0}^{k} \prod_{i=j+1}^{k} P_i G_j \qquad (5.2.9)$$

Implementation

Before we can examine the logic to produce the G and P terms for each stage, we should take another look at the equations. As far as the hardware is concerned, the combined generate and propagate function P' may be substituted for the propagate-only function. First define

$$P'_i = G_i + P_i \qquad (5.2.10)$$

Let us just see how this could be substituted in (5.2.3). We have

$$G_i + P'_i G_{i-1} = G_i + (G_i + P_i) G_{i-1} \qquad (5.2.11)$$

$$= G_i + G_i G_{i-1} + P_i G_{i-1} \qquad (5.2.12)$$

$$= G_i + P_i G_{i-1} \qquad (5.2.13)$$

The point of this discussion is to show that a combined function P' may be substituted for the propagate-only function in all equations above, and even those which follow, if the designer so decides. These may be simpler to form with the circuits at his disposal; thus,

$$P' = A + B \qquad (5.2.14)$$

$$P = A\bar{B} + \bar{A}B = \overline{(AB + \bar{A}\bar{B})} \qquad (5.2.15)$$

We choose (5.2.15) and implement it with the logic of Figure 5.2.1.

Let us now set up the logic for a five-stage lookahead unit, Figure 5.2.2. The first carry function C_1 is formed by combining two terms. The first term is produced in &1; the other term is G_1; they are combined in ∨2. In a similar fashion, the terms for each carry function are formed in an &-block and combined in a ∨-block. Thus four of the five terms for C_4 are formed by &11, &12, &13, and &14, and they are combined with G_4 in ∨15 to yield C_4. Similarly, C_5 is formed using &16 through &20, G_5, and ∨21.

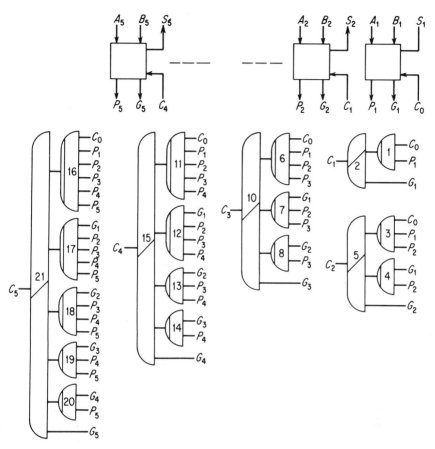

FIGURE 5.2.2   The five stage, zero level, carry lookahead logic

The number of stages for which a zero-level carry lookahead logic can be used depends upon the circuit modules available and is limited by the maximum fan-in (number of inputs) of the &-gate.

These five-stage units are used as in Figure 5.1. During the first period, the zero-level carry unit produces carries C_1 through C_5. During the second period, these are used by the sum block to produce the sum bits S_1 through S_6. At the same time, the next zero-level carry unit is producing the carries C_6 through C_{10}. During the third period, sum bits S_7 through S_{11} are produced and carry bits C_{11} through C_{15} are constructed. This arrangement continues and it can be seen that the number of periods required for a given adder is determined by dividing the number of stages by the number of stages of carries produced by the zero-level unit and adding 1 to it. The

"1" comes from the fact that an extra period is required to produce the sum bits after the last carry unit has produced its utput.

5.3 THE SUM BLOCK

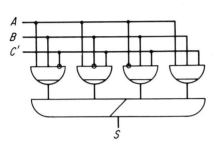

FIGURE 5.3   The sum block

The function of the sum block is to produce a sum bit. Let us consider the ith stage, but let us drop the subscript i. Then the sum block is furnished with the A and B bits and the carry from the previous stage, C'. It produces an output if only a single one of these is true or if all are true.

$$S = A\bar{B}\bar{C}' + \bar{A}B\bar{C}' + \bar{A}\bar{B}C' + ABC'$$

$$(5.3.1)$$

Chapter 4 shows several ways that this equation can be put into hardware. In addition, a straightforward, single logic level (& and $\vee$ in sequence) is found in Figure 5.3.

5.4 FIRST-LEVEL AUXILIARY FUNCTIONS

System

Figure 5.4.1 illustrates the arrangement used when first-level auxiliary functions are present. What we are going to do is produce auxiliary outputs during one time period which will be used by the carry lookahead circuits to produce the carries during the next period which, in turn, are used by the sum blocks in the period which follows. In the first period of the logic illustrated in Figure 5.4.1, we find that the initial set of carry lookaheads are produced. At the same time, the first-level auxiliary functions are produced for the next set of sum inputs. In the second period, the first sum blocks produce an output, the second set of zero-level carry lookahead produces its output, and the second set of first-level auxiliary functions produces its output.

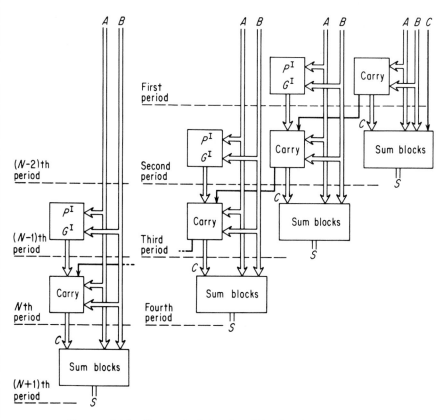

FIGURE 5.4.1 Carry lookahead with first-level auxiliary generators

Equations

To visualize the mathematics before plunging into the actual equations, let us recall that the carry for any given stage is given as a sum of products, as shown in Figure 5.4.2. Any one of these product terms consists of a

$$\Pi + \Pi + \Pi + \Pi \quad - \quad - \quad - \quad - \quad \Pi \qquad \text{Carry as the sum of products}$$

$$\overbrace{\Pi \; F \cdot F \cdot F \cdot F} \qquad \qquad \text{one term}$$

$$= \Pi \; F \cdot F \cdot F \; \Pi \; F \cdot F \cdot F \cdots F \; \Pi \; \cdots \; \Pi \; F \cdot F \cdot F \cdot \qquad \text{as the product of several products of factors}$$

FIGURE 5.4.2 Decomposition of the lookahead-carry formula

number of factor, and there is no reason why these factors cannot be grouped conveniently, as in the bottom line of Figure 5.4.2. We group the factors into products that can be conveniently formed in a single time period. In the next time period, these products are multiplied (logically) to yield the carry.

The exact statement for the carry for any given stage was defined in (5.2.9).

$$C_k = \sum_{i=0}^{k} \prod_{i=j+1}^{k} P_i G_i \tag{5.2.9}$$

Now we define the following auxiliary functions.

$$P_a^{\mathrm{I}} = \prod_{(a-1)g+1}^{ag} P_i \qquad G_a^{\mathrm{I}} = \sum_{j=(a-1)g+1}^{ag} \prod_{i=j+1}^{ag} P_i G_j \tag{5.4.1}$$

where g is the number of stages per group and a is the number of the first-level auxiliary function. The carry produced at the end of a group of stages is defined as

$$C_{ag} = C_a^{\mathrm{I}} = \sum_{0}^{ag} \prod_{j+1}^{ag} P_i G_j \tag{5.4.2}$$

$$= \sum_{0}^{a} \prod_{j+1}^{a} P_i^{\mathrm{I}} G_j^{\mathrm{I}} \tag{5.4.3}$$

Logic

The logic for forming the auxiliary functions of (5.4.1) is shown in Figure 5.4.3. The generate function is a logical sum of logical products. The logical products are formed with the &-blocks; the logical sum of these products is formed with the ∨-mixer. The propagate auxiliary function is simply a logical product and is formed using an &-block, as shown on the right side of Figure 5.4.3.

Next let us examine how these auxiliary functions are used to form the carry for any given stage. We take (5.2.6) and rewrite it in terms of the carry from the first major group. Then,

$$C_k = G_k + P_k G_{k-1} + P_k P_{k-1} G_{k-2} + \cdots + P_k P_{k-1} \cdots P_{ag+1} C_{ag} \tag{5.4.4}$$

Then this is written in summation and product notation as

$$C_k = \sum_{ag+1}^{k} \prod_{j+1}^{k} P_i G_j + \prod_{ag+1}^{k} P_i C_{ag} \tag{5.4.5}$$

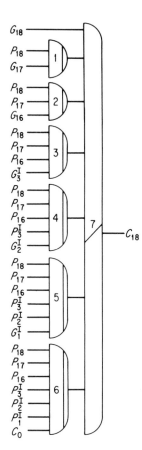

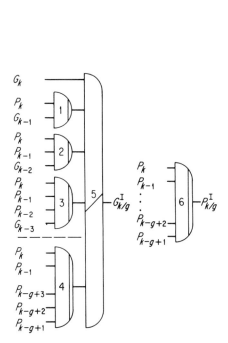

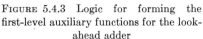

FIGURE 5.4.3 Logic for forming the first-level auxiliary functions for the look-ahead adder

FIGURE 5.4.4 Generating the carry C_{18} using first-level auxiliary functions

The second term of this equation can be further reduced by using the expression for the carry, C_{ag}, as given in (5.4.3). We then have

$$C_k = \sum_{ag+1}^{k} \prod_{j+1}^{k} P_i G_j + \prod_{ag+1}^{k} P_i \sum_{0}^{a} \prod_{j+1}^{a} P_i^{\mathrm{I}} G_j^{\mathrm{I}} \qquad (5.4.6)$$

Example

To put these principles into practice, we assume that groups consist of five stages and that we wish to produce the carry from the eighteenth stage. We, of course, have all the P's and G's available immediately. During the first time period, we prepare the auxiliary functions, P_1^I, G_1^I. In the second and third time period, we prepare P_2^I, G_2^I, P_3^I, and G_3^I.

In this instance to find the eighteenth-stage carryout, we use the logic of Figure 5.4.4, as used in the fourth time period. The equation to be implemented is,

$$C_{18} = G_{18} + P_{18}G_{17} + P_{18}P_{17}G_{16} + P_{18}P_{17}P_{16}G_3^I + P_{18}P_{17}P_{16}P_3^I G_2^I$$

$$+ P_{18}P_{17}P_{16}P_3^I P_2^I G_1^I + P_{18}P_{17}P_{16}P_3^I P_2^I P_1^I C_0^1 \quad (5.4.7)$$

If a carry is generated in the eighteenth stage, this appears directly as the first input G_{18} to $\vee 7$. If a carry is generated in the seventeenth stage and propagated through the eighteenth stage, this is determined by &1. If a carry is generated in the sixteenth stage and propagated through the seventeenth and eighteenth stages, this is determined by &2. If a carry is generated by the third group and propagated by the sixteenth, seventeenth, and eighteenth stages, this is determined by &3. Similarly, a carry generated by the first or second group is checked for by &5 and &4 respectively. A carry in the eighteenth stage which is a result of the original carry input, C_0, is determined by &6.

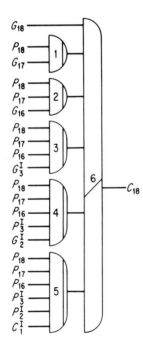

FIGURE 5.4.5 Generating the carry C_{18} using first-level auxiliary functions and C_1^I

We can combine the function of &5 and &6 in Figure 5.4.4 by simply examining the carryout of the first carry lookahead stage as in Figure 5.4.5 where &5 provides this combined function.

It should be noted before leaving these first-level auxiliary functions that these functions provide an advantage approximately proportional to the group size. Returning to Figure 5.4.1, let us assume that the carry lookahead group is of size five. Then, during the first period, auxiliary functions for five stages can be prepared. In the second period, the zero-level carry lookahead units take these auxiliary functions and prepare five carry outputs, carries C_6 through C_{10}. Similarly, in the third period, carries C_{11} through C_{15} will be prepared, and so forth.

5.5   SECOND-LEVEL AUXILIARY FUNCTIONS

System

The use of the second-level auxiliary functions is illustrated in Figure 5.5.1. We use the first-level axuiliary functions to produce second-level auxiliary functions. The advantage of this method is proportional to the

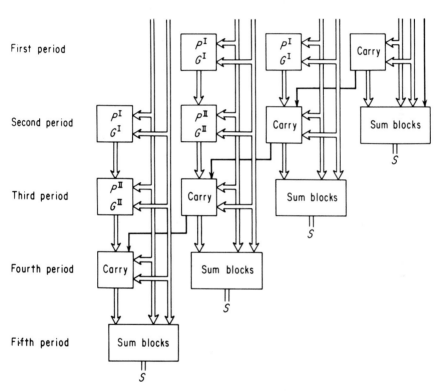

FIGURE 5.5.1   Carry lookahead using first- and second-level function generators

square of the group size. Assuming our group size again to be five, we would find, in Figure 5.5.1, that the carries for the first five stages are prepared during the first period, the first-level auxiliary functions for stages six through ten are prepared here and also the second-level auxiliary functions for stages eleven through thirty-five. In the periods that follow, the first-level functions are used to prepare the second-level functions; these are combined in the proper proportions to produce the desired stage carries. Of course, the aim of the whole setup is to produce the proper sum in as short a time as possible. Exact times are deferred to Section 6.8, where all adder times are compared.

Equations

Figure 5.5.2 shows how the equations for a given carry lookahead can be decomposed into auxiliary groups. The first line shows the sum of products,

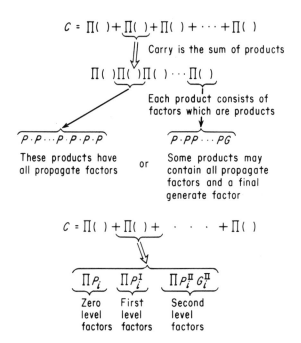

FIGURE 5.5.2 Decomposition of the carry lookahead function into first- and second-level auxiliary functions

as was presented in Figure 5.4.2. Each product will now be viewed as consisting of the product of factors. We can then break down each factor into further factors, as shown as the bottom of Figure 5.4.2. In any given term, we then have zero-level propagate factors, first-level propagate factors, and second-level factors which include one generate factor. The carry consists of a number of similar terms.

Now we define the second-level auxiliary functions as

$$P_a^{II} = \prod_{(a-1)g^2+1}^{ag^2} P_i = \prod_{(a-1)g+1}^{ag} P_i^I \qquad (5.5.1)$$

$$G_a^{II} = \sum_{j=(a-1)g^2+1}^{ag^2} \prod_{j+1}^{ag^2} P_i G_j = \sum_{j=(a-1)g+1}^{ag} \prod_{i=j+1}^{ag} P_i^I G_j^I \qquad (5.5.1)$$

These second-level functions are formed using the same principles as were employed in getting the first-level functions. The logic for forming the first-level functions was illustrated in Figure 5.4.3; the comparable logic

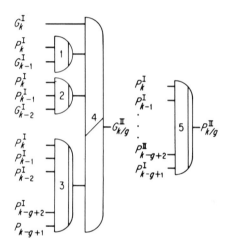

FIGURE 5.5.3   Logic for forming the second-level auxiliary functions for the carry lookahead adder

for finding the second-level functions is found in Figure 5.5.3. Here first-level functions alone are used to form the second-level functions.

The equations for the carry from a group of groups (g^2 stages) is

$$C_{ag^2} = C_{ag}^I = C_a^{II} = \sum_{j=0}^{ag^2} \prod_{i=j+1}^{ag^2} P_i G_j \qquad (5.5.3)$$

$$= \sum_{j=0}^{a} \prod_{i=j+1}^{a} P_i^{II} G_j^{II} \qquad (5.5.4)$$

where (5.5.4) gives this carry in terms of second-level functions. To find the carryout of any given stage and to write it in terms of first- and second-level functions, we refer to (5.2.6) and group the terms in such a way as to embody the desired function. This results in the following mess:

$$C_k = G_k + P_k G_{k-1} + P_k P_{k-1} G_{k-2} + \cdots + P_k P_{k-1} \cdots P_{dg+2} G_{dg+1}$$

$$+ (P_k P_{k-1} \cdots P_{dg+1})(G_d^{\mathrm{I}} + P_d^{\mathrm{I}} G_{d-1}^{\mathrm{I}} + \cdots$$

$$+ P_d^{\mathrm{I}} P_d^{\mathrm{I}} \cdots P_{d-b+2}^{\mathrm{I}} G_{d-b+1}^{\mathrm{I}})$$

$$+ (P_k P_{k-1} \cdots P_{dg+1})(P_d^{\mathrm{I}} P_{d-1}^{\mathrm{I}} \cdots P_{d-b+2}^{\mathrm{I}} P_{d-b+1}^{\mathrm{I}})(G_a^{\mathrm{II}} + P_a^{\mathrm{II}} G_{a-1}^{\mathrm{II}}$$

$$+ \cdots + P_a^{\mathrm{II}} P_{a-1}^{\mathrm{II}} \cdots P_1^{\mathrm{II}} G_0^{\mathrm{II}}) \tag{5.5.5}$$

where $k = ag^2 + ba + c$ and $d = ag + b$. The nature of this equation can be observed best by converting it into the summation and product notation as

$$C_k = \sum_{j=ag^2+bg+1}^{i,j \ ag^2+bg+c} \prod_{i=j+1} P_i G_j + \prod_{ag^2+bg+1}^{ag^2+bg+c} \sum_{j=ag+1}^{ag+b} \prod_{i=j+1}^{ag+b} P_i^{\mathrm{I}} G_j^{\mathrm{I}}$$

$$+ \prod_{ag^2+bg+1}^{ag^2+bg+c} P_i \prod_{ag+1}^{ag+b} P_i^{\mathrm{I}} \sum_{j=0}^{a} \prod_{i=j+1}^{a} P_i^{\mathrm{II}} G_j^{\mathrm{II}} \tag{5.5.6}$$

Example

Before explaining this equation, let us see how it would be used. Let us try to form the carry C_{63} using the first- and second-level auxiliary functions. The equation thus developed is given as,

$$C_{63} = G_{63} + P_{63} G_{62} + P_{63} P_{62} G_{61} + P_{63} P_{62} P_{61} G_{12}^{\mathrm{I}} + P_{63} P_{62} P_{61} P_{12}^{\mathrm{I}} G_{11}^{\mathrm{I}}$$

$$+ P_{63} P_{62} P_{61} P_{12}^{\mathrm{I}} P_{11}^{\mathrm{I}} G_2^{\mathrm{II}} + P_{63} P_{62} P_{61} P_{12}^{\mathrm{I}} P_{11}^{\mathrm{I}} P_2^{\mathrm{II}} G_1^{\mathrm{II}} \tag{5.5.7}$$

The logic to implement this equation is illustrated in Figure 5.5.4. The top input to $\vee 7$ is from a possible carry generated in stage sixty-three. If it is generated in stage sixty-two and propagated through stage sixty-three, $\&1$ indicates this. A carry propagated in stage sixty-one and propagated through the next two stages is formed in $\&2$. $\&3$ indicates when a carry is produced in group twelve and propagated through the remaining stages. A similar condition for group eleven is provided by $\&4$. $\&5$ provides for a carry generated in the second-level group and propagated onward. A carry which is produced by the first second-level group and propagated upward is detected by $\&6$. Thus all eventualities have been accounted for.

Now let us return to examine (5.5.6). The first summation term in that equation indicates carries which are generated in zero-level stages, the second term accounts for carries which are generated in the first-level functions are are propagated through the zero-level stages. The final term accounts for carries which are generated in the larger second-level groups and are propagated down the line through the other second-level groups, the other first-level groups, and, finally, up through the zero-level stages and out of this stage.

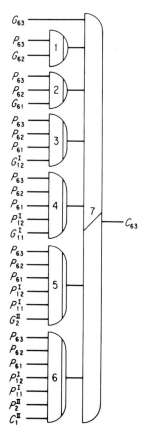

FIGURE 5.5.4 Producing the carry C_{63} using first- and second-level auxiliary functions and C_1^{II}, carry lookahead adder

5.6 FURTHER LEVELS

Of course, there is no need to stop at two levels. This process can be generalized to three, four, or more levels, but it would result in a rather large adder with many more bits than are presently used as a single computer word. However, for the sake of completeness, let us present how the carry for any given stage can be represented in terms of multiple levels of auxiliary functions. The fully generalized equation appears with appropriate notes in Figure 5.6. From the previous discussion, what happens as each new level of auxiliary function is added should be apparent.

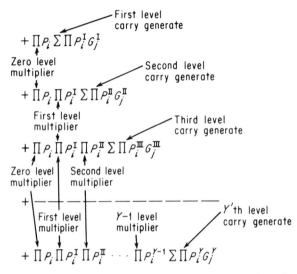

FIGURE 5.6 The generalized carry lookahead equation; the carry into the kth stage using Y levels of auxiliary functions

PROBLEMS

5.1 Design a complete 15-bit adder using zero-level lookahead principles. Lay out and interconnect all the functional blocks required. Use three sets of lookahead to do addition in five periods: one for forming the P's and G's, three for the carry sets, one for the final sums. Detail the logic required in each kind of functional block.

5.2 a. Write the equation for C_{29} for an adder using first-level auxiliary functions and the group size, g, is 5. Draw the block as in Figure 5.4.5.
   b. Again, for C_{29}, write the equation and draw the block, but assume second-level auxiliary functions.

5.3 Design a 42-bit adder with first- and second-level auxiliary functions. Choose g. Determine its speed. Compare and contrast with asynchronous adder.

5.4 Design a 54-bit adder with *third*-level auxiliary functions where $g = 3$. Sketch contents of representative block at each level. How does this compare with other design choices?

5.5 Consider a ten-bit zero-level lookahead adder. Show the output of each block
for these additions (denominator 1024):
  a. 257 + 254
  b. 767 + 000
  c. 453 + 504
  d. 783 + 015

6

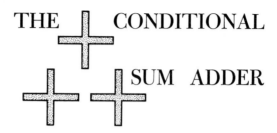

THE CONDITIONAL SUM ADDER

6.1 INTRODUCTION

The conditional sum adder is one of the faster adders available. It is of special interest to designers when circuits of small fan-in are to be used. The logic is easily redesigned so that two-input gates may be used throughout. The conditional sum adder may be an ideal means to meet the challenge of using circuits with small fan-in and fan-out when superspeed circuits are used.

Method

The conditional sum method of performing addition requires that, for each pair of bits to be added, two results are created. The first result, one sum and one carry bit per stage, is prepared as though the carry into a stage were a 0. The second result is prepared as though the carry into that stage were 1 and consists of one sum and one carry bit per stage. Next, these results are examined in pairs. The second-level result for a *pair* of stages is determined by the results of the *first* stage of the pair. This procedure is continued, examining the results in quartets, octets, and so forth.

Figure 6.1 illustrates the conditional sum adder. Two numbers are added by the conditional sum method. The decimal equivalent of the addition is at the left of that figure, the two binary qualities are at the top. In each box on the first level, the top pair of bits is the result for the addition of the two bits for a carryin of 0. The bottom pair is the sum and carry bit where the same two bits are added, but a carryin of 1 is assumed.

The left-hand box, level 1 on the first line, has 01 in it; when 1 and 0 are added with a carryin of 0, the result is a sum bit of 1 and a carry bit of 0. The second line of the left-hand box, level 1, has 10 in it; when 1 and 0 are added with a carryin of 1 present, the result is a sum bit of 0 and a carry bit of 1.

	Carry	Sum								Carryin	Level
30 Augend	0	0	0	1	1	1	1	0			
+177 Addend	1	0	1	1	0	0	0	1			
	0	1	0 0	0 1	1 0	0 1	0 1	0 1	0 1	0	
	1	0	0 1	1 0	1 1	1 0	1 0	1 0	1 0	1	1
	0	1	0	1 0	0	0 1	1	0 1	1	0	
	0	1	1	1 0	1	1 0	0			1	2
	0	1	1	0	0	0 1	1	1	1	0	
	0	1	1	0	1					1	3
207 Sum	0	1	1	0	0	1	1	1	1	0	
										1	4

FIGURE 6.1 An addition by the conditional sum method

In the second level we determine the second sum and carry bits for any given *pair* of input *stages*. In the left-hand box of level 2, both the upper and lower second set of bits are 01 because the carryouts of the first stage of this pair of stages are both 0 (see the second box from the left on level 1). The third line from the left, the carryout of the next-to-the-most significant stage, has been dropped. It was used to determine the value of both pairs of the most significant stage and is no longer of use.

Next, we go from pairs of stages on the second level to quartets on the third level. Examine the second box from the left on the second level; notice that the carryouts from the left-hand groups of this box are both 1 which indicates that we should choose the left-hand pair of outputs which results from a carryin of 1. This pair is listed in the extreme left-hand box of level 2 as 01 1, which entry is then used as the left-hand pair of both left-hand quartets illustrated in level 3.

Each time we go down a level we double the number of stages in each n-tet which we consider. We are finished when the level which we have reached has, for an n-tet, the last half of the entire result.

6.2 SYMBOLOGY

In order to discuss, describe, and properly organize the process of addition using the conditional sum method, we must devise an adequate means of visualizing any term at any level. The symbol used for this is presented in Figure 6.2.1. It allows us to describe any bit appearing anywhere in any level. If the bit under consideration is a carry bit, c appears in the large center box labeled r; if it is a sum bit, s appears in this large box. The presuperscript, the letter at the upper left-hand corner of the main character, indicates whether a 0 or a 1 is the carry into this n-tet— 0 for no-carry, 1 for carry—this is the little box labeled a. The little box labeled p, the presubscript, indicates the position of the given bit in this n-tet. The little box labeled b, the postsubscript, is the number of the bit within the word character, counting from the right.

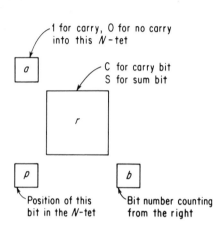

FIGURE 6.2.1 Symbology for the conditional sum logic equation

Examples

As an example, if we are examining the third sum bit from the right when we are at the third level and when there is no carry into this stage, we would designate it as $^0_3S_3$. If we are looking at the carry from the sixteenth bit from the right at the second level, for a carryin of 1 it would be indicated as $^1_2C_{16}$. Note that we designate in the same fashion the carryout of the sixteenth stage from the right for a carry of 1 at the third level, fourth level, and so forth. Also, note that some combinations of numbers in the sub- and superscript position are not admissible; thus, we would not allow the symbol $^1_4S_3$.

Figure 6.2.2 shows how the special symbol introduced above is used to convey a complete conditional sum addition in general terms. The reader should study this figure to be sure that the use of these terms is clear before he proceeds to the detailed explanation of this process.

X_{10} Y_{10}	X_9 Y_9	X_8 Y_8	X_7 Y_7	X_6 Y_6	X_5 Y_5	X_4 Y_4	X_3 Y_3	X_2 Y_2	X_1 Y_1	Carryin	Stage
$^0_1S_{10}$	$^0_1S_9$	$^0_1S_8$	$^0_1S_7$	$^0_1S_6$	$^0_1S_5$	$^0_1S_4$	$^0_1S_3$	$^1_0S_2$	$^0_1S_1$	0	1
$^0_1C_{10}$	$^0_1C_9$	$^0_1C_8$	$^0_1C_7$	$^0_1C_6$	$^0_1C_5$	$^0_1C_4$	$^0_1C_3$	$^0_1C_2$	$^0_1C_1$		
$^1_1S_{10}$	$^1_1S_9$	$^1_1S_8$	$^1_1S_7$	$^1_1S_6$	$^1_1S_5$	$^1_1S_4$	$^1_1S_3$	$^1_1S_2$		1	
$^1_1C_{10}$	$^1_1C_9$	$^1_1C_8$	$^1_1C_7$	$^1_1C_6$	$^1_1C_5$	$^1_1C_4$	$^1_1C_3$	$^1_1C_2$			
$^0_2S_{10}$	$^0_1S_9$	$^0_2S_8$	$^0_1S_7$	$^0_2S_6$	$^0_1S_5$	$^0_2S_4$	$^0_1S_3$	$^0_2S_2$	$^0_1S_1$	0	2
$^0_2C_{10}$		$^0_2C_8$		$^0_2C_6$		$^0_2C_4$		$^0_2C_2$			
$^1_2S_{10}$	$^1_1S_9$	$^1_2S_8$	$^1_1S_7$	$^1_2S_6$	$^1_1S_5$	$^1_2S_4$	$^1_1S_3$			1	
$^1_2C_{10}$		$^1_2C_8$		$^1_2C_6$		$^1_2C_4$					
$^0_2S_{10}$	$^0_1S_9$	$^0_4S_8$	$^0_3S_7$	$^0_2S_6$	$^0_1S_5$	$^0_4S_4$	$^0_3S_3$	$^0_2S_2$	$^0_1S_1$	0	3
		$^0_4C_8$				$^0_4C_4$					
$^1_2S_{10}$	$^1_1S_9$	$^1_4S_8$	$^1_3S_7$	$^1_2S_6$	$^1_1S_5$					1	
		$^1_4C_8$									
$^0_2S_{10}$	$^0_1S_9$	$^0_8S_8$	$^0_7S_7$	$^0_6S_6$	$^0_5S_5$	$^0_4S_4$	$^0_3S_3$	$^0_2S_2$	$^0_1S_1$	0	4
		$^0_8C_8$									
$^1_2S_{10}$	$^1_1S_9$									1	

FIGURE 6.2.2 A portion of an addition by the conditional sum method in symbol form

6.3 SYSTEM CONCEPT

Figure 6.3 illustrates the conditional adder system. Corresponding bits of the addend and augend are entered into a first-level block. Thus, the bits X_5 and Y_5 are entered into the first-level box A_{15}. The first digit of the subscript, 1, indicates that the A is on the first level; the second digit of the subscript, 5, indicates that this is the fifth block or stage on that level. A first-level block generally produces two sum bits and two carry bits; a pair consisting of one sum and one carry bit corresponds to one of the two postulated carryin conditions.

Each second-level box has the two pairs of outputs of an even stage of the first level; it also examines the carry outputs of the *previous even* first-level stage. It chooses two pairs of even first-level inputs (which may be the same) to be the appropriate second-level outputs depending upon the two *conditional carries* from the previous stage. For instance, examine block A_{23}: the first digit of the subscript, 2, indicates that this is a second-level block; the second digit of the subscript, 3, says this is the third of such blocks. It is

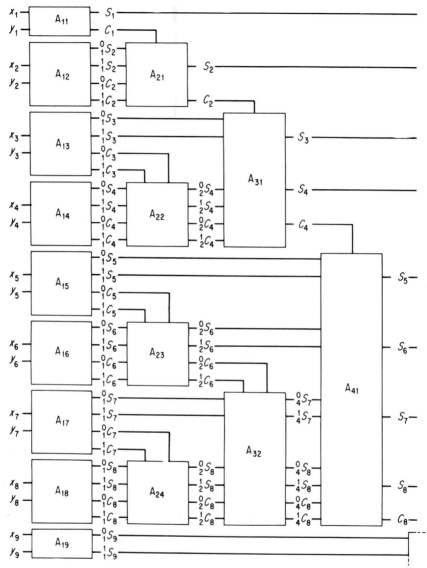

FIGURE 6.3   The system layout of the conditional sum adder

attached to the fifth first-level block A_{15}. It chooses either ${}_1^0S_6$ or ${}_1^1S_6$, to be ${}_2^0S_6$, depending on the conditional carry from the previous stage, ${}_1^0C_5$. Similarly, it chooses between ${}_1^0S_6$ and ${}_1^1S_6$ to fix ${}_2^1S_6$ depending upon ${}_1^1C_5$. The candidates for ${}_2^0C_6$ and ${}_2^1C_6$ are ${}_1^0C_6$ and ${}_1^1C_6$, and the choice for each is also made by referring to ${}_1^0C_5$ and ${}_1^1C_5$ respectively.

The sum bits for the fifth and, in fact, all odd stages are not determined in the second level, but are passed along to a higher level. Therefore, in this case, the fifth stage sum bits, $^0_1S_5$ and $^1_1S_5$, are passed along to the fourth level and, in particular, to block A_{42} where a choice will be made.

The third-level block sends two pairs of sum bits and one pair of carry bits to the next-level block. It obtains a pair of sum bits and a pair of carry bits from the preceding second-level block; it also gets a pair of sum bits directly from a first-level block. The choice of outputs for the given inputs is based upon the carries furnished by another second-level block. In fact, the second-level block whose second digit is one less than the block which is furnishing the sum bits provides the carries for this decision.

In Figure 6.3, higher level blocks have horizontal and vertical inputs. The vertical inputs are used to make the choice between the left-hand inputs to produce the right-hand outputs for a given block. Most blocks have two vertical inputs corresponding to the two conditional carries from the previous stage. When only one input is furnished, a final choice is being made!

The last level of the adder for optimum, 2^n-bit construction has a single carry choice bit entry. It produces half of the sum bit outputs or 2^{n-1}. It also produces a final or overflow carry.

At this point, the reader should review the various inputs and outputs to a higher block and see if he can derive the general case.

6.4 FIRST LEVEL

For the first level, we wish to determine the sum and carry produced by a pair of bits given the two alternatives of a 0 carryin and a 1 carryin. The equations for doing this are

$$^0_1C = XY \tag{6.4.1}$$

$$^0_1S = X\bar{Y} + \bar{X}Y \tag{6.4.2}$$

$$^1_1C = X + Y \tag{6.4.3}$$

$$^1_1S = XY + \bar{X}\bar{Y} \tag{6.4.4}$$

We have dropped the postscript in these equations which lends a feeling of generality to them; they apply to any two *corresponding* bits of the addend and augend we might consider. The logic for finding these outputs is straightforward and is presented in Figure 6.4.

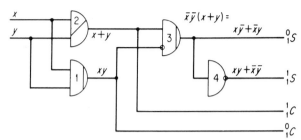

FIGURE 6.4 Conditional sum double half adder

6.5 SECOND LEVEL

Equations

The output for a second-level block is determined by the carry output of the first stage previous to that of the pair under consideration. Let us suppose that β is the number of the first stage which provides the carries to make a choice. These sum and carry bits from the β first level will pass through the second level without change; it is the adjacent set of bits from the $\beta + 1$ first level stage which is subject to change. If the carryout of the β stage is 0, we will choose the upper or 0-pair from the $(\beta + 1)$ stage in Figure 6.2.2; if the carry from the β stage is a 1, we choose the lower or 1-pair from the $\beta + 1$ stage. This is stated for the sum bit in the following two equations

$$^0_2S_{\beta+1} = {}^1_1S_{\beta+1}\,{}^0_1C_\beta + {}^0_1S_{\beta+1}\,{}^0_1\bar{C}_\beta \qquad (6.5.1)$$

$$^1_2S_{\beta+1} = {}^1_1S_{\beta+1}\,{}^1_1C_\beta + {}^0_1S_{\beta+1}\,{}^1_1\bar{C}_\beta \qquad (6.5.2)$$

Equation (6.5.1) states that the second-level sum bit of the pair which is in the $\beta + 1$ position for a 0 carryin to the β stage is determined by the following rule: "If the carry from the β stage is 1 for a 0 carry into that stage, we choose the lower bit illustrated in Figure 6.2.2; if the carry from the β stage is a 0 for a 0 carryin to that stage, we choose the upper sum bit of Figure 6.2.2." Equation (6.5.2) can be similarly analyzed. The carry bit for both cases can be summarized as

$$^a_2C = {}^1_1C_{\beta+1}\,{}^a_1C_\beta + {}^0_1C_{\beta+1}\,{}^a_1C_\beta \qquad (6.5.3)$$

Here the presuperscript a indicates that we can substitute 0 or 1 in this position throughout the equation for a 0 or 1 carryin to the β stage and the equation will be true in either case. Thus (6.5.3) is two equations in one.

Logic

The logic for implementing these equations is shown in Figure 6.5. Note that there is a separate set of blocks for the case: $a = 1$ and $a = 0$. If $^a_1C_\beta$ is 1, it opens &1 and &4; if it is 0 it opens &'2 and &'5. &1 corresponds to the first term of (6.5.1); &'2 is the second term of (6.5.1). The terms

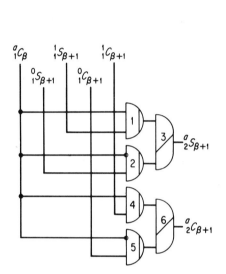

FIGURE 6.5   Second level sum
and carry generation

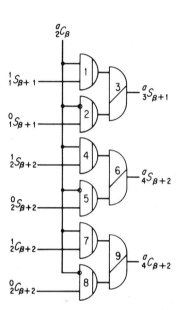

FIGURE 6.6   Third level sum
and carry generation

are combined in $\vee 3$. The output of $\vee 3$ provides the mixing or "or" function in either (6.5.1) or (6.5.2); the equation referred to depends on our choice of a in $^a_1C_\beta$. Similarly, the output of $\vee 6$ satisfies (6.5.3).

6.6   THIRD LEVEL

In the third level we are going to build two quartets of sum bits from pairs of sum bits. The right half of each quartet, the right-hand sum bit pair, will not be affected. It is the left-hand pair that makes up each quartet which is subject to choice. The choice is made by the carryout from the right-hand pair. This carryout is labeled $^a_2C_\beta$. Accordigng to our symbol definition, the postsubscript β indicates that the carry making a choice comes from the β stage; the a indicates that the carry into the quartet is a, which may be either 0 or 1. The presubscript 2 indicates that this carry occurs in position 2 of the quartet. In this level, we convert the first stage of a pair into the third stage of a quartet and the second stage of a pair into the fourth stage of a quartet. The equations for doing this are

$$\substack{a\\3}S_{\beta+1} = \substack{1\\1}S_{\beta+1}\,\substack{a\\2}C_\beta + \substack{0\\1}S_{\beta+1}\,\substack{a\\2}\bar{C}_\beta \tag{6.6.1}$$

$$\substack{a\\4}S_{\beta+2} = \substack{1\\2}S_{\beta+2}\,\substack{a\\2}C_\beta + \substack{0\\2}S_{\beta+2}\,\substack{a\\2}\bar{C}_\beta \tag{6.6.2}$$

$$\substack{a\\4}C_{\beta+2} = \substack{1\\2}C_{\beta+2}\,\substack{a\\2}C_\beta + \substack{0\\2}C_{\beta+2}\,\substack{a\\2}\bar{C}_\beta \tag{6.6.3}$$

The two quartets created are for the values $a = 0$ and $a = 1$. Scrutiny of these equations should reveal what is happening. Note in passing that the intermediate carry, $\substack{a\\2}C_\beta$, is discarded at this level.

The hardware for realizing these equations is illustrated in Figure 6.6. The output of $\vee 3$ corresponds to the sum bit of (6.6.1), of $\vee 6$ to the sum bit of (6.6.2), and of $\vee 9$ to the carry bit of (6.6.3). There is one of these logical blocks for each of the two choices for a. Notice that the carryout of the second stage of the quartet performs the choice for the third level.

6.7   GENERAL CASE

We are going to consider the case of the kth level. Recall that the second level produced two pairs, the third level two quarters, the fourth level two octets, and so forth. Therefore, the kth level produces two n-tets consisting of 2^{k-1} stages. To simplify our discussion, we say that the last previous level, the $(k-1)$th level, consists of α stages. Therefore, α is defined as 2^{k-2}. Also, the kth level produces 2α stages of output; and, for the sake of generalization, let us call the last stage of the preceding $(k-1)$th group σ. To start a permissible group, the following relationship must hold true

$$\sigma = 2c\alpha \tag{6.7.1}$$

where c is a positive integer.

Now in the kth level we wish to produce 2α stages of output. However, the first α output of this n-tet have been fixed by previous processing; it is the second set of α outputs in which we are interested. It is the last stage of the first α stages, β, which produces the carryout which will make the choice possible. Then

$$\beta = \sigma + \alpha \tag{6.7.2}$$

The stages which are of interest are numbered $\beta + 1$ through $\beta + \alpha$ (where

$\beta + \alpha = \sigma + 2\alpha)$. All of these stages will produce sum bit outputs; only the last stage numbered $\beta + \alpha$ will produce a carry output.

Now we write the general equation for a sum bit or carry bit of the second group of α stages in the kth level. These are

$$_{\alpha+i}^{a}S_{\beta+i} = {_i^1}S_{\beta+i}\,{_\alpha^a}C_\beta + {_i^0}S_{\beta+i}\,{_\alpha^a}\bar{C}_\beta \qquad 1 \leq i \leq \alpha \qquad (6.7.3)$$

$$_{2\alpha}^{a}C_{\beta+\alpha} = {_\alpha^1}C_{\beta+\alpha}\,{_\alpha^a}C_\beta + {_\alpha^0}C_{\beta+\alpha}\,{_\alpha^a}\bar{C}_\beta \qquad\qquad (6.7.4)$$

where i refers to the position of the bit whin the second set of α stages of the N-tet which ranges from 1 to α.

Let us substitute numbers into the equations to see how they were divided. Take α as 4 and σ as 8. The picture looks like that in Figure 6.7.1

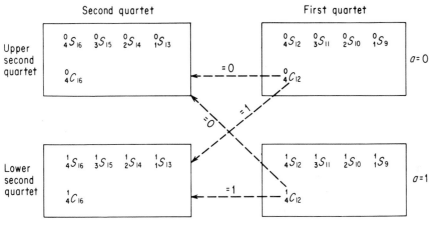

FIGURE 6.7.1   Example of how C_β chooses proper n-tet for the conditional sum adder

We are speaking of quartets. The carry bit in each of the first quartets makes the choice. It can choose between the upper second quartet or the lower second quartet. Thus, if $_4^0C_{12}$ is 0, the *upper* second quartet in toto becomes the second half of the *upper* octet. On the contrary, if $_4^0C_{12}$ is 1, the *lower* second quartet becomes the second half of the *upper* octet.

Similarly, it is the function of $_4^1C_{12}$ to choose either the *upper second* quartet or the *lower second* quartet to be the *second half* of the *lower* octet in Figure 6.7.1.

Figure 6.7.2 is a generalization of this case. The choice of second α-tets is made by $_a^a C_\beta$. Thus, if $_a^0 C_\beta$ is 0, the upper second α-tet in toto becomes the second half of the upper 2α-tet. On the contarary, if $_a^0 C_\beta$ is 1, the lower second α-tet becomes the second half of the *upper* 2α-tet.

Similarly, it is the function of $_a^1 C_\beta$ to choose either the *upper second α-tet* or the *lower second α-tet* to be the *second half* of the *lower 2α-tet* in Figure 6.7.2.

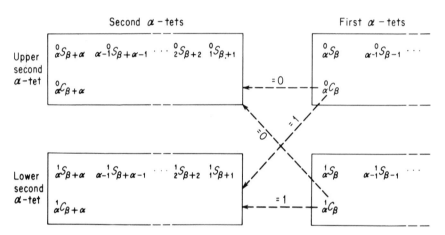

FIGURE 6.7.2   Choice to be implemented in general case, conditional sum adder

How do (6.7.3) and (6.7.4) reflect these statements? For simplicity, let a be 0. Then $_{a+i}^0 S_{\beta+i}$ in (6.7.3) is the $(\alpha + i)$th bit of the upper 2α-tet we are composing. Its value depends upon $_a^0 C_\beta$ as explained above; when $_a^0 C_\beta$ is 1, we choose the ith sum bit of the *lower second α-tet*, which is symbolized by $_i^1 S_{\beta+i}$; when $_a^0 C_\beta$ is 0, we choose the ith sum bit of the *upper second α-tet*, which is symbolized by $_i^0 S_{\beta+i}$. Finally, (6.7.4) is used to get the carry bit for the 2α-tet. Since there is only one in the upper 2α-tet and it is at the left, its presubscript is 2α. Choose the carry bit from the *upper second α-tet*, $_{2a}^0 C_{\beta+\alpha}$ if $_a^0 C_\beta$ is 0; choose the carry bit from the *lower second α-tet*, $_{2a}^1 C_{\beta+\alpha}$ if $_a^0 C_\beta$ is 1.

To compose the lower 2α-tet, let a be 1 for (6.7.3) and (6.7.4). This permits $_a^1 C_\beta$ to choose between the *upper* and *lower second α-tet* for the second half of the *lower 2α-tet*. Two such units are required on this level: one for $a = 0$, the other for $a = 1$.

The hardware for realizing these equations is illustrated in Figure 6.7.3. As the equations indicate, the carry output of the last stage of the set of first α stages of the 2α-tet makes the choice for the second set of α stages. The outputs of $\vee 3$, $\vee 6$, and $\vee 9$ satisfy (6.7.3) for values of i, respectively, of 1, 2, and α. The output of $\vee 12$ corresponds to (6.7.4).

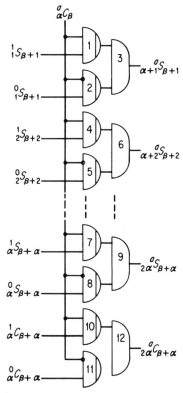

Review

The conditional sum adder consists of blocks arranged as in Figure 6.3. We have discussed the logical makeup of the boxes on each level. To speak generally, we might say that each block consists of $\alpha + 1$ units and that each unit consists of two &-gates and one $\vee$-mixer. We must double this number because the carry into each block must be considered for the alternatives of a carry into 2α-tet of both 0 and 1.

The number of levels, L, required is determined by the number of bits, B, in the adder and is given by the following relation.

FIGURE 6.7.3   General level carry and sum logic, conditional sum adder

$$L = \lceil \log_2 B \rceil \tag{6.7.5}$$

The brackets indicate an integer larger than the contents of the brackets and such that $L - 1$ is smaller than the contents.

6.8   DISCUSSION OF ADDERS

The computer designer is always compromising between speed and cost. Therefore, it is to his advantage to have methods to compare these qualities at his fingertips. For a given logic, a faster performance can be achieved with faster circuits; *ca va sans dire*. The question is, given fixed circuit speed, what are the speeds of the resulting logics, and how much hardware is required.

Comparison

Since many of the calculations we make to compare the four adder logics depend upon the word length of the machine, we make both algebraic and numerical assumptions. We consider words with N numerical bits and we further consider the case where $N = 48$. This word length is also used for the analysis of multiplication and divisions. Forty-eight is a convenient number, for it is factorable in prime factors of only 2 and 3 which allows subdivision in different ways yet does not present the special case of a power of 2.

timing

Timing analysis is in terms of what we call, for convenience, a logical stage. This consists of an & and a $\vee$, or vice versa, in cascade. The time for information to pass through such a pair is indicated as σ. Depending on the price one is willing to pay for circuits, this time may vary from several nanoseconds, (ns or billionths of a second) to several microseconds (μs or millionths of a second). For the comparison, we choose a value of one-hundred nanoseconds for time σ. This is fairly typical of many computers now being manufactured and conservative vis-a-vis the state of the art.

hardware

All the adder logics have been analyzed in terms of &- and $\vee$-blocks. It remains only to enumerate how many of these are used on each level and how many levels are needed for a given word size. There is also a choice of how to allot stages to levels but this is done arbitrarily, since the purpose of the analysis is to show *how* this is done rather than to make an exhaustive table.

The Synchronous Adder

Logic for the synchronous adder was presented earlier. This method plans for the worst case; that is, we allot time for the carry propagating in the worst case where it must travel from one end of the adder to the other. A single set of &- and $\vee$-blocks is needed in each stage for the carry function. One or several &-gates sense the simultaneous existence of the carry input from the *previous* stage and the propagate condition on *this* stage; a $\vee$-block mixes the propagate and generate conditions. Hence, the carry time per stage is σ and, for the whole adder including the sign bit, is $N\sigma$. *This time is fixed whether or not the worst case is encountered.* Therefore, it is also the average time. If we call G_s the number of &'s for the synchronous adder of word size N and the number of $\vee$'s M_s, then,

$$G_s = 3N \tag{6.8.1}$$

$$M_s = 3N \tag{6.8.2}$$

The Asynchronous Adder

The complete logic for a full stage of the asynchronous adder is found in Figure 6.8.1. Only one stage is required to pass either the 0-carry or the 1-carry. The worst case or maximum time is therefore $N\sigma$. *However,* this will be rare; we are interested in the average carry time.

The average time required for the carry-complete signal to appear is the desired figure. To see how to ascertain this, examine Figure 4.3.1. Some blocks will report to the carry-complete block immediately, for they are generate stages; others will pass through several &-$\vee$ stages. For a given word size N, we wish to determine the average, maximum length for a run of carries. Now a propagate or generate at any given stage is equally likely. Hence, we can consider this simply a problem in the theory of runs. A simple analogy would be to a coin-tossing problem. Imagine a series of experiments: a coin is tossed 48 times and the longest run of heads or tails for the trial is recorded. This is repeated many, many times. The average maximum run is obtained by averaging the maximum run length over the trials.

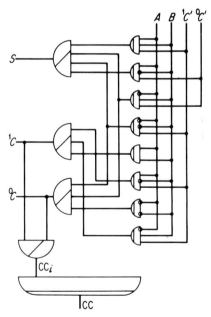

FIGURE 6.8.1   One stage of logic for the asynchronous adder

The carry problem has been looked into by four investigators, all of whom get somewhat different, though basically similar results.* Using any of their results, we find the average maximum carry length for $N = 48$ to be less than 6. In addition to this, we require one more &-∨ stage for forming the carry-complete signal. Hence, for $N = 48$ we have a carry time of 7σ. Hendrickson comes up with a nice approximation for the general case. He finds

$$\text{Average longest carry} \doteq \log_2 \left(\frac{SN}{4} \right) \qquad (6.8.3)$$

To find the hardware required, examine Figure 6.8.1. The number of &'s, G_A, and the number of ∨'s, M_A is

$$G_A = 8N + 1 \qquad (6.8.4)$$

$$M_A = 3N + 1 \qquad (6.8.5)$$

where the subscript A indicates the *asynchronous* adder.

The Lookahead Adder

For a given value of N, there are often several alternate configurations which are equivalently efficient. Therefore, it is difficult to arrive at a satisfactory formula for either the time or the hardware. This is also a function of the group size, g. It is easier to generalize about the time, however, since this primarily depends on the number of levels.

For $N = 48$, the arrangement of Figure 6.8.2 is one solution. It uses five cycles and first- and second-level auxiliary functions. The first of the timing prepares the propagate and generate functions (PG's) for all stages. The next cycle prepares the first five first-level functions. The third cycle prepares the second-level function and the remaining first-level functions. The fourth cycle prepares all the carries after which the fifth cycle uses three carries to form the sum bits.

---

* A. W. Burks, H. H. Goldstone, and J. von Neumann, *Preliminary Discussion of the Logical Design of an Electronic Computing Instrument* (Princeton, N. J.: Institute for Advanced Study, June 1946).

B. Gilchrist, J. H. Pomerene, and S. Y. Wong, "Fast Carry Logic for Digital Computers," *IRE Trans. Prof. Group on Electronic Computers*, V. EC–4, No. 4 (Dec. 1955), pp. 133–36.

G. W. Reitwiesner, "The Determination of Carry Propagation Length for Binary Addition," *IRE Trans. Prof. Group on Electronic Computers*, V. EC–9, No. 1 (March 1960), pp. 35–38.

H. C. Hendrickson, "Fast High-Accuracy Binary Parallel Addition," *IRE Trans. Prof. Group on Electronic Computers.* V. EC–9, No. 4 (Dec. 1960), pp. 469–9.

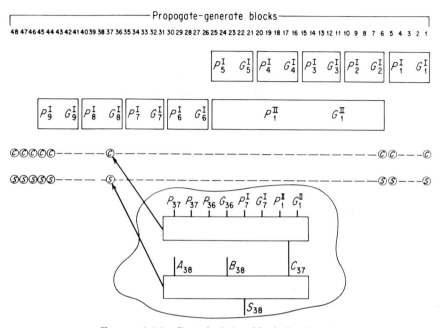

FIGURE 6.8.2   Carry lookahead logic for $N = 48$

This arrangement for $N = 48$ is by no means unique, and the reader might investigate other possibilities. However, it provides a means for comparison. Let us dig into this picture and see if we can produce some numbers.

Let us produce Table 6.8.1 as we go along. The PG logic is found in Figure 5.2.2 to consist of 2 &'s and 1 $\vee$. There are 48 of these. There are a

TABLE 6.8.1   Number of Logic Blocks for Carry Lookahead Adder
Using 48-Bit Words

Function	units/level	&'s/unit	$\vee$'s/unit	&'s/level	$\vee$'s/level
PG's	48	2	1	96	48
First level aux.	9	5	1	45	9
Second level aux.	1	5	1	5	1
Carries	48	1–8	1	216	48
Sums	48	4	1	192	48
				558	154

first-level blocks which appear in Figure 5.4.3. For $g = 5$, each contains 5 &'s and 1 $\vee$. There is only one second-level block; for $g = 5$, Figure 5.5.3 calls for 5 &'s and 1 $\vee$. Each carry block contains a variable number of &'s and 1 $\vee$. The best case uses one generate or a propagate and a generate second-level auxiliary. Hence, the number of &'s is between one and eight. An average figure of $4\frac{1}{2}$ is used in Table 6.8.1. There is one sum block for each bit and from Figure 5.3 it contains 4 &'s and 1 $\vee$. Note here that most of the &'s use more than two inputs and may in some instances require eight.

Conditional Sum Adder

The layout for a conditional sum adder is found in Figure 6.3. There is one first-level unit for each bit. There is a second-level unit for each two bits, and so forth, and we reach a level where there is but one block. For $N = 4$ there are seven levels and, in general,

$$\text{Number of levels} = 1 + \log_2 N \qquad (6.8.6)$$

A signal passes through 1 stage (time of σ) for each level. For $N = 48$, the add time is 7σ.

TABLE 6.8.2   Number of Logic Blocks for Conditional Sum Adder
Using 48-Bit Words

Level	Units/level	&'s/unit	$\vee$'s/unit	&'s/level	$\vee$'s/level
1	48	3	1	144	48
2	$23\frac{1}{2}$	8	4	188	94
3	$11\frac{1}{2}$	12	6	138	69
4	$5\frac{1}{2}$	20	10	110	55
5	$2\frac{1}{2}$	36	18	90	45
6	1			34	17
7	1			34	17
				738	345

As we determine the hardware requirements, we construct Table 6.8.2. The first-level block of Figure 6.4 is equivalent to 3 &'s and 1 $\vee$. There is a pair of units of Figure 6.5 in each second-level block consisting of 8 &'s and 4 $\vee$'s. There is a pair of units of Figure 6.6 in each third-level block consisting of 12 &'s and 6 ∨'s. In general, a pair of units as in Figure 6.7, is required. For the kth, the number of &'s, G_C, and ∨'s, M_C, is given by

$$G_C = 4(2^{k-2} + 1) \qquad\qquad k \geq 2 \qquad (6.8.7)$$

$$M_C = 2(2^{k-2} + 1) \qquad\qquad k \geq 2 \qquad (6.8.8)$$

These equations hold when

1. The block has a double carry input (like A_{32} in Figure 6.3 but not like A_{31} of that figure).
2. The block produces a full, not partial, set of outputs.

When the block is a terminal block and produces the ultimate sums and carries, it has half as many &'s and ∨'s as other blocks on that level. To

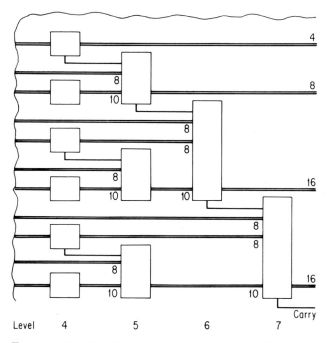

FIGURE 6.8.3 Conditional sum adder for $N = 48$, terminal portion

see this, examine Figure 6.8.3. This is a terminal view of the 48-stage adder. The seventh-level stage has 17 outputs, hence uses 17 ∨'s and 34 &'s. The sixth-level block requires the same. The fifth level has two full blocks and one terminal block. The table entry for this level is $2\frac{1}{2}$. The terminal blocks account for the $\frac{1}{2}$'s in Table 6.8.2.

TABLE 6.8.3   Time and Hardware for the Four Kinds of Adders for 48-Bit Words and Stage Time of 100 Nanoseconds

	Time			Hardware				Diodes		
	General	$N = 48$	$\sigma = 100$ns	&'s	V's	Diodes &, V	&	V	Total		
Synchronous	$N\sigma$	$48\,\sigma$	$4.8\ \mu s$	144	144	2	288	288	576
Asynchronous	$\left(1 + \log_2 \dfrac{5N}{4}\right)\sigma$	$7\,\sigma$	$0.7\ \mu s$	384	145	3	1052	435	1535*
Look-ahead	—	$5\,\sigma$	$0.5\ \mu s$	558	154	4	2232	616	2848
Conditional Sum	$(1 + \log_2 N)\sigma$	$7\,\sigma$	$0.7\ \mu s$	738	345	2	1476	690	2160

* Includes 48 for CC&.

Summary

Table 6.8.3 summarizes the results of this section. Recall that the look-ahead adder requires multiple input blocks so that a block count might be misleading. Hence, a diode count was made assuming a single diode per input per block. At the same time, the extra-large carry-complete gate for the asynchronous adder was accounted for by adding a term of size 48 in the diode count for that type.

PROBLEMS

6.1 a. Lay out the blocks required for (1) a 42-bit adder, (2) a 60-bit adder.
    b. Detail the logic required in each block.
    c. Count the functional blocks and the logical blocks.
    d. Determine the time required for an addition.
    e. Compare with the other kinds of adders.

6.2 a. Design a ten-bit conditional-sum adder.
    b. Do these additions (denominator 1024):
       1. 257 + 254
       2. 767 + 000
       3. 453 + 504
       4. 783 + 015

6.3 Suppose an &-block and ∨-block five times as fast cost five times as much. Examine the various adders. See if any would produce a major increase in speed by the judicious use of a few of these expensive, fast blocks. Contrast speed and cost for all after optimization.

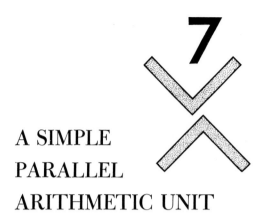

A SIMPLE
PARALLEL
ARITHMETIC UNIT

7.1 INTRODUCTION

The purpose of this chapter is to show how one would go about designing a parallel arithmetic unit. In so doing, we introduce the procedure of logic design and, at the same time, investigate the arrangement of simple arithmetic units. We will lay out a configuration of registers and then design control units to supervise addition, subtraction, multiplication, and division. We are going to develop each process separately and then combine them until we have a complete unit to perform fixed-point arithmetic. Through working out this design, we will become familiar with parallel arithmetic and its needs and limitations.

This design procedure will use the method of logical equations. The requirements of a function or subfunction, after being stated in English, will be translated into logical equations. The set of equations will then be translated, in turn, into appropriate hardware. Once we have set up the single processes, we will combine these to get a full arithmetic unit, which is accomplished by combining logical equations. This set of equations then fully describes the arithmetic unit.

To begin with, for each process we will do the following:

1. Determine how information is to be manipulated for the given process.
2. Set up a flow chart when it is required to improve comprehension.

3. Set up equations for the data manipulation.
4. Examine the equations and conditions to see when exceptions arise and determine how these exceptions should be handled.
5. Implement the equations with a control logic.

Let me stress that the methodology outlined above is the way we would go about almost any piece of logical design. It distills logical design to its most basic attributes.

Register Configuration

At this point, let us examine how the registers may be arranged so that they can do all the jobs we would like them to do. The arrangement presented is one which was devised early in the history of stored-program computers, and it is found in computers as early as the first one produced by the Institute for Advanced Study, to one as recent as the Model 212 Philco 2000. Both of these use double-rank registers as described in Section 4.1 and illustrated in Figure 4.1.5; the complete arithmetic unit register arrangement is illustrated in Figure 7.1. In later sections we will illustrate only the portions of the unit which are under consideration at that time.

Note that one data input to the adder is connected to the D register; the other data input can be connected to either the A register or the Q

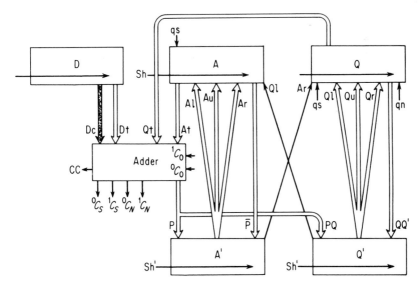

FIGURE 7.1 Arithmetic unit connected for fixed point parallel binary operations

register. The non-data inputs to the adder are the 0-carry input and the 1-carry input. The adder has indications for carry-complete and for the carry-out from the sign bit and from the most significant numerical bit. The sum output of the adder is normally connected to the A′ register; on occasion it may be connected to the Q′ register.

The adder which will be used in this chapter is an asynchronous one. Therefore, completion of its operation is somewhat unpredictable—we know that addition is complete only when the adder issues a carry-complete signal. This signal is used to initiate succeeding processing. This type of adder was chosen because, if its use is understood, the application by the reader of the synchronous adder provides no difficulty since it can be timed by a fixed means external to the adder.

Facility is provided, as can be seen in Figure 7.1, for returning the quantity from the prime register to the unprimed (main) register with a choice of a single shift to the right or to the left or without being displaced. There is also provision for the entry of single bits into selected portions of the unprimed register. Also, when we shift a datum out of one register, bits which would be lost may be shifted into another register. Thus, in shifting left from Q′, the most significant bit can be entered into the A register. Also, space created when the word is shifted may be filled with either 0's or 1's, according to the procedure being followed.

We are now ready to examine each arithmetic process individually.

7.2 ADDITION

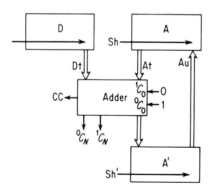

FIGURE 7.2 Connections for addition

At the beginning of addition the augend is found in the A register (Figure 7.2). It was either left over from a *previous* computation or was placed there at the beginning of *this* computation. The addend is placed in the D register before addition proper begins. We will examine addition from that point on.

At the start of addition, the true contents of the D register and the true contents of the A register are both entered into the adder regardless of the sign of either quantity. A 0-carry into the adder is also supplied at that time. The result of addition is passed directly from the adder into the

A′ register. It is then returned to the A register—that is all that is required. It is assumed to be correct as long as an arithmetic fault is not indicated. The testing for such faults is described below.

The timing of addition is accomplished by observing the carry-complete signal from the adder. This signal causes the entry of the sum into the prime register. A fixed time later the result is returned to the A register.

The only other consideration is to inhibit the return of the result to the A register when the sum exceeds the word size of the register. This condition is a function of the sign of the augend, the sign of the addend, and the carryout from the most significant bit during addition. It is covered in the next subsection.

Logical Equations

For addition the true output of the D register is connected to the adder. This is stated in equation form as

$$Dt = 1 \tag{7.2.1}$$

The true output of the A register is connected to the other input of the adder,

$$At = 1 \tag{7.2.2}$$

The carryin to the adder is

$$^1C_0 = 0 \tag{7.2.3}$$

$$^0C_0 = 1 \tag{7.2.4}$$

The means for entering the sum into the prime register is the carry-complete signal,

$$Sh' = CC \tag{7.2.5}$$

The sum is returned, unshifted from A′ to the A register,

$$Au = 1 \tag{7.2.6}$$

It is entered in to the A register by the signal Sh if no arithmetic fault occurs, which is stated as

$$Sh = \Delta \cdot Sh' \overline{Af} \tag{7.2.7}$$

where "$\Delta \cdot$" means that a fixed delay has been applied to the pulse used for entry into the prime register, Sh′. The symbol for an arithmetic fault is Af. Its condition is stated as,

$$Af = \bar{D}_s \bar{A}_s \, ^1C_N + D_s A_s \, ^0C_N \tag{7.2.8}$$

where the sign bits of the D register and the A register are respectively designated as D_s and A_s, and the carry from the most significant bit is 1 for ^1C_N and 0 for ^0C_N. This equation states that if both numbers being added are positive, a carryout of 1 from the most significant bit during addition indicates an arithmetic fault; and if both numbers being added are negative and there is no carryout from the most significant bit, an arithmetic fault has occurred. Addition is finished when the signal E is produced as the result is returned to the A register,

$$E = Sh \tag{7.2.9}$$

7.3 SUBTRACTION

Registers are arranged for subtraction as shown in Figure 7.3. The main difference between subtraction and addition is that the complement output of the D register is entered into the adder instead of its true output. The other differences are discussed as they arise. We plunge immediately into the logical equations.

Logical Equations

The complement output of the D register is connected to the adder.

$$Dc = 1 \tag{7.3.1}$$

The true output of the A register is connected to the adder,

$$At = 1 \tag{7.3.2}$$

A 1-carry into the adder is present, but not a 0-carry into the adder.

$$^1C_0 = 1 \qquad ^0C_0 = 0 \tag{7.3.3}$$

Completion of addition is indicated by the carry-complete signal, CC, from the adder. This signal is used to enter the sum into the prime register,

$$Sh' = CC \tag{7.3.4}$$

The result is returned unshifted to the A register,

$$Au = 1 \tag{7.3.5}$$

It is entered by the delayed entry pulse, Sh', if no arithmetic fault is noted.

$$Sh = \Delta \cdot Sh' \overline{Af} \tag{7.3.6}$$

An arithmetic fault is distinguished by

$$\text{Af} = D_s\bar{A}_s\,{}^1C_n + \bar{D}_sA_s\,{}^0C_N \tag{7.3.7}$$

An error occurs for a positive minuend and a negative subtrahend if there is a 1-carry of the most significant bit or if the minuend is negative and the subtrahend is positive and there is a 0-carry out of the most signifi-

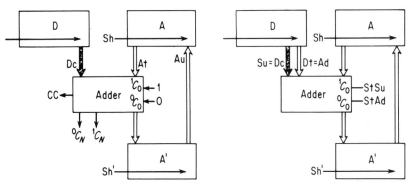

FIGURE 7.3 Connections for subtraction   FIGURE 7.4.1 Connections for combined addition and subtraction

cant bit. Subtraction is complete when the result is entered into the A register,

$$E = \text{Sh} \tag{7.3.8}$$

7.4 COMBINED ADDITION AND SUBTRACTION

In this section we will combine the logical equations of the last two sections. We will then develop the control hardware for this combined logic. The register configuration of Figure 7.4.1 is used.

Logical Equations

The true output of the D register is connected to the adder for addition (Ad) and the complement of the D register is entered there for subtraction (Su). Then,

$$\text{Dt} = \text{Ad} \tag{7.4.1}$$

$$\text{Dc} = \text{Su} \tag{7.4.2}$$

The true output of the A register is connected to the adder. The adder is connected to the prime register, and the prime register is returned, unshifted, to the A register for both processes.

$$At = 1 \tag{7.4.3}$$

$$Au = 1 \tag{7.4.4}$$

There is a 0-carry into the adder for addition and a 1-carry into the adder for subtraction.

$$^1C_0 = Su \qquad ^0C_0 = Ad \tag{7.4.5}$$

The result is entered into the prime register when the carry-complete signal appears.

$$Sh' = CC \tag{7.4.6}$$

This result is returned to the A register if there is no arithmetic fault present.

$$Sh = \Delta \cdot Sh'\overline{Af} \tag{7.4.7}$$

The condition for an arithmetic fault is a little more complicated this time and is indicated as

$$Af = {}^1C_N\bar{A}_s(Ad\bar{D}_s + SuD_s) + {}^0C_N A_s(Ad\bar{D}_s + Su\bar{D}_s) \tag{7.4.8}$$

The end of addition and subtraction occurs when the result is returned to the A register.

$$E = Sh \tag{7.4.9}$$

Arithmetic Fault Simplification

The combined equation for arithmetic fault for both addition and subtraction (7.4.8) can be simplified. We can write this as

$$Af = {}^0C_s\, {}^1C_N + {}^1C_s\, {}^0C_N \tag{7.4.10}$$

To see how this simplification results, let us examine the alternatives which exist for the combined conditions of a carryout of the most significant bit and a carryout of the sign bit.

$$^0C_s \; {}^1C_N$$

We can get a 0-carry from the sign bit with a carry entering into that stage only if both the signs of the augend and addend are positive. The condition we have is

$$^0C_s \, {}^1C_n = \bar{A}_s \, \bar{D}_s \, {}^1C_N \tag{7.4.11}$$

As we see, this is an arithmetic fault.

$$^1C_s \; {}^0C_N$$

In this case we have a 0-carry coming into the sign position and a 1-carry leaving the sign position. This means that both the sign of the augend and addend are 1, so that we have

$$^1C_s \, {}^0C_N = A_s \, D_s \, {}^0C_N \tag{7.4.12}$$

Again this is an arithmetic fault. Although the conditions we have mentioned always indicate when an arithmetic fault is present, we now wish to question whether, if these conditions are absent, an arithmetic fault is always absent.

$$^1C_s \; {}^1C_N$$

For the sign position we now have a 1 carryin and a 1 carryout. This will occur if at least one of the signs of the numbers being added is negative. We have

$$^1C_s \, {}^1C_N = (A_s \, \bar{D}_s + \bar{A}_s \, D_s + A_s \, D_s) \, {}^1C_N \tag{7.4.13}$$

The first and second terms indicate oppositely signed numbers and, hence, no arithmetic fault arises. The last term indicates two negative numbers with a carry into the sign position. This condition is correct for the addition of two negative numbers.

$$^0C_s \; {}^0C_N$$

Here we have a 0-carry into the sign position and a 0-carry out of the sign position which can occur if one or more of the numbers being added is positive. It can be written as

$$^0C_s \, {}^0C_N = (A_s \, \bar{D}_s + \bar{A}_s \, D_s + \bar{A}_s \, \bar{D}_s) \, {}^0C_N \tag{7.4.14}$$

The first two terms indicate that oppositely signed numbers are being added. The last term applies when positive numbers are being added correctly.

We have shown that (7.4.10) correctly defines the condition when an arithmetic fault occurs and that its complement defines the condition when an arithmetic fault is absent.

$$\overline{\text{Af}} = {}^1C_s\,{}^1C_N + {}^0C_s\,{}^0C_N \tag{7.4.15}$$

another way to define these conditions is

$$\text{Af:} \quad C_s \neq C_N \tag{7.4.16}$$

Control Logic

All that is needed to control addition and subtraction is presented in Figure 7.4.2. For the most part, the diagram is self-explanatory. Most of the blocks are required to form the arithmetic fault function. When Af is

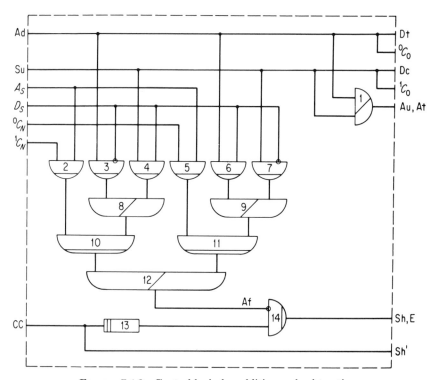

FIGURE 7.4.2   Control logic for addition and subtraction

finally formed, it is used to inhibit the production of the timing pulses Sh
and E.

7.5 MULTIPLICATION

The connection of the registers for multiplication is shown in Figure
7.5.1. Before discussing it let us review the cycle of operation as required for
multiplication.

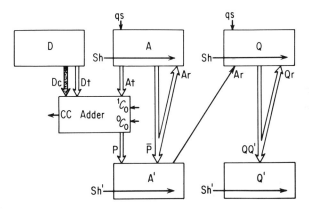

FIGURE 7.5.1   Connections for parallel binary multiplication

Cycle of Operation

As multiplication begins, we assume that the quantities in question have
been placed in their respective registers. The multiplicand has been placed
in the D register. The multiplier is in the Q register. Normally the A register
is cleared. If proper precautions are observed, it is possible to use this
scheme to perform accumulating multiplication (Section 11.5).

Figure 7.5.2 is a flow diagram showing parallel binary fixed-point multiplication. Before multiplication, we determine whether multiplication is
done by adding the multiplicand to the partial product or by adding the
complement of the multiplicand to the partial product. Next we set up to
count the number of digits in the multiplier which have been considered.
At the start we want to record that no digits of the mulitplier have been
examined yet. We are now set up to begin the multiplication itself.

The first step in each multiplication cycle is to decide if we are going to
perform an addition in this cycle or whether we are just going to perform a
shift. The criterion for this decision requires examination of the least
significant multiplier bit and the product sign.

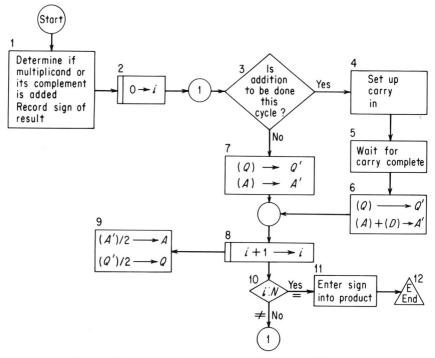

FIGURE 7.5.2   Flow diagram, parallel binary multiplication

When addition is to be performed, we first set up the carryin to the adder. Then we wait for the adder to issue a carry-complete signal. Next we enter the multiplier from the Q register to the Q' register. The sum is entered into the A' register. If addition is not performed, the multiplier can be immediately transferred from the Q register to the Q' register and the partial product can be transferred from the A register to the A' register.

Now we add 1 to the quantity in the counter to show that we have almost finished processing this digit of the multiplier. We then return the multiplier, which is sitting in the Q' register, to the Q register, shifting it one position to the right. The partial product, which is in the A' register, is returned to the A register, shifting it one position to the right at the same time. The least significant digit of the A' register will have no place to go in the A register since the quantity in the A' register is being shifted one position to the right as it is entered into the A register. However, we are providing an extra space to the left of the Q register. Therefore, it is a simple matter to enter the least significant bit from the A' register into the most significant bit of the Q register as the transfer process is occurring.

Now we are ready to examine the next bit of the multiplier which has been shifted by the previous operation into the least significant bit of the Q register. We do this if we have not already examined all the bits in the multiplier. Then we decide if addition is to be performed or whether we transfer directly from the main registers to the prime registers.

The process described above is very similar to what takes place in serial multiplication. At the end of multiplication, the two-word product will occupy the combined A and Q register, the multiplicand will be retained in the D register and the multiplier will be completely lost.

When all the digits in the multiplier have been examined, the product is complete except for the sign. This is entered before the multiplication process is terminated.

Register Function During Multiplication

The reader may be curious to know how the computer functions to simulate the multiplication activity discussed in Sections 3.3. In that discussion the multiplicand is either added or not added to the partial product. It is shifted left and then again may or may not be added to the partial product. The registers, as they are set up in this section, require shifting of the partial product to the right instead of shifting the multiplicand to the left. Since the whole thing is relative, either process should produce identical results.

Notice that when we are adding a negative number in 2's complement form, as shown in Figure 3.3.4, there are 1's in most of the left-hand portions of our number. In using the multiplicand in that figure, the sign bit has been duplicated on the left-hand side of the number and 0's are entered on the right-hand side of the number for each position it is shifted left.

Method 2 for multiplication, as illustrated in Figure 3.3.4, is implemented with the register arrangement of Figure 7.5.1 by duplicating the sign bit into the most significant bit as the A register is shifted to the right. This is best seen by looking at the example in Figure 7.5.3. This illustration seeks to duplicate the problem of Figure 3.3.4, $(+11 \times 2^{-5}) (-13 \times 2^{-5}) = -143 \times 2^{-10}$ to best suit the register configuration. At the start of multiplication, we see the multiplicand in the D register, the multiplier in the Q register, and 0's have been entered into the A register.

First examine the least significant bit, Q1. Since it is 1, an addition of D to A is called for. The result of the addition is entered into A' (the notation "prime" on the right-hand side of the figure indicates the contents of the prime register, A'). The result is returned from the A' register to the A register shifted one position to the right. As we pass the partial product from A' to A, the right-hand bit of the A register is shifted over the sign bit of the Q

Multiplicand	Product, first half	Multiplier	Do	for bit
D	$A_s A_N$ · · · A_1	$Q_s Q_N$ · · · Q_1		
1 1 0 0 1 1	0 0 0 0 0 0	0 0 1 0 1 1	Start	
	1 1 0 0 1 1		Add	$b_1 = 1$
	1 1 0 0 1 1		Prime	
	1 1 1 0 0 1	X 1 0 1 0 1	Main	
	1 1 0 0 1 1		Add	$b_2 = 1$
	1 0 1 1 0 0		Prime	
	1 1 0 1 1 0	X 0 1 0 1 0	Main	
			Nonadd	$b_3 = 0$
	1 1 0 1 1 0		Prime	
	1 1 1 0 1 1	X 0 0 1 0 1	Main	
	1 1 0 0 1 1		Add	$b_4 = 1$
	1 0 1 1 1 0		Prime	
	1 1 0 1 1 1	X 0 0 0 1 0	Main	
			Nonadd	$b_5 = 0$
	1 1 0 1 1 1		Prime	
	1 1 1 0 1 1	X 1 0 0 0 1	Main	
	1.1 1 0 1 1	1.1 0 0 0 1	Set sign	
	└─ as	└─ qs		

FIGURE 7.5.3   Register operation during multiplication
Find $(+11 \times 2^{-5})(-13 \times 2^{-5}) = 143 \times 2^{-10}$
Performed as $(Q) \times (D) \rightarrow A \cup Q$

register and entered into the left-hand numerical bit of the Q register. The arrows in Figure 7.5.3 show how this is done. Next we examine the fourth bit of the multiplier. We do this by noting that the new Q1 is 1. This calls for another addition. The result is entered into the prime register. In returning it to the main register, it is shifted one position to the right. The right-hand bit of the A′ register again is entered into the left-hand numerical bit of the Q register. Follow the arrows! As each of these shifts from the prime to the main register occurs, 1's are entered into the left-hand side of the A register by duplicating the sign bit of A′. Thus $A'_s \rightarrow A_s$ and $A'_s \rightarrow A_N$.

The third bit of the multiplier is a 0, as determined again by examining the new Q1. Therefore, the quantity in the A register is sent without addition to A′. Again, when returning A′ to A, the result is moved one position to the right of the A register, 1's are entered into the left-hand side of the A register, the right-hand bit of A′ is entered into the left-hand numerical bit of Q, and we are ready for another stage of multiplication.

Let us see, in mathematical terms, what happens when we shift from the A′ register to A in the fashion described above. It is described by

$$(A) = 2^{-1}(2 - a2^{-i}) + 2^{+1} \qquad (7.5.1)$$

The factor 2^{-1} indicates the process of shifting the number one position to the right; the term 2^{+1} is the one which is entered into the left-hand or sign position of the A register during the transfer process. This simplifies as follows:

$$(A) = 2^0 - a2^{-i-1} + 2^0 \qquad (7.5.2)$$

$$= 2 - a2^{-i-1} \qquad (7.5.3)$$

From the latter equation we find that the A register now contains one-half of the number that we started with after it has been complemented which is the desired result.

Register Connections

Returning to Figure 7.5.1, let us see how the registers should be connected during each phase of the multiplication process. When we add the multiplicand to the partial product, we may add it in either true or complemented form. When do we require the true form and when do we require the complemented form? Multiplication of 2's complement numbers was illustrated in Figures 3.3.1 through 3.3.5. We will be using what is called the second method illustrated in those figures. From these figures and from Table 3.3 it can be determined that the multiplicand is added in true form if the multiplier sign is positive; in complement form if the multiplier sign is negative. Since the multiplier is in the Q register, we will designate its sign bit as Q_s. The conditions for using the true or complement form of the D register are then,

$$Dt = \bar{Q}_s \qquad (7.5.4)$$

$$Dc = Q_s \qquad (7.5.5)$$

Throughout multiplication we will be entering the true output of the A register into the adder when we add

$$At = 1 \qquad (7.5.6)$$

The contents of the prime registers are always shifted to the right in re-entering them into the main registers,

$$Ar = 1 \qquad (7.5.7)$$

$$Qr = 1 \qquad (7.5.8)$$

Do We Add?

The adder output is connected to the A' register when we are performing addition. The condition for performing addition is denoted as P. When addition is not performed, the A register is connected directly to the A' register, the condition for this being $\bar{P}$.

Now let us find the conditions for performing addition. Whenever the multiplier is positive and the multiplier bit under examination is a 1, we wish to add. However, when the multiplier is negative we have to take the 2's complement of the multiplier to determine if addition is to be performed. This cannot be determined by simply examining the least significant bit of the multiplier. Recall the rule for finding the 2's complement of a binary number. Proceeding from right to left, if a bit is 0 the complement bit is 0; for the first 1-bit encountered, a 1 is placed in the complement; thereafter, 0's and 1's are interchanged. We will use an auxiliary bit storage device to determine whether we have so far encountered a 1 as a multiplier bit. We will designate this device F and indicate that it has not yet been set as $\bar{F}$.

We will perform an addition if the multiplier is negative, if the least significant multiplier bit is 1 and the auziliary bit storage *has not* yet been set, or if the least significant multiplier bit is 0 and the auxiliary bit storage *has* been set. We can now state the full condition for performing an addition as

$$P = \bar{Q}_s Q_1 + Q_s(\bar{Q}_1 F + Q_1 \bar{F}) \qquad (7.5.9)$$

The setting of F is discussed below.

Timing

When we are performing addition and we get a carry-complete pulse, or, when we are entering directly from the main registers, we enter quantities into the prime register. Let us show the condition for entering directly by the symbol Ed. Then,

$$Sh' = CC + Ed \qquad (7.5.10)$$

We enter directly when we are not performing addition and we are either just starting or a test reveals that we are to continue processing. We indicate with Te a successful test for continuing multiplication. Therefore, to enter directly,

$$Ed = \bar{P}(St + Te) \qquad (7.5.11)$$

The test for continuing consists of examining the multiplier bit counter.

This counter is set to zero at the beginning of the multiplication process. It is examined by looking at a decoder attached to it.

$$\text{Te} = \text{Sh D}(<N) \tag{7.5.12}$$

We state that the counter is set to zero by

$$\text{D}(0) = \text{St} \tag{7.5.13}$$

The counter is tallied after each entry of information into the prime registers. This condition is indicated as

$$\text{D}(i+1) = \text{D}(i)\text{Sh}' \tag{7.5.14}$$

Information is returned to the main register shortly after and is entered into the prime register,

$$\text{Sh} = \Delta \cdot \text{Sh}' \tag{7.5.15}$$

Multiplication is finished when the counter registers the number of bits in any given multiplier,

$$\text{E} = \text{Sh } D(N) \tag{7.5.16}$$

The auxiliary bit storage device is set to zero at the start of multiplication,

$$\bar{\text{F}} = \text{St} \tag{7.5.17}$$

We set this bit storage to 1 if it is presently set to 0, the sign of the multiplier is negative and the present least significant bit of the multiplier is 1. The time to set the F bit is *after* the first 1 in the multiplier is used and recorded but *before* the next bit is encountered. The multiplier is scanned during the Sh time; the scan is discontinued at Sh' time; another scan does not take place until the next Sh time. Therefore the time for entry is the next Sh' after the 1 is noted,

$$\text{F} = \Delta \cdot \text{Sh}'\bar{\text{F}}Q_sQ_1 \tag{7.5.18}$$

The inputs to the adder have already been described, except for the carryins. A 0 carryin is applied when we are performing addition and we have a positive multiplier,

$$^0C_0 = P\bar{Q}_s \tag{7.5.19}$$

There is a 1 carryin when we are adding and we have a negative multiplier,

$$^1C_0 = PQ_s \tag{7.5.20}$$

All that remains is to attend to the sign of the product. We wait until

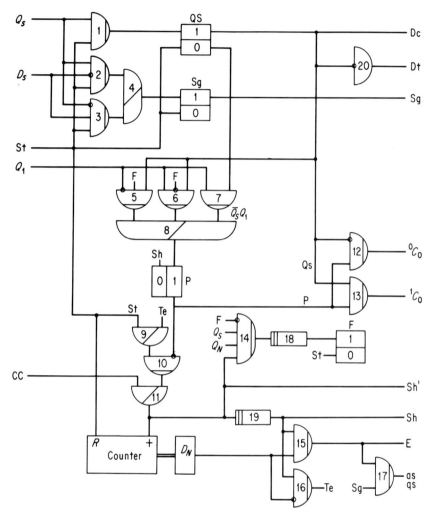

FIGURE 7.5.4 Control logic for parallel binary fixed-point
multiplication

the end of multiplication to enter this sign; however, we recognize this
information early and store it in an auxiliary flip-flop labeled Sg. We have

$$Sg = St(Q_s \bar{D}_s + \bar{Q}_s D_s) \tag{7.5.21}$$

which states that the product is negative when the multiplier and multiplicand are of different signs. A 1 is entered into the sign position of the Q
register at the end of multiplication when a negative product is specified
because the product bits are shifted *across* the sign bit of Q as they are

formed. The sign can now be entered by the pulse qs,

$$qs = \text{ESg} \qquad (7.5.22)$$

On the other hand, addition into the A register includes the sign bit, which ends up correct.

Logic

One arrangement of the logical control of parallel, binary, fixed-point multiplication is found in Figure 7.5.4. We notice that an auxiliary bit storage Q_s is used to store the sign of the multiplier so that it will not be lost during shifting. &1 checks the sign and stores the information in Q_s. This is used to operate the true and complement gates for the D register. The sign of the product is entered into Sg via &'2, &'3, and ∨4. The condition for performing addition is formed by &'5, &'6, &7 and ∨8 and is recorded in bit storage P. The pulse Sh, which occurs just before the new multiplier bit is examined at the least significant end of the Q register, clears P.

The counter is re-set to 0 by the start pulse. It is counted a short time later by the start pulse or by a subsequent test pulse passing through ∨9, &10, and ∨11 when addition is not performed or when addition is performed, by a carry-complete pulse through ∨11. The pulse which counts the counter is also the pulse for entering information into the prime registers Sh'. It is used for the testing of the setting of the auxiliary storage unit F via &'14 and Δ18.

The output of the counter is monitored by the decoder D. If we have not examined all the multiplier bits, the pulse Sh can pass through &16' as the signal Te. When we are finished, the same pulse Sh will pass through &15 and emerge as an end signal E. This pulse is used to set the sign bit of the A and Q registers through &17.

7.6 DIVISION

Before discussing the register arrangement we examine the cycle of operation.

Cycle of Operation

The flow diagram in Figure 7.6.1 shows the cycle of operation for division. To begin with, we determine the sign of the quotient we are going to develop. We also clear out the bit counter to 0. As in multiplication, we have to keep track of the digits of the quotient that have been formed.

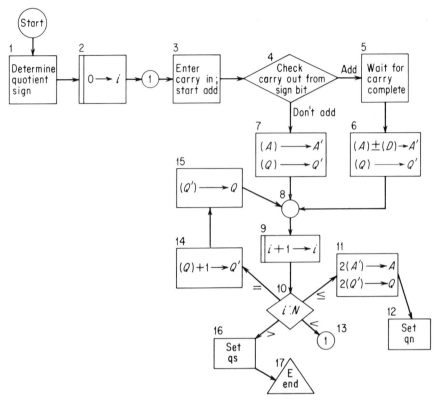

FIGURE 7.6.1   Flow diagram for parallel binary division

The method for performing division that we examine here requires that we start addition each cycle; however, addition is not carried through to its completion if it will not be "successful." Recall that in early discussions under division, performing addition is called successful when the sign of the partial remainder is not changed. We will anticipate whether the sign of the partial remainder is about to change by starting addition and observing what happens to the carry from the sign position of the sum. In most cases we will know what happens to the sign bit before the carries for addition have rippled through the entire adder. However, even if the sign digit is the last one to indicate its carry, no harm will occur. We do not process the sum until we get the result on the sign digit.

If we determine that addition is to occur, we transfer the sum to the A' register; if addition is not to be performed, we transfer the unchanged partial remainder to the A' register. In either case the quotient that we have developed so far is transferred to the Q' register. These alternatives are shown in boxes 4, 5, 6, and 7 of Figure 7.6.1. After the transfer to the prime registers, the counter is tallied. Then we check to see if all the bits of the quotient have been developed. If they have not, we return via circle 1 to box 3 and start another addition. In any case, the partial remainder and the partial quotient are returned to their respective main registers, shifted one position to the left. At the same time, the most significant numerical bit from the register is entered into the least significant position of A. Also, the least significant bit of the quotient is recorded; whether it is to be a 0 or a 1 is determined by criteria discussed a little later. Division continues thus until all the quotient bits have been determined. At that time, when we enter box 10 in the flow chart, we will find that i is equal to N, which means the count in the counter is that of the proper number of quotient bits.

We are not through yet because even though the division has been performed using 2's complement notation, a negative quotient is developed as the 1's complement of its positive equivalent. We must add 1 to this to get the proper result. Box 14 shows the process of adding 1 to the quotient and entering this result into the Q' register. The proper quotient is returned from the Q' register, unshifted, to the Q register in box 15. We go back to box 9 and count the counter again. Now the count in the counter should be $N + 1$. When we compare $N + 1$ to N, we find the result to be "greater." We can now set the proper sign into the quotient and thus end the division process.

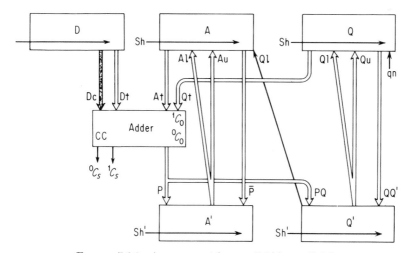

FIGURE 7.6.2 Arrangement for parallel binary division

Register Connections

The register configuration is found in Figure 7.6.2. The control logic in Figure 7.6.3 makes the connections for the registers as is described here.

The true output of the A register is connected directly to the adder during division, except when a correction cycle is being performed.

$$\text{At} = \overline{\text{PQ}} \qquad (7.6.1)$$

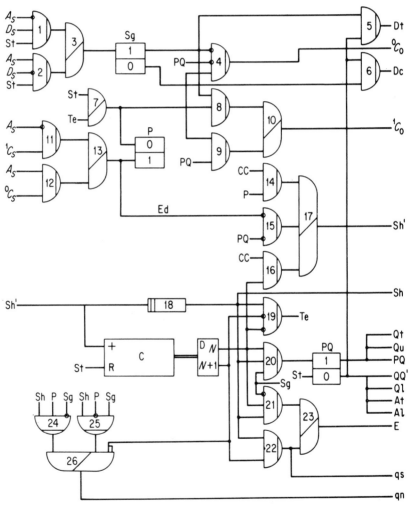

FIGURE 7.6.3 Control logic for parallel binary fixed-point division

where PQ indicates that a correction cycle is in progress ($\overline{PQ}$ denies this). Whenever the quantity in A′ is returned to A it is shifted to the left. Since A and A′ are not used during the correction cycle,

$$Al = \overline{PQ} \tag{7.6.2}$$

Whether we use the true D output or the complemented D output is determined by the sign of the quotient being developed. The sign information is stored in an auxiliary storage device denoted by Sg. The D register is always used, except on the correction cycle, so that

$$Dt = Sg\,\overline{PQ} \tag{7.6.3}$$

$$Dc = \overline{Sg}\,\overline{PQ} \tag{7.6.4}$$

The sign of the quotient is negative whenever the signs of the dividend and the divisor are unlike,

$$Sg = \bar{D}_s A_s + D_s \bar{A}_s \tag{7.6.5}$$

The Q register is always entered into the Q′ register directly and the Q′ register is returned to the Q register shifted one position left, so that

$$QQ' = \overline{PQ} \tag{7.6.6}$$

$$Ql = PQ \tag{7.6.7}$$

For the correction cycle the contents of Q is passed through the adder, entered into Q′ and then returned unshifted into Q, so that

$$Qt = PQ \tag{7.6.8}$$

$$Qu = PQ \tag{7.6.9}$$

Is Addition Completed?

For each cycle of division we are going to try to add (D) (in either true or complement form) to (A). This addition will be completed if the result will not cause (A) to reverse its sign. To determine if a sign reversal is going to occur, we monitor the carryout of the sign position of the adder. If the partial remainder in A is positive, a change in its sign is indicated by a 1 carryout of the sign position during addition; if the partial remainder is negative, a change in sign is indicated by a 0 carryout of the sign position during addition. Thus we continue addition to completion and transfer the sum for P given by,

$$P = A_s\,{}^0C_s + \bar{A}_s\,{}^1C_s \tag{7.6.10}$$

Timing

This requires reference to Figure 7.6.3. When addition does not occur, as tested against the criterion above, we enter the contents of A directly into A'.

$$\text{Ed} = A_s\, {}^1C_s + \bar{A}_s\, {}^0C_s \qquad (7.6.11)$$

Although this is equivalent to $\bar{P}$, it is generated in a definite fashion by observing if certain adder carryouts are present instead of whether they are absent. The signal Ed is an intermediate one which does not appear in Figure 7.6.2. It is used to prepare Sh'. However, it does appear in Figure 7.6.3.

The signal for entering information into the prime register is determined by whether we are adding; if so, the carry-complete signals this. Otherwise, as soon as we know addition will not be completed, we can enter information into the prime register,

$$\text{Sh}' = \text{PCC} + \text{Ed} \qquad (7.6.12)$$

Information is returned to the main registers a little later,

$$\text{Sh} = \Delta \cdot \text{Sh}' \qquad (7.6.13)$$

The test to see if further cycles should be performed depends on the quantity contained in the counter. If we have not yet performed N cycles, we will continue.

$$\text{Te} = \text{Sh}\, D(<N) \qquad (7.6.14)$$

The counter is set to 0 at the start of the division process.

$$D(0) = \text{St} \qquad (7.6.15)$$

We tally up the counter during each entry into the prime registers.

$$D(i+1) = D(i)\text{Sh}' \qquad (7.6.16)$$

Termination and Correction

A correction cycle is required when we are developing a negative quotient. This cycle is designated as the $(N+1)$th cycle. It is started after we have entered the uncorrected quotient into the A register,

$$\text{PQ} = \text{Sh}\, D(N)\text{Sg} \qquad (7.6.17)$$

We will terminate division after N cycles if we are developing a positive quotient and after $N + 1$ cycles if we are developing a negative quotient.

$$E = Sh[D(N)\overline{Sg} + D(N + 1)Sg] \qquad (7.6.18)$$

Register Entries

During division we must record each quotient bit as it is generated. This bit is a 1 and is recorded by the pulse ql if we are developing a negative quotient and have performed addition or if we are developing a negative quotient and have not performed addition. No quotient bit is recorded during the correction cycle,

$$ql = Sh(\overline{Sg}P + \overline{Sg}P)\ \overline{D(N + 1)} \qquad (7.6.19)$$

The sign bit for the quotient sign is entered by the pulse qs at the end of division,

$$qs = ESg = Sh\ D(N + 1) \qquad (7.6.20)$$

Adder

We enter a 0-carry into the adder during the start of division and in succeeding cycles if the sign of the quotient is positive,

$$^0C_0 = (St + Te)\overline{Sg}\ \overline{PQ} \qquad (7.6.21)$$

A 1 carryin to the adder is provided at these times if the sign of the quotient we are producing is negative. It is also entered during the correction cycle,

$$^1C_0 = (St + Te)(Sg + PQ) \qquad (7.6.22)$$

Notice that in (7.6.21) no qualifying term $\overline{PQ}$ is necessary since a correction cycle does not occur when the sign of the quotient is positive.

7.7 COMBINED DESIGN

The problem now is to combine all the functions—addition, subtraction, multiplication, and division—into one single unit. The register configuration presented as Figure 7.1 is displayed again as Figure 7.7.1. All the inputs

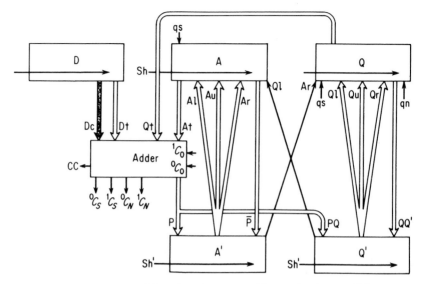

FIGURE 7.7.1   Arithmetic unit connected for fixed-point parallel
binary operations

and output in Figure 7.7.2 are required to construct a functioning logic to
control the configuration of Figure 7.7.1. Once we have developed the equation which connects the inputs and outputs as we have in the foregoing, the
next step is fairly simple. We take the equations from the previous sections
and combine them into composite equations representing the connections
which obtain when any one of the processes under consideration takes
place. This has been done and the full set of equations appears as Table 7.7.
Let us examine a few of the equations to see how this was done.

The conditions for connecting the true output of register D to the adder,
Dt, are:

1. Addition is being performed.
2. Multiplication is being performed and the sign of the multiplier is
    positive.
3. Division is being performed, a negative quotient is being developed
    and a correction cycle is not in process.

These conditions are summarized in (7.7.1) (the first equation in Table
7.7). The reader would do well to go down the list of equations to be sure
that each one makes sense and he can see its derivation. Even the most
complicated one can be so analyzed.

For instance, equation 13 of that table (7.7.13), which tells us when the

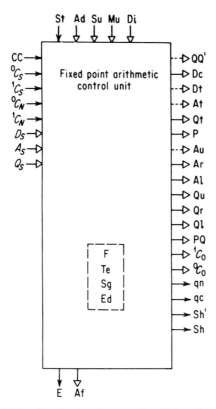

FIGURE 7.7.2 Signals to, from and within, the arithmetic control unit

result produced by the adder is entered into the prime register, is now analyzed. The conditions for this are:

1. Addition.
2. Subtraction.
3. Multiplication where a positive product is being developed and the multiplier digit under consideration is a 1.
4. Multiplication where a negative product is being developed and this is the first 1 we have encountered in the multiplier.
5. Multiplication where a negative product is being developed, we have already encountered a 1 in the multiplier, and the multiplier bit under consideration is a 0.
6. Division where no sign change will take place in the partial remainder, except on the correction cycle.

7.8 TIMING CONSIDERATIONS

The way we have approached the design of the arithmetic unit has neglected entirely the problem of determining at what instant connections should be made among the various functional and logical units and how long these connections should be maintained. This is, to some extent, a function of the kind of logic (*nor*, DCTL, etc.) used. In general, though, there are rules which apply to most kinds of logic, and we will now examine a few of these considerations.

Adder

As soon as we apply the inputs to the adder, it begins to develop a sum. A carry-complete signal will appear as soon as this result is ready for use. After the completion of one addition, if we immediately switch the inputs to the adder from one set of quantities to another, information which is presently in the adder will be trapped and might cause erroneous signals indicating the completion of an addition when really the sum being presented at the output of the adder is incorrect.

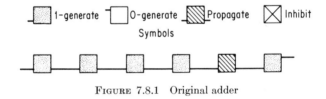

FIGURE 7.8.1 Original adder

To see what might happen, let us examine Figures 7.8.1 through 7.8.5. The first of these figures shows the result being produced by an adder when two particular numbers have been presented at its input for addition. In

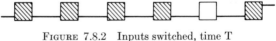

FIGURE 7.8.2 Inputs switched, time T

Figure 7.8.2 the inputs are switched. In the case illustrated, an input consisting of all 1's was changed to all 0's, a particular case. The adder has not had time to recover and it continues to produce carries between stages

FIGURE 7.8.3   Switched adder, time T + 1

identical with those it had produced for the last addition. In Figure 7.8.3 we
see the adder after it has had time to partially recover. It is only fully re-

FIGURE 7.8.4   Switched adder, time T + 3

covered in Figure 7.8.5. The time required for recovery is the time required
for the carry trapped in the adder to pass down five stages. In the very

FIGURE 7.8.5   Switched adder, time T + 5

worst case, a carry can be trapped in the first stage of the adder and may
have to travel all the way down to the very end of the adder.

FIGURE 7.8.6   Original adder, input removed, time T

The solution for this is indicated in Figure 7.8.6; all inputs are removed
from the adder for a short period before new information is entered. The
X's in that figure indicate that no input is present. Notice that the carries
between stages are maintained for a short period of time. Then, since no

FIGURE 7.8.7   As above but time T + 1

signals are present to generate these carries, they disappear, Figure 7.8.7.
A little later when the new numbers are entered into the adder, no carries
are present so that the adder is free to form the proper sums. Since no carries
are present, no carry-complete signal will appear until carries have been
formed at each stage of the adder. This means that the carry-complete
signal will truly indicate the moment when the sum formed by the adder is
correct and ready for use.

FIGURE 7.8.8   As above, a little later

Proper switching of most connections can be obtained by using an auxiliary bit storage device which is set at the beginning of each cycle and re-set by the carry-complete pulse, or, in the case of multiplication or division, by the "enter directly" pulse. The setting of this device, T, is given by

$$T = St + Te \tag{7.8.1}$$

$$\overline{T} = CC + Ed \tag{7.8.2}$$

To make use of this device, we modify the inputs to the adder so that when they are called for by a given equation they are only applied during the portion of the cycle when the auxiliary device is in state T. Below are examples of the use of this device:

$$Dt = T(Ad + MuQ_s + D(i)Sg\overline{PQ}) \tag{7.8.3}$$

$$At = T\overline{PQ} \tag{7.8.4}$$

The logic for the implementation of (7.8.1) and (7.8.2) is obvious.

Clearing the Registers

In the previous discussion we have simply indicated that information is passed from one register to another. This can be done if we **jam** information into a register. The term **jam transfer** is applied when a bit storage is forced to either its 0 or 1 state, according to the state of the setting input. If jam transfer is not used, it is necessary to clear a destination register before information is entered into it. Then, only 1's are passed from a source register to a destination register.

To implement the clear signal, it is sufficient to use the entry signal for the destination register as the clear signal for the source register. Then, when return is made to the old source register—when it becomes the destination register—it will be clear. With present high-speed circuitry, the time for a signal to be cleared from a register is still sufficient for reliable entry into a destination register. Thus, if we clear A and enter it into A′ at the same moment, the signal from A is maintained long enough to be used as the source for entering information into A′. Indicating the signal to clear the main registers by Cl and the prime registers by Cl′, we then may have

$$Cl = Sh' \tag{7.8.5}$$

$$Cl' = Sh \tag{7.8.6}$$

TABLE 7.7   Equations for the Design of a Combined Parallel Binary,
Fixed-Point Arithmetic Unit

Function	Symbol	Equation
Register connections		
1. D, True out to adder	Dt	$Ad + Mu\bar{Q}_s + DiSg\overline{PQ}$
2. Complement to adder	Ds	$Su + Mu\bar{Q}_s + Di\overline{Sg}\overline{PQ}$
3. A, True to adder	At	$\overline{PQ}$
4. Unshifted from A'	Au	$Ad + Su$
5. from A', shifted right	Ar	Mu
6. from A', shifted left	Al	Di
7. Q, True to adder	Qt	PQ
8. from Q', unshifted	Qu	PQ
9. from Q', shifted right	Qr	Mu
10. from Q', shifted left	Ql	$Di\ \overline{PQ}$
11. set sign bit	qs	$ESg(Mu + Di)$
12. set least significant bit	ql	$DiShD(N + 1)\ (P\overline{Sg} + \overline{P}Sg)$
13. A' from adder	P	$Ad + Su + Mu(Q_i\overline{Sg}$ $+ Sg(Q_i\overline{F} + \bar{Q}_iF))$ $+ Di(A_s\bar{C}_s + \bar{A}_sC_s)$
14. from A	$\overline{P}$	$\overline{P}$
15. Q' from Q	$\overline{PQ}$	St
16. from adder	PQ	$ShSgD(N)$
Adder Connections		
17. Carryin, zero	$^1C_0$	$Ad + (Mu\bar{Q}_sP$ $+ Di\overline{Sg}PQ)(St + Te)$
18. Carryin, one	$^0C_0$	$Su + (MuQ_sP + DiSg)(St + Te)$ $+ DiPQ$
Timing		
19. Start	St	
20. Enter into A', Q'	Sh'	$CC(Ad + Su + PQ)$ $+ (CC + Ed)(Mu + Di)$
21. Enter into A, Q	Sh	$\Delta \cdot Sh'\overline{Af}$
22. Test for next add cycle	Te	$Sh\ D(<N)D(\neq C)$
23. Enter directly, do not add	Ed	$Mu\overline{P}(St + Te)$ $+ Di(A_s\ ^1C_s + A_s\ ^0C_s)PQ$
24. End of arithmetic	E	$Sh(Ad + Su + Mu\ D(N)$ $+ Di(\overline{Sg}D(N) + SgD(N + 1))$
Auxiliary		
25. Arithmetic fault	Af	$^1C_N\bar{A}_s(Ad\bar{D}_s + Su D_s)$ $+ {}^0C_N\ A_s(AdD_s + Su\bar{D}_s)$
26. Sign of result	Sg	$Mu(Q_s\bar{D}_s + \bar{Q}_sD_s)$ $+ Di(A_s\bar{D}_s + \bar{A}_sD_s)$
27. Two's complement bit complement	F	$\overline{F} = St \qquad F = \Delta \cdot Sh'MuQ1Q_s\overline{F}$

PROBLEMS

7.1 Make all changes in the equations of Table 7.7 so that a synchronous adder can be used.

7.2 Redo Table 7.7 to include clear logic, Cl and Cl', as well as a timing device, T, noted on page 148.

7.3 Make all changes in the equations of Table 7.7 so that the arithmetic unit will handle 1's complement numbers.

7.4 What basic changes are required so that the arithmetic unit will handle sign and magnitude numbers?

7.5 Redesign the arithmetic unit for sign and magnitude numbers. Make a new table similar to Table 7.7 to describe the unit.

7.6 What kind of configuration is required to do integer arithmetic?
a. Describe the 2's complement integer representation.
b. Design the unit.
c. Set up equations like those in Table 7.7 for the system.

8

MULTIPLICATION

8.1 INCREASING MULTIPLICATION SPEED

Most computational problems require multiplication. Problems which involve division often can be re-stated in terms of multiplication or the division can be done using multiplication and referring to a stored table of reciprocals. Reciprocals for division can also be prepared by a programming method using multiplication, addition, and subtraction. Thus, there are many ways of "getting around" division—being able to perform it without providing special hardware to do it.

Multiplication cannot be "gotten around." The only possibility to avoid constructing the product is to refer to a table of multiplication. This is inefficient in terms of storage space in parallel machines. The only known example of serial table lookup multiplication is found in the IBM 1620. Any programmed method of multiplication requires repeated additions, and these could not be performed nearly as fast as when a built-in, short-cut method of multiplication is provided. Hence, it is important for any computer which is doing scientific problems to have a built-in, fast method of multiplication. The reader should be well-acquainted by now with serial multiplication and with the simple method of parallel multiplication which was discussed in Chapter 7. In this and the next three chapters we will discuss methods for increasing the speed of multiplication.

There are only the following ways of speeding up multiplication:

1. Reduce the average time required to perform the repeated additions during multiplication.
2. Provide prefabricated multiples of the multiplicand.
3. Provide means for doing both addition and subtraction during the multiplication process so that certain multiples of the multiplicand can be formed in less steps than the direct method.
4. Combine the above to produce gains over any single method.

The next section gives a preview of this chapter and the three that follow by summarizing the principles applicable to each method in the order in which they appear.

8.2   PREVIEW OF METHODS

In Section 2.1 we explained that the speed for multiplication is highly dependent upon add time, which, in turn, is a function of the add logic and the circuit speed. In what follows, the adder is assumed to be fixed in design and, consequently, in speed. An increase in multiplication speed can hence be achieved only through the logical design of the multiplier unit, to which we address ourselves.

Speeding Up Multiple Additions

Normally, multiplication is performed by adding the multiplicand to the partial product. Each addition requires a propagation of the carry through the length of the adder. The multiplication process must wait while carry propagation takes place. The time for a single addition in a series of additions can be reduced immensely if we save the information about the carries and use it on the next cycle.

Thus, each addition in the series will require only the time necessary for the transit of the operands through the adder and the formation of a single carry. During the next addition, the carry information, together with the new operands, is entered into the adder and the carry from this process is again saved. Only on the last cycle of multiplication need the addition be carried to completion. Hence the last stage of multiplication is treated as a normal addition cycle (Section 8.3).

Multiplicand Multiples

Before we formally start the process of multiplication, we can form and store multiples of the multiplicand in special registers. Then, during multiplication, we can refer to the bits of the multiplier in sets. Each set will call for a distinct multiple of the multiplicand to be added to the partial product. We gate this multiple into one input of the adder and the partial product into the other input. This procedure will speed up multiplication by a factor proportional to the number of multiples we can handle in one cycle (Sections 8.4, 8.5, and 8.6).

Ternary Multiplication With Fixed Steps

Four multiples of the multiplicand are available automatically and immediately by reference only to the multiplicand, if we provide a choice in the central circuitry for addition or subtraction of the multiplicand and if we allow for single or double shifts of the operand during multiplication. This method, discussed in Chapter 9, allows us to decode bits of the multiplier in pairs, triplets, etc., rather than singly and without the need for extra registers to store multiples.

Variable Shift Multiplication

An effective means for speeding up multiplication is to provide facility for shifting operands a variable number of times. This method conveniently uses runs of bits in the multiplier. Thus, shifting of length i occurs when a run of i 0's or i 1's occurs in the multiplier. Between each shift, either an addition or a subtraction of the multiplicand occurs with the partial product. The theory of this method and improvements upon it are discussed in Section 10.1, 10.2, and 10.3. The hardware and equations required to implement the theory are discussed in the remainder of Chapter 10.

Extension

Some of the combinations of the methods mentioned above are discussed in Chapter 11. Following this, all the methods discussed are compared. Further problems, such as rounding and double-length multiplication, and so forth, are discussed in Section 11.5.

8.3 CARRY-SAVE ADDERS FOR MULTIPLICATION

Principle

We are going to save the carry generated during the multiple additions required for multiplication. This means that a complete register must be assigned the sole function of storing carry information.

Figure 8.3.1 shows two stages of addition during multiplication at some intermediate point in the complete adder. The left-hand adder stage (subscripted i) has information from one bit of the A register and one bit of the D register as inputs. Of course, the input from the D register may be inhibited or may be the true or complement output of the D register. This decision is made by the control circuitry. The third input to the adder stage normally comes from the previous adder stage and is used to propagate the carry during addition. This link is now broken and a **carry-save** register is inserted.

Figure 8.3.1 has omitted the timing circuitry incidental to the proper operation of this logic. At the same time addend and augend bits are entered into the X and Y inputs of one adder stage, the output of the previous stage of carry-save register is entered into the C' input of this adder stage. The sum of the addition is sent to the appropriate bit of the A' register. The adder stage also produces a carry output which would ordinarily be sent to the next higher stage of the adder to be propagated up the line. Instead, it is sent to the appropriate bit of the carry-save register.

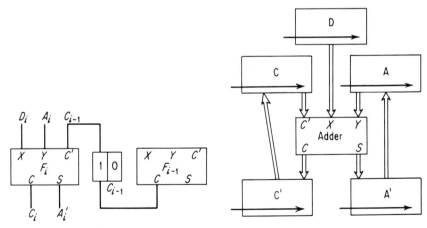

FIGURE 8.3.1 A single carry-save adder stage and the one just previous

FIGURE 8.3.2 Carry-save adder accumulator with double rank register

As soon as the carry and sum for all stages are stored respectively in the C and A′ registers, this partial addition cycle is said to be completed. Incidentally, carry and sum storage should occur at approximately the same time for all stages.

The carry-save principle can be incorporated in either the single-rank or double-rank register configurations. To be consistent in our presentation, let us examine how we would incorporate it into a double-rank register arithmetic unit. In Figure 8.3.2 we see how double-rank registers labeled C and C′ have been incorporated for when multiple additions are called for. This figure shows simply how multiple numbers can be accumulated rather than how multiplication is performed. The A register is used to accumulate the "uncarried" sum; new numbers to be added to the sum-so-far are entered between cycles into the D register. The prime carry register, C′, receives the new carries produced by the adder on each cycle. Notice that these carries are shifted one position to the left as they are entered from C′ into the main carry register. During the next addition these carries, which have now been moved over one position, are entered, together with the accumulated sum and a new addend, into the adder.

When the *last* addend is entered into the adder, we wish the adder to function to give us the final sum. This can de done in two ways. We can operate the adder in a carry-propagate rather than a carry-save mode. Secondly, we can operate the adder for the first cycle as described previously. We follow with other cycles, inhibiting the D input and continuing operation until the carries produced by the adder are all 0's. Thus, in succeeding cycles we are adding the partial sum to the partially assimilated carry until the carry is fully assimilated. Although this last alternative does not seem appealing, when we come right down to it, it is not so bad. The average propagation length has been investigated by several authors and is about six stages for an adder of forty bits. This means that only six extra cycles are required, on the average, to "flush out" the carries and obtain the proper sum.

Multiplication With Carry-Save Adders

To apply the carry-save principle of Figure 8.3.2 in order to increase the speed of multiplication, we must take several things into consideration:

1. Provide storage for the multiplier and for the less significant word of the double-length product. We use the Q register for both these jobs.
2. Provide a shift to the right of both the multiplier and the product after each addition or suppressed-carry addition.

3. Provide for shifting the new product bit across from the A′ register to the Q register.
4. Provide for the effect of the right shift of the product upon the carry storage.

These items have been taken into consideration in Figure 8.3.3. Here you notice that there is no shift when information is transferred from C′ to C. This is because the single, right shift of information being transferred from A′ to A causes the required relative shift of the partial sum with respect to carry storage. In fact, only one register can be used for the functions of both C and C′.

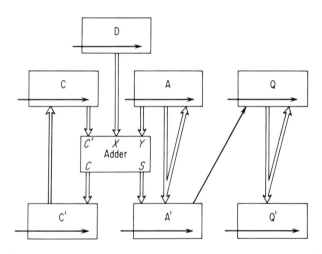

FIGURE 8.3.3 Carry-save adder configuration for simple multiplication, double rank registers

When a non-add cycle is requested by the control logic, the A register can be shifted to the prime register directly through the adder without much increase in time, since no propagation is necessary. This means that the adder sees only the partial sum and the stored carries during a non-add cycle—the D register input is inhibited. The non-add cycle produces a "sum" which is entered into A′ and new carries for this cycle which are entered into C′. As usual, the shift to the right is performed as the partial sum is returned from A′ to A.

Application

The carry-save adder of Figure 8.3.3 reduces multiplication time directly; the reduction amounts to the carry propagation time for all additions required in multiplication except the last. The carry-save concept can also be incorporated into some of the speed-up methods for multiplication described in forthcoming sections.

One might conjecture as to the effect of storing carries and then using them in the final addition stage. Will this increase, decrease, or have no effect upon the time taken for addition in this final add cycle? This topic was studied both theoretically and empirically by G. Estrin, B. Gilchrist and J. H. Pomerene* who found no perceptible difference in the time required for the final cycle with the two kinds of addition, carry-save and asynchronous propagation.

8.4 MULTIPLES—PAIRS

Notation

We use the notation and register configuration of Chapter 7. That is, the multiplicand is stored in the D register; the multiplier is in the Q register; the partial product is entered into the A register. To indicate what happens from one sequence to another, we use the arrow notation, so that

$$(A) + (D) \longrightarrow A \tag{8.4.1}$$

indicates that the contents of the A register and the contents of the D register are added together and returned to the A register.

In discussing a sequence, we refer to the *present* contents of the A and D register but the *original* contents of the Q register. This may simplify the thinking, but in any case it makes the result valid regardless of the register configuration we are discussing. Thus, the ith bit of the multiplier is referred to as Q_i regardless of where this bit is setting in the Q register. In most cases where we examine the multiplier bits from right to left, the present bit under examination has been shifted to the right end of the register and hence we might more truly refer to it as Q_1. However, this mixed notation allows us to use the simpler Q_i no matter where the bit is within the register.

Simple Bit-at-a-Time, Positive-number Multiplication

The multiplication described in Chapter 4 can be put into the notation used above as follows:

$$\tfrac{1}{2}[(A) + Q_i\,(D)] \longrightarrow A \tag{8.4.2}$$

* G. Estrin, B. Gilchrist, and J. H. Pomerene, "A Note on High-Speed Digital Multiplication" (correspondence), *IRE Trans. Prof. Group on Electronic Computers*, V. EC–5, No. 3 (Sept. 1956).

If the multiplier bit under examination Q_i is 0, the A register is merely shifted with respect to itself. In contrast, if the multiplier bit is a 1, the multiplicand is added to the A register which is then shifted with respect to itself. As mentioned previously, a shift is performed by passing the output of the adder into the prime register and then returning the contents of the prime register moved over one bit, to the main register.

Examining Multiplier Bits in Pairs

It would certainly speed up multiplication if we could examine pairs of multiplier bits and, in one step, do the additions requested by this bit pair. To perform the addition required by the bit pairs in one step, we would have to realize the following equation:

$$\tfrac{1}{4}[(A) + 2Q_{i+1}(D) + Q_i(D)] \longrightarrow A \qquad (8.4.3)$$

Four alternatives may arise for the combination of bit pairs $Q_{i+1} \cdot Q_i$. Three of these alternatives are easily disposed of as

$$00: \quad \tfrac{1}{4}(A) \longrightarrow A \qquad (8.4.4)$$

$$01: \quad \tfrac{1}{4}[(A) + (D)] \longrightarrow A \qquad (8.4.5)$$

$$10: \quad \tfrac{1}{4}[(A) + 2(D)] \longrightarrow A \qquad (8.4.6)$$

After each pair we go on and examine the next pair which we may note as

$$i + 2 \longrightarrow i \qquad (8.4.7)$$

What do we do when both of the bits of the pair are 1? This requires that the multiplicand and twice the multiplicand both be added to the A register. Different ways of handling this are now examined.

Methods for Handling
Multiplier Bit Pair, 11

The first way to solve the problem is to ignore it; that is, when we encounter a pair of 1's we revert to the simple method of doing multiplication a bit at a time. This we can indicate as

$$11: \quad \tfrac{1}{2}[(A) + (D)] \longrightarrow A \qquad i + 1 \longrightarrow i \qquad (8.4.8)$$

The latter half of (8.4.8) indicates that instead of going on to the next pair of bits we take the left bit of this pair and the next bit to the left of it and call it a pair for the purposes of the next sequence. In doing multiplication, we will go down the line of multiplier bits, examining them in pairs and sometimes accomplishing the full request of the pair of bits and other times doing only half the job. On a random statistical basis, we would expect that three-quarters of the time we could handle the complete bit pair; only one-quarter of the time would we revert to the single-bit case.

Another alternative is to form, before multiplication begins, a triple of the multiplicand. This requires an extra register, call it T, where three times the multiplicand is stored. To place it there, we enter into the adder, at one input, one times the multiplicand and, at the other input, twice the multiplicand; we obtain three times the multiplicand at the output and insert it into the T register. Recall that twice the multiplicand is merely the multiplicand shifted once to the left. Now we have

$$2(D) + (D) \longrightarrow T \tag{8.4.9}$$

$$11: \ \tfrac{1}{4}[(A) + (T)] \longrightarrow A \quad i + 2 \longrightarrow i \tag{8.4.10}$$

Another alternative is to use ternary multiplication, which performs multiplication with *additions and subtractions*. It is discussed in detail in the next chapter.

8.5 MULTIPLES—TRIPLETS

We may examine the multiplier bits in sets of three. The desired result for this examination is

$$\tfrac{1}{8}[(A) + 4Q_{i+2}(D) + 2Q_{i+1}(D) + Q_i(D)] \longrightarrow A$$

$$i + 3 \longrightarrow i \tag{8.5.1}$$

When the triplet contains a single 1 or no 1 at all, then it is simple to perform the requested additions in one stage. Hence,

$$000: \ \tfrac{1}{8}(A) \longrightarrow A \tag{8.5.2}$$

$$001: \ \tfrac{1}{8}[(A) + (D)] \longrightarrow A \tag{8.5.3}$$

$$010: \ \tfrac{1}{8}[(A) + 2(D)] \longrightarrow A \tag{8.5.4}$$

$$100: \ \tfrac{1}{8}[(A) + 4(D)] \longrightarrow A \tag{8.5.4}$$

How do we deal with the cases where there are two or more 1's in the triplet? The first method is to revert to a simpler form; the other, to provide one or more multiples.

Reversion to Fewer Bits per Cycle

The remaining bit triple combinations not covered by (8.5.2)–(8.5.5) can be written in this form when no multiples of the multiplicand are provided.

$$011, 111: \quad \tfrac{1}{2}[(A) + (D)] \longrightarrow A \qquad i + 1 \longrightarrow i \qquad (8.5.6)$$

$$101: \quad \tfrac{1}{4}[(A) + (D)] \longrightarrow A \qquad i + 2 \longrightarrow i \qquad (8.5.7)$$

$$110: \quad \tfrac{1}{4}[(A) + 2(D)] \longrightarrow A \qquad i + 2 \longrightarrow i \qquad (8.5.8)$$

For (8.5.6) we revert to the simple one-bit-at-a-time method. For (8.5.7) and (8.5.8) we perform examination in pairs instead of triplets. In each case the bits which have not been considered for this cycle are passed on to the next cycle for examination. Using this method, a statistical examination shows that for randomly distributed multipliers, 50 per cent of the time we perform multiplication at triple speed; 25 per cent of the time we operate at double speed, and 25 per cent of the time at single speed.

Provide Triples

The next alternative which we inherit from the previous section uses the triple of the multiplicand which is stored in the D register at the start of multiplication. This serves us in two of the cases. The triple is used when we require six times the multiplicand, since, when we shift the triple left, this produces six times the multiplicand. We then have

$$011: \quad \tfrac{1}{8}[(A) + (T)] \longrightarrow A \qquad i + 3 \longrightarrow i \qquad (8.5.9)$$

$$110: \quad \tfrac{1}{8}[(A) + 2(T)] \longrightarrow A \qquad i + 3 \longrightarrow i \qquad (8.5.10)$$

The case 101 is accommodated as in (8.5.7); for 111 we have,

$$111: \quad \tfrac{1}{4}[(A) + (T)] \longrightarrow A \qquad i + 2 \longrightarrow i \qquad (8.5.11)$$

Thus with the triple provided we do three-quarters of the triplets at triple speed and one-quarter at double speed. This averages out to $2\tfrac{3}{4}$ bits per cycle, which isn't bad.

Use Triples, Quintuples, and Septuples

In examining the bit triplet of the multiplier, we can perform multiplication for this triplet in a single step if we have available not only the triplet of the multiplicand, but also the quintuple and the septuple. This would of course dispose of the two cases left over in the preceding paragraph. It is obvious how these multiples of the multiplicand are added into the partial product when they were available in the separate registers, F and S.

$$101: \quad \tfrac{1}{8}[(A) + (F)] \longrightarrow A \quad\quad i + 3 \longrightarrow i \quad\quad (8.5.11)$$

$$111: \quad \tfrac{1}{8}[(A) + (S)] \longrightarrow A \quad\quad i + 3 \longrightarrow i \quad\quad (8.5.12)$$

Another alternative is the ternary method discussed later.

8.6   QUADRUPLETS ET CETERA

We may examine the multiplier bits in sets of four, five, and so forth. As the number of bits examined increases, the additional logic required increases at a high rate. If we want to handle all cases in one cycle of addition, we must incorporate a large number of auxiliary registers. These are used to hold the prime or relatively prime multipliers of the multiplicand. Thus, in the case of quadruplets, we need extra registers for the following multiplets of the multiplicand (in addition to those required for the case of triplets) : nine, eleven, thirteen, and fifteen.

Again, compromises may be used so that when an unmanageable case arises we examine only one, two, or three bits of the multiplier instead of four (in the case of quadruplets).

It is interesting to note that the case examined in the next subsection results if we have the capability for multiple shifts but do not use extra registers for storage of multiples of the multiplicand.

Considering Multiple Zero Bits in the Multiplier

Sometimes this method is called shifting over 0's. Let us consider that the computer has a capability of performing in one operation k shifts to the right. Placing this in our notation, we see that we can do the following:

$$\underbrace{100\cdots00}_{k}: \quad (\tfrac{1}{2})^k(A) \longrightarrow A \quad\quad i + k \longrightarrow i \quad\quad (8.6.1)$$

Of course, we also wish to perform all shifts less than k, between 1 and k. We also include in our computer a decoder on the right-hand multiplier bits which is capable of recognizing patterns in the form $100\cdots01$ where there may be none, one or up to $(k - 1)$ 0's between the two 1's. When there are the maximum number of 0's between the 1's, the notation is

$$100\cdots01: \quad (\tfrac{1}{2})^k[(A) + (D)] \longrightarrow A \qquad i + k \longrightarrow i \qquad (8.6.2)$$
$$\underbrace{}_{k-1}$$

Where there are fewer 0's between the 1's the notation may be

$$100\cdots01: \quad (\tfrac{1}{2})^{k-j}[(A) + (D)] \longrightarrow A \qquad i + j \longrightarrow i \qquad (8.6.3)$$
$$\underbrace{}_{k-j-1}$$

One may calculate the increase in speed over the simple method for the case of randomly distributed multiplier numbers. This is a more complicated derivation depending upon the length in bits of the multiplier and requiring the application of the statistical theory of runs.

Shifting Over Zeros Combined With the Multiplicand Multiple Method

The logic required for examining the multiplier bits in larger and larger multiples increases rather rapidly. The logic required for making multiple shifts, however, does not become more complicated nor require more registers, but simply increases the number of gates hanging on to the prime register connecting it to the main register. A compromise can be made by combining multiple shifts with the multiple multiplicand method.

For instance, we can combine the method of bit pairs using triples and shifting over 0's. The equations to be modified are (8.4.4), (8.4.5), (8.4.6), and (8.4.10). These become, respectively,

$$100\cdots00: \quad (\tfrac{1}{2})^j(A) \longrightarrow A \qquad\qquad i + j \longrightarrow i \qquad j \leqq K \qquad (8.6.3)$$
$$\underbrace{}_{j}$$

$$100\cdots01: \quad (\tfrac{1}{2})^{j+1}[(A) + (D)] \longrightarrow A$$
$$\underbrace{}_{j}$$
$$i + j + 1 \longrightarrow i \qquad j < K \qquad (8.6.4)$$

$$100\cdots010: \quad (\tfrac{1}{2})^{j+2}[(A) + 2(D)] \longrightarrow A$$
$$\underbrace{}_{j}$$
$$i + j + 2 \longrightarrow i \qquad j + 1 < K \qquad (8.6.5)$$

$$100\cdots011: \quad (\tfrac{1}{2})^{j+2}[(A) + (T)] \longrightarrow A$$
$$\underbrace{}_{j}$$
$$i + j + 2 \longrightarrow i \qquad j + 1 < K \qquad (8.6.6)$$

where K is the maximum number of shifts of which the hardware is capable.

PROBLEMS

8.1 a. Lay out a configuration, including all interconnections, for an arithmetic unit with a carry-save adder.

    b. Examine Table 7.7. Annex any equations, specifying new equations to incorporate the new carry-save register for multiplication.

    c. Alter any old equations of Table 7.7 for the same purpose.

8.2 Perform the same task as 8.1 for the multiplication by pairs, using a triplet register this time.

8.3 To multiply two $N + 1$-bit numbers (extra bit for sign), how many bits are required for D, A, Q, and especially A' and the adder for the methods of Problems 8.1 and 8.2?

8.4 Draw the configuration for implementing (8.6.3) through (8.6.6).

8.5 Propose a method for multiplication by examining multiplier bits in quadruplets. Assume that the multiplicand triple is available and that difficult multiples are handled by reversion to fewer bits per cycle.

    a. Enumerate the sixteen formulas.

    b. Compare the time with other methods in the chapter.

    c. Is this method attractive?

9

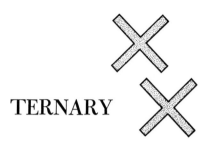

TERNARY

MULTIPLICATION

9.1 INTRODUCTION

A simplification in the number of additions and subtractions that may be required during a multiplication results from the ability to add or subtract the multiplicand from the partial product at will. When this is combined with the ability to perform multiple shifts, a powerful tool for multiplication results. The multiplier bits may be examined in pairs, triplets, and so forth, but increasing complexity results as more bits are examined simultaneously.

Ternary multiplication is so-named because examination of the *set* of multiplier bits may require one of *three* decisions: add or subtract a multiplicand multiple and shift or simply shift without arithmetic.

There are several factors that enter into a description of ternary multiplication: the number of bits examined at one time, the direction in which the multiplier digits are examined (both of which are choices made by the designer), and the sign of the multiplier (which is a function of the calculation but also affects the explanation). We cover the simplest sets of alternatives first and then examine the more elaborate ones.

164

9.2 POSITIVE MULTIPLIERS, MULTIPLIER BIT PAIRS

First Look

When the two bits of the multiplier examined are 00, 01, or 10, the procedure that is adopted is that described in (8.4.4), (8.4.5) and (8.4.6). This only requires the ability to shift the multiplicand one position to the left and to shift the partial product to the right twice when returning it from the prime register to the main register. We have the remaining case where the multiplier bit pair is 11. This requires the addition of three times the multiplicand to the partial product. We note that this can be accomplished by adding four times the multiplicand to the partial product and subtracting one times the multiplicand from the partial product. If these were done simultaneously, of course, the result would be the addition of three times the multiplicand to the partial product, but there is no reason why we cannot perform these in sequence in either order.

When the pair 11 is detected, it is used to request a subtraction of one times the multiplicand from the partial product. This is noted as

$$11: \quad \tfrac{1}{4}[(A) - (D)] \longrightarrow A \qquad i + 2 \longrightarrow i \qquad (9.2.1)$$

The addition of four times the multiplicand has not yet been performed. It is not done in this cycle but is carried over into the examination of the next multiplier bit pair.

When the multiplier bits are examined after a request in the last cycle for an addition of four times the multiplicand, the procedure for each contingency must be changed.

Second Look

Table 9.2.1 indicates the action which is to be performed for each possible pair of multiplier bits under examination. It assumes that no request

TABLE 9.2.1   Ternary Multiplication for
Positive Numbers, No Carry

Bits	Add D	Carryout
00	0	0
01	1	0
10	2	0
11	−1	1

for four times the multiplicand was made in the preceding cycle. Examination at *this* time might indicate a request in the *next* cycle for an addition of four times the multiplicand. This is indicated in the table as a carryout of 1. Thus, for the bit pair 11, we subtract the multiplicand and enter a request for four times the multiplicand to be processed later.

TABLE 9.2.2   Ternary Multiplication for
Positive Numbers with Carryin

Bits	Add D	Carryout
00	1	0
01	2	0
10	−1	1
11	0	1

Table 9.2.2 lists what we are to do for possible bit-pair combinations, provided that, in the last cycle, a request was placed for four times the multiplicand. Between the last cycle and this cycle, a shift to the right of two places has occurred. In other words, the partial product has been multiplied by four. Therefore, to accomplish an addition of four times the multiplicand called for in the last cycle, we add one times the multiplicand in this cycle.

To interpret what must be done for each bit-pair combination, we take its numerical equivalent and add 1 to it. Thus the first entry for the bit combination 00, which would normally request no additions of the multiplicand, is now interpreted to mean one addition of the multiplicand because of the request for four times the multiplicand which was issued in the last cycle. The interpretation of the bit combination 01 is obvious.

For the bit combination 10 we would normally add twice the multiplicand during this cycle. But a request for four times the multiplicand issues in the previous cycle requires an extra addition of one times the multiplicand in *this* cycle. This plus twice the multiplicand required by 10 yields a request for three times the multiplicand. This is interpreted, as the entry 11 was in Table 9.2.1, as a subtraction of the multiplicand and a request to be passed on the next stage to add four times the multiplicand.

The bit combination 11, requesting three times the multiplicand, is now interpreted as a request for four times the multiplicand. This is passed along to the next stage as a carryout and nothing need be added in this cycle.

Combining Tables 9.2.1 and 9.2.2, we have all the conditions which prevail for multiplying positive numbers using the ternary method.

Third Look, Special Cases, Positive Numbers

It should be apparent that we may have a request for a subtraction of the multiplicand occurring on the first examination of the multiplier—the least significant multiplier bits might both be 1's. This means that the partial product is negative. Does this present a problem?

To carry this question a little further, the next pair of bits might be 10 so that the partial product would continue to become more negative. This may continue throughout our examination, but eventually it will be compensated for: a number larger than the partial product accumulated so far will be added to it and the partial product will become positive. Hence, there should be no fear that overflow will occur.

Another problem, which is related to some extent to the one mentioned above, is the extra final cycle which may be required. After looking at the two most significant bits of the multiplier, we may have registered a request for four times the multiplicand. Normally, we would have completed multiplication after examining the most significant multiplier bits. In this case, the product is not complete and another cycle is forthcoming.

The extra cycle is performed if the most significant bit pair is 11 or if there was a carry into this cycle and the most significant bit pair is either 11 or 10. After the last cycle, the partial product is shifted into its proper position in the computer registers. This shift of two places to the right means that a request for four times the multiplicand has now changed to one times the multiplicand. In fulfilling that request, we must be sure that no shift to the right (or left) is performed: then our result will be the correct product. Our extra cycle is noted as

$$[(A) + (D)] \longrightarrow A \qquad (9.2.2)$$

9.3 SIGNED NUMBERS, 2's COMPLEMENT NOTATION

Negative Multiplicand, Positive Multiplier

As long as the multiplier is positive, the negative multiplicand poses no problems which have not already been discussed in previous paragraphs: Again, we add the multiplicand to the partial product in the same fashion as illustrated in Figure 3.3.1. The only difference is that we examine the multiplier two bits at a time. Note especially, that when the partial product

is negative and the right shift is performed, the sign bit which is a 1 is duplicated in the most significant position just as in Figure 3.3.1.

Sometimes we may request the subtraction of the multiplicand from the
partial product. We do this by complementing the multiplicand and adding
it, plus the end-around carry, to the partial product. Of course, complementing a negative number produces a positive number; this too presents
no problem. Finally, we may begin multiplication with the combination 11
which requests a subtraction of the multiplicand (which is negative) or
the addition of the multiplicand complement which is positive which produces a positive partial product. This will be automatically cured, since
one of the succeeding cycles will add a negative number of larger magnitude
into the partial product, thus producing a negative number as a final result.

Negative Multiplier

Negative multiplication, as described here, is performed using Method
2, illustrated in Figure 3.3.4, which requires the 2's complement of the
multiplier. Then each addition called for is interpreted as a request for the
complement of the multiplicand; each subtraction requests the true multiplicand.

To find the 2's complement of the multiplier, even if we examine it in
bit pairs proceeding from right to left, we use the method described in
Chapter 7 whereby we note whether a 1 has been encountered and act
accordingly. The interpretation of the multiplier bit pair now depends on
two factors: Has a 1 previously been encountered in the multiplier? Has a
carryin occurred from the previous cycle (a request for four times the
multiplicand)? The actions to be taken are summarized in Table 9.3.1. If no

TABLE 9.3.1   Ternary Multiplication for Negative Multipliers

| | No previous 1 | | | Previous 1 encountered | | | | |
| | | | | | No carry | | Carry in | |
Bits	Comp	Add D	Carryout	Complement	Add D	Carryout	Add D	Carryout
00	00	0	0	11	−1	1	0	1
01	11	−1	1	10	2	0	−1	1
10	10	2	0	01	1	0	2	0
11	01	1	0	00	0	0	1	0

previous 1's have occurred, then it is impossible to have a carryin. To determine our action, we now find the proper complement of the bit pair under consideration and then interpret that as in Table 9.2.1. If a 1 was previously encountered, the complement of the bits now under consideration is different from those just listed. If no carryin is present, we obtain the entries in the middle of Table 9.3.1 by interpreting the complement of the bit pair using Table 9.2.1. If a carryin is present, we interpret this bit pair complement as in Table 9.2.2.

Control Equations

We are now going to combine the conditions of Tables 9.2.1, 9.2.2, and 9.3.1 to derive the adder control equations. The first step toward doing this

TABLE 9.3.2   Register Connections for Ternary Multiplication of Signed Numbers by Examining Bit Pairs of the Multiplier from Right to Left

| Q_s | | 0 | | 0 | | 1 | | 1 | | 1 | |
| F | | X | | X | | 0 | | 1 | | 1 | |
C'		0		1		0		0		1	
Q_{i+1}	Q_i	D	C_{i+2}	D	C_{i+2}	D	C_{i+2}	D	C_{i+2}	D	C_{i+2}
0	0	0	0	Dt	0	0	0	Dt	1	0	1
0	1	Dt	0	Dtl	0	Dt	1	Dcl	0	Dt	1
1	0	Dtl	0	Dc	1	Dcl	0	Dc	0	Dcl	0
1	1	Dc	1	0	1	Dc	0	0	0	Dc	0

is to make a new, combined table, as shown in Table 9.3.2. Let us now consider how we will devise this table.

What information contributes to the determination of what action takes place in this stage? First, we have the sign of the multiplier, Q_s, which will determine whether the multiplier bits are complemented. Second, we have the fact of whether a 1 has been encountered in examining the multiplier for complementation. (This is the variable F and is pertinent only in dealing with negative multipliers.) Third, there is the carryin from the previous stage, a request for an addition of four times the multiplicand (indicated in the Table as C'). Finally, there are the two multiplier bits, the less significant of which is Q_i, and the more significant of which is Q_{i+1}.

dependent variables

The variables enumerated in the foregoing paragraph will determine the connections and settings made in this stage. We wish to communicate, to the next cycle, whether a carry is requested, which is recorded by the setting of C.

The other consideration is the connection of the multiplicand register to the adder: it can be connected directly, Dt; its true output can be connected after having been shifted one position to the left to yield twice the multiplicand, Dtl; it can be complemented before connection, Dc; it can be complemented and shifted left, Dcl.

equation conditions

In retabulating the information in Table 9.3.1, it must be remembered that the column listing entitled "Add D" is to be interpreted as the addition or subtraction of the complement of D, since the method of Figures 3.3.4 and 3.3.5 are being implemented. Hence, a positive number in one of these columns calls for a complement connection for D or a complement shift left connection for D; alternatively, a negative entry requires a true connection for D.

equations

From Table 9.3.2 we can make up equations which will define the connections required in each cycle. Although there are four connections required, we can simplify this to three with the following definition: Let DT represent a true connection of D to the adder whether D is shifted left or not. Similarly, DC is a complement connection of D to the adder whether shifted left or not. Then L indicates whether a left shift is performed. We have, for instance,

$$Dt = DT\bar{L} \qquad (9.3.1)$$

The conditions of Table 9.3.2 are difficult to simplify using Karnaugh maps or Boolean equations. It seems that juggling the equations around may yield the most efficient result. A form which I have been able to derive is found in the following equations:

$$DT = \bar{Q}_s[C'\bar{Q}_{i+1} + \bar{C}'(\bar{Q}_{i+1}Q_i + Q_{i+1}\bar{Q}_i)]$$

$$+ Q_s[\bar{F}C'Q_{i+1}Q_i + F(C'\bar{Q}_{i+1}Q_i + \bar{C}'\bar{Q}_{i+1}Q_i)] \tag{9.3.2}$$

$$DC = \bar{Q}_s[C'Q_{i+1}\bar{Q}_i + \bar{C}'Q_{i+1}Q_i]$$

$$+ Q_s\{\bar{F}\bar{C}'Q_{i+1} + F[C'Q_{i+1} + \bar{C}'(\bar{Q}_{i+1}Q_i + Q_{i+1}\bar{Q}_i)]\} \tag{9.3.3}$$

$$L = \bar{Q}_s(\bar{C}'\bar{Q}_{i+1}Q_i + C'Q_{i+1}\bar{Q}_i)$$

$$+ Q_s[\bar{C}'(Q_{i+1}\bar{Q}_i\bar{F} + \bar{Q}_{i+1}Q_iF) + C'FQ_{i+1}\bar{Q}_i] \tag{9.3.4}$$

$$C = \bar{Q}_s(\bar{C}'Q_{i+1}Q_i + C'Q_{i+1}\bar{Q}_i)$$

$$+ Q_s[Q_{i+1}(\bar{F} + C') + \bar{C}'F(\bar{Q}_{i+1}Q_i + Q_{i+1}\bar{Q}_i)] \tag{9.3.5}$$

The reader may try to simplify these further or derive his own simpler equations. He should note that DT is not equal to DC.

9.4 PAIRS, HARDWARE

Configuration

Figure 9.4 illustrates a suggested configuration for ternary multiplication by pairs. The reader should be familiar by now with the symbology. The one exception may be the connections Ar2 and Qr2. Each of these

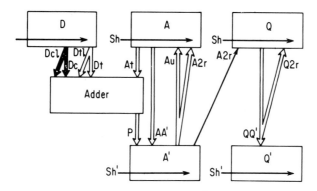

FIGURE 9.4 Register configuration for two-bit ternary right-to-left multiplication

represents connections between the prime register and the main register whereby the quantity in the prime register is shifted two places to the right as it is returned to the main register. It should also be noted that the kind of shift called for here requires the entry of two least significant bits of A′ into the main Q register as the shift of two places right is performed. This is in order to produce the double-length product. Note also that the connection labeled Au, which is required to perform the correction cycle after the most significant bits of the multiplier have been considered.

Timing

We now present the equations for timing the interchange of data during 2-bit ternary multiplication. Entry into the prime register is performed when carry-complete is detected at the adder,

$$Sh' = CC \tag{9.4.1}$$

Information is returned to the main registers a little later,

$$Sh = \Delta Sh' \tag{9.4.2}$$

We keep track of how many bits of the multiplier have been examined in a counter which is set to 0 at the start of multiplication. The symbol for the output of this counter is $D(\quad)$. The counter is reset to 0 by the start pulse,

$$D(0) = St \tag{9.4.3}$$

The counter is incremented by two a short time after the contents of the adder is entered into the prime register,

$$D(i + 2) = Sh' \, D(i) \tag{9.4.4}$$

To determine when multiplication is complete, we have two alternatives: all multiplier bits have been examined; all multiplier bits have been examined *and* a termination cycle has been done. The termination cycle is required if a carry signal is evident after the regular $N/2$ multiply cycles and not otherwise. When a termination cycle is required, the counter will be tallied *past N* and, on completion of the extra cycle, will read $N + 2$. Therefore, we can say that multiplication is complete if

$$E = Sh \, D(N)C + Sh \, D(N + 2) \tag{9.4.5}$$

We wish to continue processing and issue a test signal, Te, when the counter reads less than N or for the termination cycle when the counter reads N and a carry signal has been recorded,

$$Te = Sh[D(<N) + C \, D(N)] \tag{9.4.6}$$

The unshifted connections, Au and Qu, between the prime and main A and Q registers are called for only on the correction cycle when the counter reads N,

$$Au = Qu = D(N) \qquad (9.4.7)$$

A double right shift from the prime registers A′ and Q′ to the main register, A and Q is called for at other times,

$$Ar2 = Qr2 = D(<N) \qquad (9.4.8)$$

The further timing signals, which are required to connect (T) and disconnect ($\overline{T}$) the adder, are given as

$$T = St + Te \qquad (9.4.9)$$

$$\overline{T} = CC \qquad (9.4.10)$$

which signals are discussed in Section 7.8 and given there as equations (7.8.1) and (7.8.2).

Adder Connections

When the D register is connected directly into the adder, whether shifted left or not, we enter a 0-carry into the adder,

$$^{0}C_0 = DT \qquad (9.4.11)$$

When the unshifted complement of the D register is entered into the adder, a 1-carry into the adder must be present,

$$^{1}C_0 = DC\overline{L} \qquad (9.4.12)$$

Now we note a special case where two times the complement of the multiplicand is to be added to the partial product. In this case, we must not enter carryin of 1 into the first stage of the adder. Rather, it must be entered into the second stage of the adder to get a correct result because the complement has been shifted one place to the left and the end-around carry must be entered into that position. Therefore,

$$^{1}C_1 = DCL \qquad (9.4.13)$$

Register Connections

We want to connect the true output of the D register into the adder for non-termination cycles when the proper equations apply or during the termination cycle for a positive multiplier,

$$Dt = D(<N)DT \bar{L} + D(N)C\bar{Q}_s \qquad (9.4.14)$$

The shifted true D register connection is made only on non-termination cycles,

$$Dtl = D(<N)DT\ L \qquad (9.4.15)$$

The unshifted complement connection of the D register is required on non-correction cycles when the proper equations apply and on the correction cycles for a negative multiplier,

$$Dc = D(<N)DC\ \bar{L} + D(N)CQ_s \qquad (9.4.16)$$

The left shifted complement of the D register is connected on non-termination cycles.

$$Dcl = D(<N)DC\ L \qquad (9.4.17)$$

Auxiliary Functions

The complement assist bit storage F is set to 0 at the beginning of multiplication,

$$F = St \qquad (9.4.18)$$

It is set to 1 a little time later than the entry of the adder into the prime register if

1. It has not already been set to 1—F.
2. We have a negative multiplier—Q_s.
3 And at least one of the pair of bits examined is a 1—$Q_1 + Q_2$,

$$F = \Delta Sh'\bar{F}Q_s(Q_1 + Q_2) \qquad (9.4.19)$$

We also need to record the sign of the product at the beginning of multiplication so that we can set the sign of the Q register when multiplication is complete. Hence, we provide the sign register Sg and a setting pulse qs when a negative product is produced.

$$Sg = Sf(Q_s\ D_s + Q_s\ D_s) \qquad (9.4\ 20)$$

$$qs = ESg \qquad (9.4.21)$$

9.5 A SIMPLER 2-BIT CONDITION MATRIX

We have seen how multiplication can be speeded up by examination of the multiplier in pairs of bits. The logical equations for this operation were set up on the basis of examining the bit pairs in the multiplier from the right end of the multiplier to the left. Regardless of the direction in which we examine the multiplier, there is a better set of equations that governs this process. We will develop these by first setting up a table of conditions as we did in the first part of this section.

No-Borrow Condition

Suppose, for the moment, that we examine multiplier bits in pairs, this time from left to right. We initially set up our conditions so that the partial product is always a positive number (in the case of two positive operands), as shown in Table 9.5.1. If the bits represent the quantities 0 or 2, we add

TABLE 9.5.1   Ternary Multiplication for Positive
Numbers, Method 2, No Borrowin

Bits	Add D	Borrow
00	0	0
01	2	1
10	2	0
11	4	1

nothing to the partial product or twice the multiplicand to the partial product respectively. If the bit pair represents the quantities 1 or 3, we add in one more than this. Thus, for 01, we add in twice the multiplicand and, for 11, four times the multiplicand. In each case, we "owe" a subtraction of the multiplicand. This is worded in Table 9.5.1 as a borrow of 1.

After each addition, the partial product is shifted two places to the left, which is equivalent to division by four. When examining a bit pair, it may be after a borrow is recorded or after no borrow is recorded. The no-borrow case is presented as Table 9.5.1.

Borrow Condition

For a borrow condition, we always wish to subtract one times the multiplicand from the partial product. However, because of the shift *to the right* after the previous cycle, we must subtract four times the multiplicand instead of one times the multiplicand. The various contingencies are presented in Table 9.5.2. When the bit pair under examination is 00, we subtract four times the multiplicand and record no borrow. Similarly, the bit pair 10 calls for a subtraction of four and an addition of two so that the result is a subtraction of twice the multiplicand. The bit pair 01 calls for

TABLE 9.5.2   Ternary Multiplication for
Positive Numbers, Method 2, with Borrowin

Bits	Add D	Borrow
00	−4	0
01	−2	1
10	−2	0
11	0	1

a subtraction of four and an addition of one which is a subtraction of three. This is accomplished by subtracting twice the multiplicand now and recording a borrow for the next cycle. Similarly, the bit pair 11 calls for subtracting four and adding three for a total of −1. This is performed by subtracting nothing now and recording a borrow for the next cycle.

Examining both tables, we see that a borrow condition arises when the least significant bit of the bit pair is a 1. This is a useful fact in itself, but it also communicates to us what has happened on the previous cycle. Thus, the least significant bit of *this* pair tells us the borrow for *this* cycle, and the least significant bit of *the pair to the left of this pair* tells us whether a borrow occurred on the *previous* cycle and, therefore, whether we are using Table 9.5.1 or 9.5.2.

Termination

One minor problem arises in the method outlined above the required extra termination cycle. If the least significant bit, the extreme right-hand bit of the multiplier, is a 1, then a borrow is recorded in examining the rightmost bit pair of the multiplier. This requires then an extra cycle be performed to subtract one times the multiplicand from the uncorrected product.

This correction can be performed in one of three possible fashions. First, we can perform an extra cycle only when the least significant bit of the multiplier is a 1. Second, we can try to perform an adjustment cycle after we have formed the uncorrected product. In this case, we pass the product through the adder, subtracting the multiplicand when the multiplier bit is 1 and shutting off the multiplicand completely when the multiplier bit is 0. The third alternative is used when this method is applied to examining the bits in sequence from right to left. In that case, at the start of multiplication the partial product is 0. Instead of entering 0 into the adder, something else may be entered. One input to the adder on the initial cycle is determined by Tables 9.5.1 and 9.5.2; the other input is determined by whether the least significant bit is a 1 and is the complemented multiplicand applied to the input normally reserved for the partial product.

Direction of Examination

This method does not depend for its effectiveness upon the direction in which the multiplier bits are examined. In advancing leftward we pick up a pair of bits. The *next bit to the left* tells the borrow condition. If it is 1, we subtract according to Table 9.5.2; if it is 0, we add according to Table 9.5.1. *Termination* is done with a possible extra initial cycle as above.

Signed Numbers

When we have a negative multiplicand and a positive multiplier, multiplication proceeds exactly as described above: we add the number when required and subtract the number by complementing it and adding in the end-around carry.

A negative multiplier is handled differently according to whether we are using 1's complement notation or 2's complement notation. In the case of 1's complement notation, the complement of a multiplier bit is obtained directly. For 2's complement notation, the F function we have been using right along is applied here. In the latter case, it is *essential* that we proceed from right to left so that this F function has meaning. Since we are concerned primarily with 2's complement notation, the complete table for positive and negative numbers is presented as Table 9.5.3.

In Table 9.5.3 we find entries for the sign bit of the multiplier, Q_s, the F function, and three bits of the multiplier. These three bits are the bit pair under consideration, $Q_{i+1}Q_i$, and the left adjacent bit, Q_{i+2}. The latter indicates whether a borrow condition applies to the bit pair now under examination. Each set of columns contains, when necessary, the 2's complement of the three bits being considered, the multiples of the multiplicand which are to be added or subtracted, the connections between the D register and the adder to produce this multiple, and, finally, the setting of the F bit storage when this is appropriate.

TABLE 9.5.3   Register Connections for Ternary Multiplication of Signed Numbers by Examining Bit Pairs of the Multiplier from Right to Left by Method 2

| $Q_{i+2}Q_{i+1}Q_i$ | $Q_s = 0$ | | $Q_s = 1$ F = 1 | | | $Q_s = 1$ F = 0 | | | |
	Add D	Con- nect	Comple- ment	Add D	Con- nect	Comple- ment	Add D	Con- nect	Set F
000	0	0	111	0	0	000	0	0	0
001	2	Dt	110	−2	Dt	111	0	0	1
010	2	Dt	101	−2	Dt	110	−2	Dt	1
011	4	Dtl	100	−4	Dtl	101	−2	Dt	1
100	−4	Dcl	011	4	Dcl	100	−4	Dtl	1
101	−2	Dc	010	2	Dc	011	4	Dcl	1
110	−2	Dc	001	2	Dc	010	2	Dc	1
111	0	0	000	0	0	001	2	Dc	1

Equations

From Table 9.5.3 we can now produce the following equations for the three functions: true multiplicand, DT; complement multiplicand, DC; multiplicand shift left, L.

$$\text{DT} = (\bar{Q}_s + \text{F})\bar{Q}_{i+2}(Q_{i+1} + Q_i)$$
$$+ Q_s\bar{\text{F}}(\bar{Q}_{i+2}Q_{i+1} + Q_{i+2}\bar{Q}_{i+1}\bar{Q}_i) \tag{9.5.1}$$

$$\text{DC} = Q_{i+2}[(\bar{Q}_s + \text{F})(\bar{Q}_{i+1} + \bar{Q}_i) + Q_s\bar{\text{F}}(Q_{i+1} + Q_i)] \tag{9.5.2}$$

$$\text{L} = (\bar{Q}_s + \text{F})(\bar{Q}_{i+2}Q_{i+1}Q_i + Q_{i+2}\bar{Q}_{i+1}\bar{Q}_i)$$
$$+ Q_s\bar{\text{F}}Q_{i+2}\bar{Q}_{i+1} \tag{9.5.3}$$

These equations would replace (9.3.2) through (9.3.5) They are combined with (9.4.1) through (9.4.21) to produce a ternary multiplication unit with a simpler control logic.

9.6   LEFT-TO-RIGHT   BIT-PAIR EXAMINATION

It seems odd that the system which was devised originally by examining bit pairs from most to least significant position is *not applicable to 2's complements negative multipliers* when scanned in that sequence. For positive multipliers, scanning from left to right can be performed as described earlier. This presents an advantage in that the partial product maintains the sign of the multiplicand throughout multiplication. Although a termination cycle is required, it is easy to perform. The big disadvantage is the extra length of adder required—usually enough to eliminate this sequence from consideration.

The explanation for the identity of the connections in the two cases can be presented in a double negative philosophy. Multiplier bit combinations (see center three columns of Table 9.5.3) requiring addition for a positive multiplier require subtraction for a negative multiplier and vice versa. However, a negative multiplier for addition requires complementation of the multiplicand first. These two sign reversals cancel each other leading to a consistent interpretation regardless of multiplier sign.

Equations (9.5.1) through (9.5.3) can now be simply written as

$$\mathrm{DT} = \bar{Q}_{i+2}(Q_{i+1} + Q_i) \tag{9.6.1}$$

$$\mathrm{DC} = Q_{i+1}(\bar{Q}_{i+1} + \bar{Q}_i) \tag{9.6.2}$$

$$L = \bar{Q}_{i+2}Q_{i+1}Q_i + Q_{i+2}\bar{Q}_{i+1}\bar{Q}_i \tag{9.6.3}$$

Procedure

The most significant bit of the partial product is formed first. If the less significant bits of the product are formed, the most significant bits are shifted out of the A' register and across into the Q register. Thus, by the end of multiplication, the double-length product is stored in the Q and A register and the multiplier has been completely lost. The more significant word is in the Q register and the less significant word is in the A register. The multiplicand is preserved throughout multiplication.

Since 2's complement notation is most prevalent, the right-to-left examination of the multiplier bits is what is recommended for this high-speed multiplication method.

The left-to-right scan is particularly applicable when we are using 1's complement notation because the 1's complement of any bit in a number does not depend in any way upon the bits to the right of it. As we know, this is not true in 2's complement notation and is the reason why the F function is required. The only way we can use the method above to perform multiplication with a negative multiplier using 2's complement notation is to require a special initial cycle which finds the 2's complement of a multiplier and inserts it in an appropriate register. As with positive numbers, a final correction cycle is also required.

Configuration

The register configuration for performing multiplication, when examining the multiplier from left to right, is different from that used when examining the multiplier from right to left. This form of configuration is presented in Figure 9.6. The multiplier is stored in the Q register, the prod-

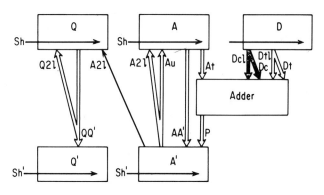

FIGURE 9.6   Register configuration for two-bit, ternary, left-to-right multiplication

uct is accumulated in the A register, and the multiplicand is stored in the D register. The multiplicand can be used directly in true or complement form or multiplied by two in true or complement form. As left-hand multiplier bits are examined, they are discarded as the Q′ register is shifted left into the Q register.

Equations

For 1's complement, left-to-right multiplication, the control equations can be immensely simplified; primarily because the auxiliary F function is eliminated. Examine Table 9.5.3. The column labeled "$Q_s = 0$" is applicable to positive multipliers. The one labeled "$Q_s = 1$; F = 1" is *always* applicable for negative multipliers. Notice that the multiplicand connections for both these columns are identical!

9.7   TRIPLETS

Introduction

Ternary multiplication with triplets is similar to ternary multiplication with pairs except that now three bits of the multiplier are examined instead of two. It assumes the ability to subtract or add the multiplicand as desired. It also requires the ability to shift the multiplicand prior to entering it into the adder either one, two, or three places. Besides this, it is necessary to be able to add or subtract three times the multiplicand shifted accordingly.

This method offers the advantage of speed. It is as fast as the improved method of shifting over 0's and 1's described later. It has the advantage of requiring a uniform shift of three bits of both the multiples and the partial product. Further, no 2's complement correction cycle need be provided as long as adequate decoding hardware is used.

As far as disadvantages are concerned, an additional register is required to store the triple of the multiplicand. This necessitates an additional cycle to prepare the triple by adding the multiplicand to the multiplicand shifted once to the left. Further, provision must be made for a correction according to the least significant multiplier bit. This may be done with an extra termination cycle or may be incorporated into the first addition cycle performed during multiplication.

Method, Positive Numbers

We are going to proceed by pretending that we are going to examine the multiplier right word (from left to right) and thus develop the control equations, even though we are going to apply the control equations by examining the multiplier leftward, which is required when dealing with negative numbers in 2's complement notation.

In the last section, we examined three bits to determine how to use the two, right-hand remaining bits of the multiplier. In this case, to use three bits of the remaining multiplier, we examine the four right-hand bits of the multiplier. The high-order bit of this quartet determines whether a borrow will be requested in the next cycle.

To determine what is required on each cycle, we set up Table 9.7.1. This is similar to what would result in combining Table 9.5.1 and 9.5.2 in a three-bit case. Let us examine Table 9.7.1. Line 3 says, that when the least significant multiplier bits are 0010, we add twice the multiplicand and produce no borrow; this should be clear. Line 2 says that, when the least significant bits of the multiplier are 0001, we request an addition of twice the multiplicand and a borrow from the next cycle of 1. Of course, we could add once the multiplicand and let it go at that. However, this would require that the circuitry make available not only the eight, four, and two multiples of the multiplicand, but also the one multiple of the multiplicand. This can be circumvented by using twice the multiplicand and subtracting once in the next cycle. Similarly, three times the multiplicand is formed by adding four and subtracting one; seven times the multiplicand is formed by adding eight and subtracting one.

A request for six times the multiplicand now requires reference to the multiplicand triple which was formed on the initial cycle. Five times the multiplicand is formed by adding six and subtracting one.

TABLE 9.7.1   Ternary Three-Bit Multiplication for Positive Numbers Using Multiplier Bit Triplets

Line	Borrow	Bits	Request	Add D	New Borrow
1	0	000	0	0	0
2	0	001	1	2	1
3	0	010	2	2	0
4	0	011	3	4	1
5	0	100	4	4	0
6	0	101	5	6	1
7	0	110	6	6	0
8	0	111	7	8	1
9	1	000	−8	−8	0
10	1	001	−7	−6	1
11	1	010	−6	−6	0
12	1	011	−5	−4	1
13	1	100	−4	−4	0
14	1	101	−3	−2	1
15	1	110	−2	−2	0
16	1	111	−1	0	1

The bottom half of Table 9.7.1 arises from a borrow when the lowest bit of the triple to the left is a 1. This appears as a 1 in the high-order bit when examining the multiplier bit in quartets. Line 9 says that, when a request for a borrow is accomplished by no request for multiplication in this cycle, we subtract eight times the multiplicand. This is true because the borrow applies to the cycle coming up in the next three positions to the left. The borrow corresponds to eight times the multiplicand used for that bit set. The other entries may be interpreted similarly. Thus, in line 16, we have a borrow corresponding to eight times the multiplicand and a multiplier triplet of 111 corresponding to seven times the multiplicand, so that our request is to subtract one times the multiplicand. This is performed by not adding the multiplicand at all but simply by recording a new borrow.

Method, Signed Numbers

In order to see how this method applied to signed numbers, we prepare Table 9.7.2 which corresponds to Table 9.5.3 for the method of bit pairs. The description which applies to the earlier table is also applicable here because of the similarity of the methods. Notice that the column corre-

TABLE 9.7.2. Register Connection for Ternary Multiplication of Signed Numbers by Examining Bit *Triplets* of the Multiplier from Right to Left

Q_{i+3}	Q_{i+2}	Q_{i+1}	Q_i	Request	Con-nect	Comp	Request	Con-nect	Comp	Request	Con-nect
	Multiplier bits			$Q_s = 0$			$Q_s = 1$				
							$F = 1$ Dc			$F = 0$ Dc	
0	0	0	0	0	—	1111	−1	—	0000	0	—
0	0	0	1	1	Dt	1110	−2	Dt	1111	−1	—
0	0	1	0	2	Dt	1101	−3	Dt	1110	−2	Dt
0	0	1	1	3	Dtl	1100	−4	Dtl	1101	−3	Dt
0	1	0	0	4	Dtl	1011	−5	Dtl	1100	−4	Dtl
0	1	0	1	5	T	1010	−6	T	1011	−5	Dtl
0	1	1	0	6	T	1001	−7	T	1010	−6	T
0	1	1	1	7	Dt2	1000	−8	Dt2	1001	−7	T
1	0	0	0	−8	Dc2	0111	7	Dc2	1000	−8	Dt2
1	0	0	1	−7	Tc	0110	6	Tc	0111	7	Dc2
1	0	1	0	−6	Tc	0101	5	Tc	0110	6	Tc
1	0	1	1	−5	Dcl	0100	4	Dcl	0101	5	Tc
1	1	0	0	−4	Dcl	0011	3	Dcl	0100	4	Dcl
1	1	0	1	−3	Dc	0010	2	Dc	0011	3	Dcl
1	1	1	0	−2	Dc	0001	1	Dc	0010	2	Dc
1	1	1	1	−1	—	0000	0	—	0001	1	Dc

sponding to a positive multiplier corresponds closely to the entries in Table 9.7.1. True and complement shift entries for the D register should be clear from the previous usage. It remains to note that the register containing the multiplicand triple is labeled T and its complement is labeled Tc. The right-hand portion of the chart is devoted to the cases which arise when the multiplier is negative. As previously, we must monitor the multiplier bits, recording when a 1 is first encountered by setting the bit storage F to 1. When the bit storage F is 1, the complement of the multiplier bits is formed by taking the 1's complement of each bit; when F is 0, we form the complement of the multiplier bits as discussed previously. We interpret the request for multiples of the multiplicand by referring to the multiplier bit complement.

When dealing with a negative multiplier, we must keep in mind that the request for a multiplicand multiples has to be interpreted as a request for negative multiplicand multiples as long as we are performing multiplication by the second method for 2's complements discussed in Chapter 3. The multiplicand complement would be found at the complement bus from the D register. Interpreting our request as applying to multiplicand complements, we can set up appropriate connections so that the result will be the desired one.

9.8   TERNARY TRIPLET
MULTIPLICATION HARDWARE

Register Configuration

Figure 9.8 shows a configuration of registers which could be used to perform three-bit, ternary, right-to-left multiplication of signed numbers. The

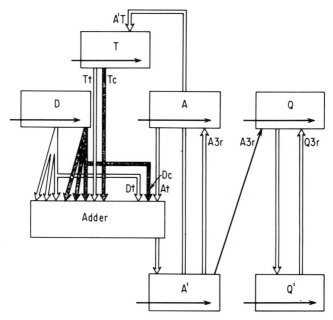

FIGURE 9.8   Three-bit   ternary   right-to-left   multiplication.
Logic, signed numbers

register labeled T is provided to store the multiplicand triple. Notice that the right input to the adder has provisions for receiving the contents of the A register, the D register, or the complemented D register. The left input to the adder has provision for receiving eight different quantities: the T register and its complement; the three multiples of the multiplicand; the three multiples of the multiplicand complement.

Shifting between prime and main requires duplication of the sign bit in the higher order bits of A in order that the Method 2, 2's complement multiplication procedure be followed. Also, the shift of low order bits from A′ in the high order of Q is indicated in Figure 9.8.

Cycle of Operation

This description is rather cursory, as the reader should now be familiar with the operation of multiplication hardware. There are three different cycles we are concerned with: the preparation of the multiplicand triple; the first multiplication cycle during which a correction for the least significant bit may be applied; the other multiplication cycles.

Preparing the Triple

The adder setup allows us, on the first cycle, to apply one times the multiplicand on the right side and twice the multiplicand on the left. The result, three times the multiplicand, is passed over to the A′ register. It is returned via the line labeled A′T into the T register.

Since we have at our disposal not only the means for preparing the multiplicand triple but also the multiplicand complement triple, we could prepare it in a similar fashion. The choice as to whether to prepare the proper triple and use only one output of the T register, as against preparing the same triple all the time and gating the output of the T register, is up to the designer.

Initial Multiply Cycle

One way to handle the correction necessitated by a 1 in the least significant bit position of the multiplier is to perform this correction during the first cycle of multiplication. This requires that the multiplicand be shifted once, twice, or three times, as against a multiplicand shift of 0, once, or twice if a separate correction cycle is used.

We examine, on the first cycle, the three right-hand bits of the multiplier, applying the decisions listed in Table 9.7.2. This permits us to enter the proper multiple of the multiplicand, properly signed, into the adder on the first cycle. Since the A register has been cleared, nothing would normally be entered into the right-hand input of the adder. If the least significant multiplier bit is a 1, we can now enter the properly signed multiple of the multiplicand into the adder, thus performing the correction during the first multiplication cycle.

Succeeding Multiply Cycles

Cycles that follow refer to the multiplication table of Table 9.7.2 to determine the correct multiple of the multiplicand to be added to the partial product. As the new partial product is formed, it is entered into the prime register and then returned to the main register, shifted three positions to the right. This shift is the type which usually occurs in multiplication wherein the least significant portion of the A′ register is shifted across to the most significant portion of the Q register. During a cycle, the multiplier is shifted across from the main register to the prime register and then back across to the main register where it is displaced three positions to the right. This means that the least significant three bits of the multiplier are lost as to the less significant word of the product is developed.

Termination

After each cycle, 3 is added to the shift counter. Before each new cycle, the shift counter is tested to determine whether multiplication is finished. If the counter has been counted up to the number of bits of the multiplier being used, multiplication is terminated after the sign of the product is set into the A register; otherwise, new cycles of multiplication continue.

PROBLEMS

9.1 Write the control equations for ternary multiplication by examining the multiplier bits in triplets as in Section 9.7.

9.2 Propose a combination of ternary triplets and shifts over 0's of up to four bits.

9.3 Contrast ternary multiplication for
   a. Sign and magnitude representation.
   b. 1's complement representation.
   c. 2's complement representation.

10
MULTIPLICATION
BY SHIFTING

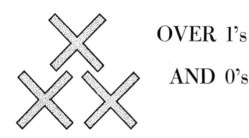

OVER 1's
AND 0's

10.1 INTRODUCTION

Multiplication performed by shifting over 1's and 0's, as previous methods, depends for its speed on the way in which the multiplier word is examined. In this case, we look for runs of 1's and 0's; a run consists of a number of consecutive, identical bits. For each run of 1's, this method requires one subtraction and one addition; nothing but shifting is required for a run of 0's. Since a run of 0's always occurs between runs of 1's, we may say that this process performs one addition or subtraction for *each* run of 0's or 1's in the multiplier.

The theory of runs indicates that a saving occurrs by this method if the bits of the multiplier are randomly distributed 1's and 0's. When the data is structured so that more or longer runs result than for the random case, the savings are greater still; for example, calculations with few places of significance where many 0's appear.

An improvement on the first method is made in Section 10.3. In the next sections the implementation in hardware of both the improved and unimproved method is presented. In Section 10.3 the control equations are also developed.

Section 10.4 builds up the hardware and equations required for a system which uses the method of shifting over 1's and 0's to multiply signed numbers. First, a register configuration is presented. The procedure for manipulating positive multipliers using a simple method is then outlined in Section 10.5. This is extended to include negative multipliers in 2's complement notation. Then the improved method for handling positive multipliers is implemented in Section 10.6. It is extended in Section 10.7 to handle negative multipliers in 2's complement notation. Finally we combine the equations in Section 10.8.

System

The register configuration for this method must be such that addition or subtraction of the multiplicand from the partial product is possible. If multiples of the multiplicand can be *added or subtracted*, this produces a further speedup in operations; but this topic is postponed to Chapter 11.

In returning the new partial product from the prime register to the main register, a variable number of shifts is performed upon it. This requires multiple gating; the more shifts that are possible, the greater will be the resulting speedup. As would be expected, this facility costs money. Once the number of shifts is increased beyond a certain point, somewhere near the fan-out limit of the gates, the cost per shift takes a sharp rise.

A decoder of the right-hand K multiplier bits is attached to the multiplier register, where K is the largest number of shifts which may be performed at any one time.

Auxiliary devices are required for such things as recording the last action taken on a multiplication cycle.

10.2 THEORY

An alternative representation for a string of 1's appearing any place in a binary number is sought. First, consider the binary number consisting only of a string of 1's.

Initial Run of 1's

The number $11\cdots11$ is translated by adding up consecutive powers of 2, starting from 0. Thus, when the number we are concerned with consists of k 1's, it represents $2^{k-1} + 2^{k-2} + \cdots + 2^1 + 2^0$.

When we add these powers of 2 the result is $2^k - 1$. Here is a simple intuitive proof of this fact. If we add 1 to the number consisting of k 1's, each 1 in turn down the line becomes a 0 and causes a carry into the 1 above it. This continues until we encounter the first 0 to the left. Thus, if we add 1, the number we obtain consists of 1 followed by k 0's, that is,

$100\cdots00$. This latter number is 2^k which was obtained by adding 1 to our original number. Hence our original number is 1 less than this number, 2^k, or $2^k - 1$.

The simplification above indicates that a number consisting of a string of 1's can be represented by subtracting 1 and by adding a power of 2 which is 1 greater than the highest power of 2 encountered in our number. Thus,

$$\overbrace{011\cdots11}^{k} = \overbrace{100\cdots00}^{k} - 00\cdots001 \qquad (10.2.1)$$

1's Followed by 0's

Next let us consider a number consisting of k 1's followed by m 0's. This multiplies the previous result by 2^m. Thus our number, consisting of k 1's followed by m 0's, can be represented as $2^m(2^k - 1)$. Then,

$$\overbrace{011\cdots11}^{k}\overbrace{00\cdots00}^{m} = \overbrace{100\cdots00}^{k+m} - \overbrace{0100\cdots00}^{m} \qquad (10.2.2)$$

Alternating Runs

The simplification of (10.2.2) remains valid when we consider a number consisting of alternating runs of 1's and 0's. We can abstract a run of 1's from our number, considering it to consist of all 0's following this run of 1's, and using the method specified above for simplifying our number. To make a first try at this, let us examine a number V, consisting of k 1's followed by m 0's followed by r 1's followed by s 0's.

$$V = \overbrace{11\cdots11}^{k}\overbrace{0000\cdots00}^{m}\overbrace{0011\cdots11}^{r}\overbrace{0000\cdots00}^{s} \qquad (10.2.3)$$

The first set of 1's is then represented as $2^{m+r+s}(2^k - 1)$. The next run of 1's is represented by $2^m(2^r - 1)$. We are examining this number as though it had two runs superimposed:

$$V = \overbrace{11\cdots11}^{k}\overbrace{00000\cdots00}^{m+r+s} + \underbrace{11\cdots11}_{r}\underbrace{0000\cdots00}_{s} \qquad (10.2.4)$$

Hence our number is

$$V = 2^{k+m+r+s} - 2^{m+r+s} + 2^{r+s} - 2^s \qquad (10.2.5)$$

This procedure can be generalized to any run of 1's in a number in any position in that number.

The Multiplier Considered as Alternating Runs

When the number we are referring to is a multiplier, a run of 1's requests a number of rapid additions and shifts. This can now be replaced by a subtraction for the right-hand 1 in the run followed by an addition one position to the left of the left-most 1 in the run. This tongue-twister can be better visualized by noting how the multiplier below can request additions and subtractions of the multiplicand:

multiplier	0	1	1	1	0	0	1	1	1	1	0	1	0	0	0	1	1	1
multiplicand additions	1	0	0	0	0	1	0	0	0	0	1	0	0	0	1	0	0	0
multiplicand subtractions	0	0	0	1	0	0	0	0	0	1	0	1	0	0	0	0	0	1

How would the equipment function to perform multiplication with the multiplier discussed in the preceding paragraph? The multiplier register is scanned from right to left, say, by the decoder. The decoder sees a run of 1's beginning and requests a subtraction of the multiplicand. It detects that there are three 1's in this run and, therefore, both the multiplier and the partial product should be shifted three positions.

On the next cycle, the decoder perceives a run of 0's. This calls for an addition of the multiplicand to the already-shifted partial product. After the addition is performed, the multiplier and partial product are shifted corresponding to the number of 0's in the 0 run—in this case three places.

Next, the decoder detects a run of one 1. This requests a subtraction of the multiplicand and a shift of one position. The one 0 which follows requests an addition and a shift of one position. The four 1's which follow request a subtraction followed by a shift of four places, and so forth.

When the number of 1's or 0's in a run exceeds the number of shifts which can be performed by the computer, the decoder detects that the run which it is presently examining is not a new run but part of an old run. At this point, no addition or subtraction is performed. Shifting of the multiplier and partial product continues until the long run under consideration is completed.

A run of 1's at the left of a number requires an addition at a position exceeding the most significant position in the partial product. This will not cause an overflow, since a subtraction has preceded this operation which will compensate for this large addition.

10.3   AN IMPROVEMENT

The Lone One

We can improve the method outlined above if we notice what happens when we encounter a lone 0 in a run of 1's or a lone 1 in a run of 0's. Let us take the case of what happens when a single 1 appears in a run of 0's. We have such a case presented below:

$$
\begin{array}{ll}
\text{multiplier} & 0\cdots010\cdots0 \\
\text{subtract multiplicand} & 0\cdots010\cdots0 \\
\text{add multiplicand} & 0\cdots100\cdots0
\end{array}
$$

A single 1 in the 0's in the multiplier requires that we perform a subtraction of the multiplicand immediately followed by an addition of the multiplicand. This shortcut method requires longer than the simple method; this is really no saving!

It would be well if we could use the shortcut method in all cases except when single 1's appear in strings of 0's. These could be treated in the regular fashion by performing a single addition corresponding to the 1 encountered.

When a 0 occurs in a run of 1's, we handle this by requesting a subtraction at the position at which the 0 occurs, using our shortcut method as previously.

Example

The discussion is best illustrated by the following example:

Old method

$$
\begin{array}{ll}
\text{multiplier} & 0111011 \\
\text{add multiplicand} & 1000100 \\
\text{subtract multiplicand} & 0001001
\end{array}
$$

Improved method

$$
\begin{array}{ll}
\text{multiplier} & 0111011 \\
\text{add multiplicand} & 1000000 \\
\text{subtract multiplicand} & 0000101
\end{array}
$$

Notice that through the first method we make up 59 by $64 + 4 - 8 - 1$; through the second method we form 59 by $64 - 4 - 1$

Let us see if we can show mathematically the validity of the procedure above. Let us take, proceeding from left to right, a run of k 1's after which we find a single 0 followed by r 1's and then s 0's. We know that this can be represented as $2^{r+s+1}(2^k - 1) + 2^s(2^r - 1)$. We propose to treat this as a run of $k + r + 1$ 1's, but we will subtract a 1 corresponding to the position of the 0. The 0 occupies the position numbered $r + s + 1$ which corresponds to a power of 2 of $r + s$. Therefore, what we propose to perform is given by $2^s(2^{k+1+r} - 1) - 2^{r+s}$. We have the following questionable equalities:

$$2^{r+s+1}(2^k - 1) + 2^s(2^r - 1) \overset{?}{=} 2^s(2^{k+1+r} - 1) - 2^{r+s} \qquad (10.3.1)$$

Expanding we have,

$$2^{k+1+r+s} - 2^{r+s+1} + 2^{s+r} - 2^s \overset{?}{=} 2^{k+1+r+s} - 2^s - 2^{r+s} \qquad (10.3.2)$$

Eliminating terms, this results in

$$-2^{r+s+1} + 2^{s+r} \overset{?}{=} -2^{r+s} \qquad (10.3.4)$$

Transposing, we have

$$-2^{r+s+1} = -2^{r+s} - 2^{r+s} = -2^{r+s+1} \qquad (10.3.5)$$

Since this last is truly an equation, it shows the validity of our original assumption.

It is left up to the reader to show that this procedure is valid for a single 1 in a string of 0's. This property holds no matter where the lone 1 is in relation to the binary multiplier considered as a strong of 1's and 0's.

Recapitulation

To summarize, the improved method treats isolated 1's in runs of 0's by performing an addition corresponding to the location of the 1; an isolated 0 in a run of 1's is treated as a subtraction at the location of the isolated 0.

Negative Multipliers

In 1's complement notation, runs of 0's represent runs of 1's and vice versa. For 2's complement notation, the method for complementing a number requires that we note the point at which the first 1 is recognized, examining the multiplier from right to left. This means that the first run of 0's is treated as a run of 0's. When a 1 is encountered, 1's in the complement will appear for 0's to the left of the first 1 in the original number. Therefore, this case requires special treatment. After a 1 has been encountered, runs of 0's are treated as runs of 1's and vice versa.

The control equations required to handle negative multipliers in 2's complement notation are discussed in great detail in Section 10.5 with respect to implementing multiplication using this fast method of shifting over 0's and 1's.

Direction of Examination of Multiplier

All that is said with regard to positive multipliers can be applied to examining the multiplier from left to right as well as from right to left.

When starting at the left, the beginning of a run of 1's calls for addition of the multiplicand; the beginning of a run of 0's calls for subtractions. Negative multipliers in 1's complement notation can be implemented in either direction.

2's complement multipliers require right-to-left examination of the multiplier because of the method for determining the multiplier complement.

10.4   HARDWARE CONFIGURATION, SHIFTING OVER 1's AND 0's

Registers and Hardware

The register configuration is shown in Figure 10.4.1. The multiplicand is stored in the D register; it may be required by the adder in true or complement form, Dt or Dc. The product is stored in the A register; it is always used by the adder in true form. The result produced by the adder is passed along to the A' register. Before being returned to the A register, the quantity in the prime register may be subjected to a variable number of shifts to the right. The minimum number is 1, and the maximum, K, is fixed by both design and economical considerations.

As addition takes place, the multiplier is transferred directly from the Q register to the Q' register. After addition, this multiplier, as it is returned to the Q register, is shifted the same number of places that the product is shifted.

As multiple-bit shifting takes place, information from the least significant part of the A' register is transferred to the most significant part of the Q register. Thus in shifting right i places we find that the right-most bit of the A′ register, A_1, is entered into the $(N - i + 1)$th position of the Q register, Q_{N-i+1}, and so forth, as follows:

$$\text{Ari:} \qquad A_1' \longrightarrow Q_{N-i+1}$$

$$A_2' \longrightarrow Q_{N-i+2}$$

$$A_i' \longrightarrow Q_N$$

$$A_{i+1}' \longrightarrow A_1$$

$$A_{N-1}' \longrightarrow A_{N-i-1}$$

$$A_N' \longrightarrow A_{N-i}$$

$$A_S' \longrightarrow A_{N-i+j} \quad \text{for all } i \text{ such that} \quad 1 \leqq j \leqq i$$

The condition shown in the last line is required when dealing with negative multipliers and, consequently, with negative partial products. In that case, we are shifting in 1's at the left, as required in Method 2, 2's complement multiplication.

If we have the facility to shift K bits, we also require the ability to decode the last K bits of the multiplier in order to make the most use of our shifting ability. In addition to the decoder, several bit storage devices are provided that serve auxiliary functions. One of these functions is to remember whether the last run consisted of 0's or 1's. Another function is the familiar F function which indicates when we have encountered the first 1 when forming the 2's complement of a number.

Alternate Representation and Configuration

Now that we understand the configuration of Figure 10.4.1, let us look into another way of presenting this information. Figure 10.4.2 supposedly conveys this more simply. The box labeled "variable shifter" is energized by the decoding network observing the K least significant bits of the multiplier as it sits in Q′. This decoder determines whether 1, K, or an intermediate number of shifts are to be performed. The large number of gates and mixers required to perform the variable shift is contained in the "variable shifter" box. The oblique arrow through this box indicates a cross-shift from the least significant bits of A′ to the most significant non-sign bits of Q.

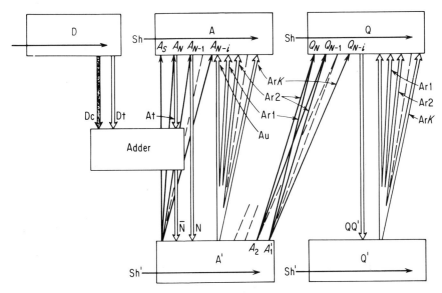

FIGURE 10.4.1 Register configuration for multiplication by shifting over 1's and 0's, examining multiplier from right to left

Fabricators of Stretch-like machines may complain that this is not the only conceivable configuration. Thence, for completeness, Figure 10.4.3 is presented. Its similarity with Figure 10.4.2 is immediately apparent; the difference is that the variable shift is performed here *before*, not *after*, addition. Again, the oblique arrow through the shifter shows a cross-shift from the lower end of A to the upper end of Q′.

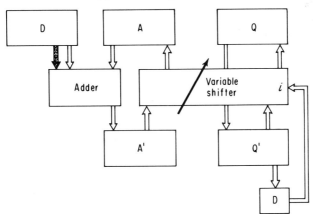

FIGURE 10.4.2 Simple representation of hardware for multiplying by shifting over 0's and 1's of Figure 10.4.1

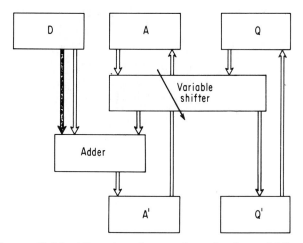

FIGURE 10.4.3   Alternate register configuration for multiplication by shifting over 0's and 1's.

The first arrangement works in an add-and-shift fashion: the second performs shift-and-add. Actually, the difference is minor and depends on the multiplier encountered. When the first multiplier bit calls for addition, the first arrangement performs the add-and-shift effectively; the second can only do the add on the first cycle and must do the shift as part of the second shift-and-add cycle. In contrast, if a multiple shift followed by an add is called for on the first cycle, the first method requires that the shift be performed without the add and that the add be done on the second cycle of add-and-shift; the second method does both on the first cycle. On the average, as far as the number of cycles is concerned, the two methods come out about even.

We continue the discussion now turning to the logical equation and assuming the configuration of Figure 10.4.1.

10.5   EQUATIONS, SIMPLEST METHOD

History Bit Storage

We are going to use the bit storage device labeled H to indicate the recent history of runs—what the *last* run was. When we first examine the multiplier it is assumed that the previous run consisted of 0's.

$$\bar{H} = St \tag{10.5.1}$$

When the least significant multiplier bit is 1, H is set to 1. This is done after the historical information has been used. It is safe to do this when passing information over to the prime register,

$$H = Q_1 \qquad (10.5.2)$$

Otherwise, it is 0,

$$\bar{H} = \bar{Q}_1 \qquad (10.5.3)$$

Here, and in what follows, on shifting over 0's and 1's, Q_1 refers to the *present* rather than *absolute* position of a multiplier bit.

For positive multipliers, we are interested in noting the beginning and end of a run of 1's. If we have just finished with a run of 0's and are beginning a run of 1's, you recall that we wish to subtract the multiplicand from the partial product. This means that the complement of the multiplicand is entered into the adder.

$$Dc = Q_1\bar{H} \qquad (10.5.4)$$

Since we are performing subtraction, it is also required that a 1 be entered into the carryin of the adder.

$$^1C_0 = Q_1\bar{H} \qquad (10.5.5)$$

At the end of the run of 1's, we find that H has been set to 1, but the least significant multiplier bit is now 0. This requires a true entry of the multiplicand into the adder.

$$Dt = \bar{Q}_1H \qquad (10.5.6)$$

and the appropriate carryin to the adder.

$$^0C_0 = \bar{Q}_1H \qquad (10.5.7)$$

Long Runs

The decoder examines the multiplier to determine the length of the run of multiplier bits. In most cases this will be a number smaller than K, the maximum number of shifts of which the mechanism is capable. In this case, addition or subtraction is performed, as discussed above, and the first bit of the next run will then end up as the new least significant multiplier bit. However, the case does arise when the run of multiplier bits now under examination exceeds, or is the same as, the shift ability of the mechanism. Suppose, for instance, we have a run of 1's or length greater than K. The decoder sees K 1's and then requests a shift of maximum length, K. The previous run bit storage, H, is set to 1 during this cycle. At the start of the next cycle, the least significant bit of the multiplier is again a 1. Since the previous run and this run both consist of 1's, this indicates that no addition is to be performed in this cycle.

To summarize, when the least significant multiplier bit agrees with the setting of the previous run bit storage, we perform no addition or subtraction for that cycle.

$$N = Q_1 H + \bar{Q}_1 \bar{H} \tag{10.5.8}$$

Run Length

The number of shifts to be performed is determined by the decoder. A shift of one place is required when the first and second multiplier bits differ. This is a run of 1 bit,

$$\text{Ar}1 = Q_2 \bar{Q}_1 + \bar{Q}_2 Q_1 \tag{10.5.9}$$

If the first and second bits of the multiplier are the same and the third bit differs from these two, a shift of two places is requested.

$$\text{Ar}2 = Q_3 \bar{Q}_2 \bar{Q}_1 + \bar{Q}_3 Q_2 Q_1 \tag{10.5.10}$$

In general, a shift of i bits is requested when the first i bits of the multiplier are the same and the $(i + 1)$th is different from the others,

$$\text{Ar}i = Q_{i+1} \bar{Q}_i \cdots \bar{Q}_1 + \bar{Q}_{i+1} Q_i \cdots Q_1 \tag{10.5.11}$$

A full-length shift is requested when all the multiplier bits are the same,

$$\text{Ar}K = \bar{Q}_K \bar{Q}_{K-1} \cdots \bar{Q}_1 + Q_K Q_{K-1} \cdots Q_1 \tag{10.5.12}$$

Negative Multipliers in 2's Complement Notation

When we deal with signed multiplers, runs of 1's and 0's with positive multipliers are handled as discussed in the last subsection. The effect of taking the 2's complement of a number is to change the appearance of some of the runs. The initial run of 0's in a multiplier, if such should occur, is unaffected. The first 1 encountered in examining the multiplier, from right to left, has a strange effect on the first run of 1's. What appears to be a run of 1's turns out to be not a run at all, so that we have, for instance,

$$\begin{array}{ll} \text{multiplier} & 011\cdots1100\cdots00 \\ \text{complement} & 100\cdots0100\cdots00 \end{array}$$

Also, what does not seem to be a run, turns out to be a run as

$$\text{multiplier} \qquad 100\cdots00100\cdots00$$
$$\text{complement} \qquad 011\cdots11100\cdots00$$

Initial 1 Bit Storage, F

In order to determine how to handle this problem, we have to store information concerning what to do when a 1 has been encountered in the multiplier. The bit storage device is set to 0 at the start of multiplication,

$$\bar{F} = St \qquad (10.5.13)$$

It is set to 1 the first time that the least significant multiplier bit is recognized as a 1,

$$F = Q_1\bar{F} \qquad (10.5.14)$$

Previous Run Storage, H

H is now used to indicate the character of the previous run when it is considered in complement form; that is, for a negative number we only examine the complement of the multiplier and consider a run of 0's and 1's in this multiplier complement. We set the device H accordingly.

At the beginning of the operation, we assume that a run of 0's has preceded,

$$\bar{H} = St \qquad (10.5.15)$$

If we have not yet encountered a 1 and the least significant multiplier bit is 0, we are examining a run of 0's. If we have already encountered a 1 and the least significant multiplier bit is a 1, we are examining a run of 0's in the multiplier complement. Hence,

$$\bar{H} = St + FQ_1 \qquad (10.5.16)$$

A run of 1's begins when we encounter our first 1 (not having encountered a 1 previously) or when we encounter a 0 after having previously encountered a 1,

$$H = \bar{F}Q_1 + F\bar{Q}_1 \qquad (10.5.17)$$

Run Length

In determining how many shifts to perform, we have to consider three cases:

1. If we have not yet encountered a 1, we shift according to the number of 0's presently in the multiplier.

2. For the first 1 encountered, the 0's to the left of it will become 1's in the complement. Therefore, we should shift over the first 1 and all the 0's that follow it.

3. When we have already encountered a 1, the number of shifts is the same as the number of 0's or 1's in the present run.

Register Connection to the Adder

Our action with respect to addition and subtraction of the multiplicand depends on complement runs in the multiplier. Assume that we can recognize a run of 1's in the complement of the multiplier. Using the second method for multiplication discussed in Chapter 3, you recall that we complement the multiplier and then add the complement of the multiplicand accordingly. In the case under consideration, the beginning of a run of 1's calls for the subtraction of the complement of the multiplicand; the end of a run of 1's in the complement of the multiplier calls for the addition of the complement of the multiplicand. Now subtracting a complement is the same as adding the true quantity and adding the complement is the same as subtracting. Hence, we can say that at the beginning of a run of 1's in the complement of the multiplier we add the true multiplicand,

$$Dt = Q_s Q_1 (\bar{F} + F\bar{H}) + \bar{Q}_s \bar{Q}_1 H \qquad (10.5.18)$$

The expression above incorporates the cases of both the positive and negative multiplier.

The end of a run of 1's of the complement of the multiplier for negative numbers is always recognized as the beginning of a 0-run; this will require, in complement form, that a 1 be in the least significant position. When the case of a positive multiplier is included, we have

$$Dc = Q_s H Q_1 + \bar{Q}_s \bar{H} Q_1 = Q_1 (Q_s H + \bar{Q}_s \bar{H}) \qquad (10.5.19)$$

Shift Length

The number of positions which we must shift depends on the setting of F. Initial 0-runs are treated the same as with positive multipliers. One condition for shifting just one place is that the least significant bit of the multiplier is a 0 and the bit to the left of it is a 1. If we have not encountered a 1 previously and we are dealing with a negative multiplier, then we will have a run of one position if the least significant bit is a 1 and the one next to it is also a 1. Except for the case of $\bar{F}$, $\bar{Q}_2Q_1$ also requests a single shift. These conditions are combined to yield

$$\text{Ar}1 = Q_2\bar{Q}_1 + Q_s\bar{F}Q_2Q_1 + (F + \bar{Q}_s)\bar{Q}_2Q_1 \qquad (10.5.20)$$

Similarly, we shift two places for the following cases: when the two right-hand bits of the multiplier are 0's and the next one is a 1; when we have a positive multiplier or have already encountered a 1 in a negative multiplier and $Q_3Q_2Q_1$; when we have not previously encountered a 1 in a negative multiplier and $Q_1 = 1$, $Q_2 = 0$, $Q_3 = 1$. This is summarized as

$$\text{Ar}2 = Q_3\bar{Q}_2\bar{Q}_1 + Q_s\bar{F}Q_3\bar{Q}_2Q_1 + (F + \bar{Q}_s)\bar{Q}_3Q_2Q_1 \qquad (10.5.21)$$

For i shifts,

$$\text{Ar}i = Q_{i+1}\bar{Q}_i \cdots \bar{Q}_2\bar{Q}_1 + (F + \bar{Q}_s)\bar{Q}_{i+1}Q_i \cdots Q_2Q_1$$
$$+ \bar{F}Q_sQ_{i+1}\bar{Q}_i \cdots \bar{Q}_2Q_1 \qquad (10.5.22)$$

For a full-length shift of K places,

$$\text{Ar}K = \bar{Q}_K\bar{Q}_{K-1} \cdots \bar{Q}_2\bar{Q}_1 + (F + \bar{Q}_s)Q_KQ_{K-1} \cdots Q_2Q_1$$
$$+ \bar{F}Q_s\bar{Q}_K \cdots \bar{Q}_2Q_1 \qquad (10.5.23)$$

which completes the implementation for the simple method.

10.6 IMPROVED METHOD, POSITIVE MULTIPLIER

The aim of the method covered in this section is to distinguish a single 1 in a run of 0's and to identify a single 0 in a run of 1's. It is possible to achieve a further improvement if we are able to identify a number of isolated 1's in a run of 0's or a number of isolated 0's in a run of 1's and to take appropriate action. However, we will be satisfied with the speedup obtained from the method described here without any lookahead for multiple isolated bits.

Table of Action Alternatives

In order to investigate the alternatives which are possible in this method, see Table 10.6. It is based upon an examination of the final three bits of the multiplier. In general, the decoder will examine K bits of the multiplier. However, three bits will suffice to indicate what cases must be accommodated by the hardware.

Suppose that we have just had a run of 0's. We refer to the center set of columns of Table 10.6. Entry 1 says that a row of k 0's is now encountered which means we are continuing our run of 0's from the previous run. For $k < K$, the run consists of $(k + K)$ 0's. In any case, this is a *continuing* run of 0's. We do no arithmetic (N); we just shift k places and set H to 0 for the 0 run.

TABLE 10.6 Shifting over 0's and 1's, Improved Method, Positive Multiplier, Alternatives A for add, S for Subtract, N for do Nothing

Entry	Present multiplier bits	Last run 0's			Last run 1's		
		Do	Then shift	Set H	Do	Then shift	Set H
1	$\overbrace{10000\cdots0}^{k}$	N	k	0	A	k	0
2	$\underbrace{011\cdots11}_{k}$	S	k	1	N	k	1
3	$\underbrace{011\cdots110}_{k}$	N	1	0	S	k	1
4	$\underbrace{100\cdots001}_{k}$	A	k	0	N	1	1

Entry 2 is the beginning of a run of 1's. This calls for a subtraction (S) and a shift of k places. This is a 1-run, so H is set to 1.

Entry 3 is a special case of entry 1 and so has similar entries.

Entry 4 is an isolated 1 in a run of 0's. We add (A) to compensate for it. We shift over both the 1 and the 0's that follow, a total of $k(\leq K)$ places. Set H to 0.

When a 1-run preceded, the last column set of Table 10.6.1 is referred to. Then entry 1 represents a new run of k 0's. Entry 2 is a continuing run of k 1's. Entry 3 is an isolated 0. Entry 4 is a special case of entry 2.

Arithmetic Criterion

We do no arithmetic when the first multiplier bit, Q_1, and the previous run are the same; thus,

$$N = H Q_1 + \bar{H}\bar{Q}_1 \qquad (10.6.1)$$

Once we have eliminated these do-nothing cases, it is easy to determine whether we add or subtract by simply examining the second multiplier bit. Thus,

$$\text{Dt} = \bar{\text{N}}\bar{Q}_2 \qquad (10.6.2)$$

$$\text{Dc} = \bar{\text{N}}Q_2 \qquad (10.6.3)$$

Now how did we get this criterion? Well, this can be obtained directly by examining Table 10.6. We see that where addition is to be performed, the second bit is a 0 and, conversely, for subtraction the second bit is a 1. But there must be some rationale for this. There are two cases where we add. A new run of 0's is one of these. To have such a run, it must contain at least two 0's, guaranteeing a 0 for Q_2. The other case is an isolated 1 in a run of 0's. Since the 1 at Q_1 is isolated, it has a 0 on either side, again guaranteeing a 0 at Q_2.

Similar observations are made for subtraction. Subtraction occurs for a *new* 1-run or an isolated 0, both of which require $Q_2 = 1$.

Run Bit Storage, H

Let us now determine how to set the bit storage device H. Returning to Table 10.6, notice that H is set to 0 when both Q_2 and Q_1 are 0. Also, if Q_2 and Q_1 are not both 1 and we had a run of 0's ($\bar{\text{H}}'$), H remains set ot 0. H must be set to 0 to start, for then we act as if we had just encountered a run of 0's. The conditions for setting H to 1 are similar, except for the start,

$$\bar{\text{H}} = \text{St} + \bar{Q}_2\bar{Q}_1 + \overline{Q_2Q_1}\bar{\text{H}}' \qquad (10.6.4)$$

$$\text{H} = Q_2 + Q_1 + (Q_2 + Q_1\text{H}') \qquad (10.6.5)$$

Shift Length

We rarely require a shift of one bit length. This is a testimony to the efficiency of the system. The case where a single shift is required is when we are continuing an old run, one that started earlier and exceeded the capability of the shifting network. Also, this old run must terminate on the second multiplier bit. Thus the condition for a single shift is that H and the first multiplier bit are the same but the second multiplier bit is different.

$$\text{Arl} = Q_2\bar{Q}_1\bar{\text{H}} + \bar{Q}_2Q_1\text{H} \qquad (10.6.6)$$

Examining Table 10.6, we see that a double shift is called for when the second and third multiplier bits are different, except where a single shift has already been defined. Thus,

$$Ar2 = (Q_3\bar{Q}_2 + \bar{Q}_3Q_2)\overline{Ar1} \qquad (10.6.7)$$

A triple shift is called for when the second and third multiplier bits are the same but the fourth multiplier bit is different, except for those cases covered by the single shift.

$$Ar3 = (Q_4\bar{Q}_3\bar{Q}_2 + \bar{Q}_4Q_3Q_2)\overline{Ar1} \qquad (10.6.8)$$

We now generalize to a shift of i positions. This requires that the multiplier bits 2 through i are the same and the $(i + 1)$th bit is different. Again we exclude the case of the single shift covered above.

$$Ari = (Q_{i+1}\bar{Q}_i\bar{Q}_{i-1} \cdots \bar{Q}_2 + \bar{Q}_{i+1}Q_1Q_{i-1} \cdots Q_2)\overline{Ar1} \qquad (10.6.9)$$

The full shift of K places is called for when all the bits 2 to K inclusive are identical, except when dealing with the old run which terminates at the first bit. Again, excluding Ar1,

$$ArK = (\bar{Q}_K\bar{Q}_{K-1} \cdots \bar{Q}_2 + Q_KQ_{K-1} \cdots Q_2)\overline{Ar1} \qquad (10.6.10)$$

10.7 IMPROVED METHOD, NEGATIVE MULTIPLIERS

In the improved method, we must identify an isolated bit in a run of bits of opposite nature for both a positive multiplier and for the 2's complement of a negative multiplier. This requires that we establish an F function, as we have done previously in dealing with negative multipliers.

Action Alternatives

As previously, our procedure is to establish a table which will tell us what to do for the various eventualities which may arise. This table will correspond to Table 10.6, except that we must consider the different possibilities for both F and H.

Examine Table 10.7. The case where F is 0 indicates that we have not yet encountered a 1. Hence, we only have the condition that H is 0; otherwise we would have encountered a 1 already. Again, in Table 10.7 we consider only the last three bits of the multiplier. Since it is a negative multiplier, we must complement these bits before deciding what to do. The complement depends on whether a 1 has been encountered previously.

TABLE 10.7 Multiplication Shifting over 1's and for 2's Complement Negative Numbers Using the Improved Method and F Storage. Circled Entries Indicate Old Runs

	$F = 0$				$F = 1$				
	$H = 0$				$H = 0$			$H = 1$	
Bits	Comple-ment	Shifts	Subtract Add or Neither	Set H	Comple-ment	Shifts A/S/N	Set H	Shifts A/S/N	Set H
000	000	(3+	N	0)	111	3+ S	1	(3+ N	1)
001	111	3+	S	1	110	(1 N	0)	3+ S	1
010	110	(1	N	0)	101	2 A	0	(1 N	1)
011	101	2	A	0	100	(2 N	0)	2 A	0
100	100	(2	N	0)	011	2 S	1	(2 N	1)
101	011	2	S	1	010	(1 N	0)	2 S	1
110	010	(1	N	0)	001	3+ A	0	(1 N	1)
111	001	3+	A	0	000	(3+ N	0)	3+ A	0

From the complement, we wish to determine the number of shifts to be performed, whether we add, subtract or neither, and how we set H. As previously, we first set about to find the "old" cases, the cases where we neither add nor subtract. These cases occur when the setting of H and the right-most multiplier complement bit coincide. Note here that our setting of H applies to the runs that we have encountered in the *complement* of our negative multiplier. Table 10.7 reveals the identity of these multiplier complement bits, but in order to write out the equation we must reinterpret these in terms of the original bits, the F function, and the H function. Notice for $\bar{F}$ no arithmetic is done for $\bar{Q}_1$. When F is 1, do nothing if Q_1 and H are oppsoite. These conditions are combined as follows:

$$N = \bar{F}\bar{Q}_1 + F(\bar{H}Q_1 + H\bar{Q}_1) \qquad (10.7.1)$$

Add or Subtract

A look at the table will show us that this time we are lucky: the determination for add or subtract can be made simply by examining the second bit of the *true* multiplier. Of course, first we exclude the old runs ($N = 1$). Then if Q_2 is 1, addition is called for; if it is 0, subtraction is called for. Before we quit, however, we should notice that the addition we call for is of the complement of the multiplicand. This can be seen by referring to

Figures 3.3.4 and 3.3.5. Now if we are going to add the complement of the multiplicand, it is the same as calling for the entry of the complement of the multiplicand into the adder; subtraction calls for the complement of the complement of the multiplicand and therefore is a request for the entry of the true multiplicand into the adder. Remembering this, we have

$$Dt = \bar{Q}_2\bar{N} \tag{10.7.2}$$

$$Dc = Q_2\bar{N} \tag{10.7.3}$$

History Bit Storage, H

The reader can do as an exercise the derivation for the present setting of H which is

$$H = \bar{F}\bar{Q}_2Q_1 + F\bar{H}'\bar{Q}_2Q_1 + FH'(\bar{Q}_2 + \bar{Q}_1) \tag{10.7.4}$$

Shift Length

There are several conditions under which a single shift can be performed. The first is when a 1 has not yet been encountered, Q_1 is 0, and Q_2 is 1. If we are initially examining the negative multiplier and it consists of $\cdots X10$, we shift just once.

Suppose we have a large number of right-hand 0's requiring a number of full (length K) shifts. If, when the first 1 is finally encountered, it lies in the second position to the right, this condition again arises.

If Q_1 is 0 and Q_2 is 1 and we have been examining a run of 1's in the complement of the multiplier, this is a run of 1's which continues for only one bit position and therefore calls for a single shift. Initial right-hand bits of negative multiplier of 10 are interpreted as 10 leading to a shift of one place also. A continuing run of 0's in the multiplier complement after a 1 has been encountered, and only one bit requires a single shift. It is detected when Q_2 is 0, Q_1 is 1, F is 1, and H is 0. The complete condition is, therefore,

$$Ar1 = Q_2\bar{Q}_1(\bar{F} + H) + \bar{Q}_2Q_1F\bar{H} \tag{10.7.5}$$

For shifts of length 2 or greater, we examine the bits of the *true* multiplier proceeding left from the second bit. The number of adjacent bits which are the same determines the length of the shift we perform. Thus, we have the following set of equations:

$$Ar2 = (Q_3\bar{Q}_2 + \bar{Q}_3Q_2)\overline{Ar1} \tag{10.7.6}$$

$$Ar3 = (Q_4\bar{Q}_3\bar{Q}_2 + \bar{Q}_4Q_3Q_2)\overline{Ar1} \tag{10.7.7}$$

$$Ari = (Q_{i+1}\bar{Q}_i\bar{Q}_{i-1} \cdots \bar{Q}_2 + \bar{Q}_{i+1}Q_iQ_{i-1} \cdots Q_2)\overline{Ar1} \tag{10.7.8}$$

$$ArK = (\bar{Q}_K\bar{Q}_{K-1} \cdots \bar{Q}_2 + Q_KQ_{K-1} \cdots Q_2)\overline{Ar1} \tag{10.7.9}$$

10.8 FULL EQUATIONS, IMPROVED METHOD, SIGNED NUMBERS

From the two previous sections, we have all the information that we need to build a control unit for a multiplier that does multiplication by the improved method of shifting over 1's and 0's.

Counter

Since multiplication is done for a fixed number of multiplier bits, N, we require a counter to keep track of the number of bits of the multiplier which have been used so far. This counter is set to 0 at the beginning of multiplication.

$$D(0) = \text{St} \qquad (10.8.1)$$

During each cycle, we determine how many places are going to be shifted. When a shift of i places is done, this amount is added to the count presently stored in the counter. Let us call the present contents of the counter j; a shift of i places is indicated by the presence of the Ari signal, Thus,

$$D(j + i) = \text{Sh}' D(j) \text{Ar}i \qquad j + i \leq N, i \leq K \qquad (10.8.2)$$

Now our counter will function to indicate the number of multiplier bits which have been scanned so far. The question arises as to what occurs as we approach the completion of the multiplication process. That is, when we have used up almost N digits of the multiplier, how can we be assured that the counter does not try to use a number of multiplier digits greater than N? This is the same as asking whether it is possible for the circuitry to request a number of shifts which will bring the total over the prescribed limit of N. This is a definite problem, for recall that the least significant portion of the partial product and the most significant multiplier bits are next to each other in the same register. It would be easy to mistake product bits for multiplier bits.

At this point, we will remove the problem for later consideration by saying that we will prevent a final shift which will bring the total in the counter over N.

Timing

As in all our algorithm control units, we require pulses to indicate the proper sequence of events. The pulse, St, as used above, indicates the start of the multiplication procedure. Next we indicate the time at which information from the adder or the main register is entered into the prime register. This is indicated as

$$\text{Sh}' = \text{CC} \qquad (10.8.3)$$

Information is returned to the main register a short time later, as indicated by

$$\text{Sh} = \Delta\text{Sh}' \qquad (10.8.4)$$

There is a choice on non-add cycles of entering information directly from the main register to the prime register and shifting it on the way back into the main register. The alternative is to pass the information *through* the adder, inhibiting the entry of the addend into the adder. Using the second alternative slightly simplifies the presentation.

2's Complement First 1, F

The F function is initially set to 0,

$$\bar{\text{F}} = \text{St} \qquad (10.8.5)$$

When there is 1 in the multiplier in any position up to the ith for a negative multiplier, we wish to set the F function to 1 when we are through with the multiplier. This is done as the partial product is entered into the prime register,

$$\text{F} = \text{Sh}'Q_s(Q_1 + Q_2 + \cdots + Q_{i-1} + Q_i)\text{Ar}i \qquad (10.8.6)$$

History Storage

The bit storage labeled H stores the information about the previous run. Initially, it is set to 0. It is also set to 0 when there is a 0 in the least significant bit position of the multiplier for a positive multiplier; for a negative multiplier having already encountered a 1 in the multiplier, a 1 in the least significant bit position should cause H to set to 0. These conditions are

$$\bar{\text{H}} = \text{St} + \text{Sh}'(\bar{Q}_s\bar{Q}_1 + \text{F}Q_1) \qquad (10.8.7)$$

Notice that the last condition does not seem to include the requirement that we are dealing with a negative multiplier. However, from (10.8.5) we see that as multiplication begins, F is reset to 0 regardless of the multiplier sign and will remain so for positive multipliers.

We wish to set H to 1 when there is a 1 in the least significant bit position of the multiplier and we have a positive multiplier or F is presently set to 0 for a negative multiplier. Notice that in both of these cases F is set to 0 so that it is the single criterion. For a negative multiplier where a 1 has already been detected, the expression is derived from Table 10.7

$$H = \text{Sh}'[\bar{F}Q_1 + F(\bar{H}'\bar{Q}_2\bar{Q}_1 + H'\overline{Q_2Q_1})] \qquad (10.8.8)$$

Termination

As was noted earlier, a 1-run may continue up to the Nth bit of the multiplier. This requires an add cycle after the final multiplier cycle. This termination cycle is indicated by the setting of a termination flip-flop, TM, to 0 at the beginning of multiplication,

$$\overline{TM} = \text{St} \qquad (10.8.9)$$

We record the necessity of a final cycle when the counter stores the count of N and we are performing a 1-run for a positive multiplier or a 0-run for a negative multiplier,

$$TM = D(N)(\bar{Q}_s H + Q_s \bar{H}) \qquad (10.8.10)$$

which means that an add cycle must be performed in both cases. In the case of a negative multiplier, we wish to add the complement, which is included in the D register connection equations discussed below.

Also, after the termination cycle addition is performed, the quantity in the prime register must be returned to the main register, *unshifted*. This is accomplished by

$$A'A = TM \qquad (10.8.11)$$

To keep track of the termination cycle, we add 1 to the counter during its performance; that is,

$$D(N + 1) = \text{Sh}''TM\, D(N) \qquad (10.8.12)$$

which allows us to detect the end of multiplication by

$$E = \text{Sh}[D(N)\overline{TM} + D(N + 1)] \qquad (10.8.13)$$

Thus completion is indicated on return to the main register when the counter stores $N + 1$ or when it stores N and no completion cycle is called for.

Determination of Addition, Subtraction, or Neither

The condition for performing neither addition nor subtraction is determined by combining (10.6.1) and (10.7.1), to yield

$$N = \bar{Q}_s(\bar{H}\bar{Q}_1 + HQ_1) + Q_s[\bar{F}\bar{Q}_1 + F(\bar{H}'Q_1 + H'\bar{Q}_1)] \qquad (10.8.14)$$

The condition for addition—entry of the D register to the adder in true-form—is given by combining (10.6.2) or (10.7.2) (they are the same) and the termination condition, to yield

$$Dt = \bar{N}\bar{Q}_2 + \bar{Q}_s\mathrm{TM} \qquad (10.8.15)$$

Similarly, for the complement entry of the D register,

$$Dc = \bar{N}Q_2 + Q_s\mathrm{TM} \qquad (10.8.16)$$

Shift Length

The shift length is a function of the bits of the multiplier which are presently under examination: the present least significant bit and those to the left as far as we need investigate. The shift length is also a function of the number stored in our bit counter. We do not wish to examine more than N bits of the multiplier; if we go beyond N, we will begin to look at sign bits and bits of the product.

single-length shifts

The one exception for the need to investigate the counter is where a single-length shift is concerned, because we will not examine our multiplier bit if the *last* cycle made the counter register N. This would either signal the end of multiplication or the beginning of a correction cycle. Therefore, if we examine the multiplier bits at all, we know that at least one more shift is tolerable. The condition for a single shift when dealing with a positive multiplier is found in (10.6.6); that for negative multipliers is found in (10.7.5). These are combined to yield the requirement for the full system.

$$Ar1 = Q_2\bar{Q}_1[\bar{Q}_s\bar{H} + Q_s(\bar{F} + H)] + \bar{Q}_2Q_1(\bar{Q}_sH + QF\bar{H}) \qquad (10.8.17)$$

double shift

The equations already posed for double shift are given by (10.6.7) for positive multipliers and by (10.7.6) for negative multipliers. These are combined when two other conditions are not: when we do not perform a single shift: when there is room in the counter for a count of 2 or more. Now if there is room in the counter for exactly two counts and the bit decoder indicates that we should perform a shift of more than two bits, we perform a shift of exactly two bits. These conditions are all tied together as

$$Ar2 = \overline{Ar1}[D(\leq N - 2)(Q_3\bar{Q}_2 + \bar{Q}_3Q_2)$$
$$+ D(N - 2)(Q_3Q_2 + \bar{Q}_3\bar{Q}_2)] \qquad (10.8.18)$$

i shifts

The decoder will indicate that i shifts are to be performed if bits 2 through i of the multiplier are the same and the $(i + 1)$th bit is different, provided there is not a request for a single shift and there is room in the counter to increase the count by i. In addition, if there is room in the counter for a count of exactly i but the decoder requests a shift of more than i places, then a shift of i places will be done.

$$\text{Ar}i = \overline{\text{Ar1}}[D(\leq N - i)(Q_{i+1}\bar{Q}_i \cdots \bar{Q}_2 + \bar{Q}_{i+1}Q_i \cdots Q_2)$$
$$+ D(N - i)(\bar{Q}_{i+1}\bar{Q}_i \cdots \bar{Q}_2 + Q_{i+1}Q_i \cdots Q_2)] \qquad (10.8.19)$$

K shifts

We perform the maximum allowable number of shifts, K, if a single shift is not requested; if there is room in the counter for a count of K; if the bits 2 through K of the multiplier are the same. This yields

$$\text{Ar}K = \overline{\text{Ar1}} \, D(N - K)(\bar{Q}_K\bar{Q}_{K-1} \cdots \bar{Q}_3 + Q_K Q_{K-1} \cdots Q_2) \qquad (10.8.20)$$

PROBLEMS

10.1 Make up three examples of binary multiplication and show how they are done by shifting over 0's and 1's.

10.2 What differences are there in shifting over 0's and 1's for
   a. Sign and magnitude representation.
   b. 2's complement representation.
   c. 1's complement representation.

10.3 Discuss rightward examination of the multiplier for the three representations.

10.4 How could shifting over 0's and 1's be improved to consider isolated pairs of 0's or pairs of 1's instead of just isolated 0's and 1's?

10.5 Discuss a full register length shifter $(K = N)$ for
   a. Feasibility.
   b. Usefulness.
   c. Speed.
   d. Cost.

11

COMPOUND MULTIPLICATION; COMPARATIVE SUMMARY

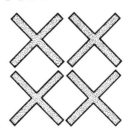

11.1 INTRODUCTION

The first purpose of this chapter is to review the methods of performing multiplication already discussed. The reader should then have an understanding of the hardware configuration required for each method and the operation cycles needed for the hardware to perform the multiplication as outlined. This review enables us to propose combinations of hardware which might speed up the multiplication process. This section prepares us to make an evaluation and comparison of the various methods available. In Section 11.3 we make certain assumptions and discuss their rationale. Then, in Section 11.4, we algebraically analyze the time required for each method proposed within the constraints inherent in the method and the circuitry as of the present state of the art. The result of that section is distilled into Table 11.4 which contrasts all the methods for multiplication discussed in this book. Other problems associated with multiplication are present in Section 11.5.

Technical Summary

Let us recall the means for speeding up multiplication:

1. Increase addition speed by such devices as the carry-save adder.
2. Provide prefabricated multiples of the multiplicand.
3. Use subtraction as well as addition in forming the product.

The No-Add Option

At this point, we should note that many of the methods call for shifting the partial product without performing any addition. This can be done in two ways. Suppose that our partial product is stored in the A register. We can pass the quantity directly to the A' register and then shift it as we return to the A register. This means that when addition is called for, we enter the A register contents into the adder; when addition is not called for, we shift it directly across to the prime register. An alternative to this is to *always* pass information from the A register to the A' register *through the adder*. When nothing is to be added, we *inhibit the other input* to the adder. In that way the information is transcribed to the A' register without any modification. This eliminates gating at the output of the A register during multiplication. To compensate for this gain, we introduce an extra delay due to the adder circuitry through which the information must pass.

The analysis of Section 11.4 (see Table 11.4, entries A1 and A2) indicates that the time saved by shifting directly across is small in comparison to the total time and, therefore, may, in general, be neglected. This means that in all cases where shifting of the partial product is performed without any addition or subtraction of the multiplicand, it may be done by passing the partial product through the adder.

11.2 DISCUSSION OF METHODS ANALYZED

We discuss, in the sequence in which they are analyzed, multiplication methods and combinations thereof, labeling each with a letter for reference in the next sections.

A. Bit-by-Bit Multiplication

Hardware for bit-by-bit multiplication is illustrated in Figure 7.1. Only two kinds of cycles are required: add and non-add. Only two choices exist for entering the multiplicand into the adder: true or complement form. Each cycle, whether add or non-add, increases the count in the shift counter by 1. Multiplication terminates when the shift counter reaches N. No corrections are required.

B. Bit-by-Bit, Carry-Save Multiplication

For bit-by-bit, carry-save multiplication, multiplication is performed with two kinds of cycles exactly as in A. The only difference is the use of the carry-save adder instead of the full carry-propagate adder. Termination is the same. The only difference is in the completion. In the last cycle, addition must be carried to completion in one of two ways.

If only a carry-save adder is available, we can perform cycles of addition until the carry signal indicates that the addition process has been completed. This is done by performing addition cycles in the same fashion as the multiplication cycles were performed: removing the multiplicand input to the adder.

Since we would not expect a carry-save adder to be used on an addition command, we would expect that any decent computer has a carry-propagate adder or that the adder incorporated in the computer could be switched from one mode to the other. It is this last alternative which will be assumed in the analysis that follows. In that case, when the last cycle of multiplication is announced, the adder is switched to function as a carry-propagate adder.

C. Multiplication With Bit Pairs Except 11

Multiplication with bit pairs requires no extra registers. The hardware for it is the same as that in Figure 7.1. We must be able to shift the multiplicand or its complement either one place left or not at all. We must also be able to inhibit any input of the multiplicand when the multiplier bit pair under examination is "00." Normally, we shift two places when we return information from the prime register to the main register, except when the bits we have been examining are both 1's. In that case, a single shift of the partial product is required. Termination and completion are as before.

D. Multiplication by Bit Pairs Using a Register to Store the Multiplicand Triple

Method D is illustrated in Figure 9.8, with the exception that fewer lines are required to connect the D register to the adder.

A premultiplication cycle is required to prepare the multiplicand triple by adding the multiplicand to twice the multiplicand, passing the result into the A′ register, and, thence, to the T register. The multiplicand must be available in true or complement form, in single or double multiples, or may be inhibited entirely. All shifts from the prime to the main register are in multiples of two. Termination and completion, as previously, are determined by examining the shift counter.

E. Bit Pairs With Triple Register and Carry-Save

Method E is illustrated in Figure 11.2.1, if the reader will mentally eliminate the extra lines from the D register into the adder. This method operates exactly the same as D, with the exception that the adder operates in a carry-save mode in all except the last cycle. Carry information is passed from the adder into the C′ register and then returned to the C register, properly shifted, so as to be in step with the partial product. A premultiplication cycle for preparing the multiplicand triple is required, as well as a final multiplication cycle where the adder is switched into the carry-propagate mode.

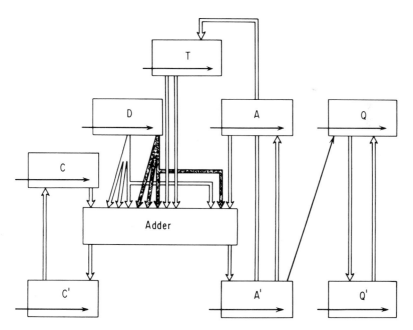

FIGURE 11.2.1 Logic for bit triplets or ternary triplets multiplication with carry-save/propagate facility.

F. Bit Triplets With the Exception of Certain Combinations

Method F does not use prepared multiples. We examine the multiplier bits in triplets. If these bits are found to be in one of the four combinations which allows us to make a triple shift, we perform the addition required and then do the triple shift. If the triplet is one of the four combinations where a triple shift cannot be performed, a single or double shift is resorted to, depending upon the combination. The hardware of Figure 9.4 does this job. Termination requires that the shift counter be examined to be sure that the number of shifts performed during a given cycle does not exceed the number of shifts which are left to be performed before multiplication is terminated.

G. Bit Triplets With Triple Multiplicand Register

The hardware of Figure 9.8 performs multiplication by bit triplets with a triple multiplicand register. There are now six combinations of bits of the multiplier bit triplet for which a triple shift can be performed. The other two combinations can be performed with a double shift.

H. Complete Bit Triplet

For completeness, let us mention that multiplication can be performed examining the multiplier bits in triplets and always performing a triple shift, if the quintuple and septuple are available, as well as the multiplicand triple. These quantities can be formed in a total of three additional registers using three premultiplication cycles. Method H is less efficient time-wise than the method of ternary triplets, besides requiring more hardware than that method; for that reason, Method H may be neglected.

I. Ternary Pairs

Method I uses the hardware of Figure 9.4. We add or subtract the multiplicand, depending upon the examination of the least significant bits of the multiplier. No extra registers or cycles are required and all shifting from prime to main registers is done in pairs.

J. Ternary Pairs With the Carry-Save Adder

Method J is similar to that illustrated in Figure 11.2.1. The carry-save adder is used on all cycles except the last.

K. Ternary Triplets

Method K is illustrated in Figure 9.8. A triple of the multiplicand is prepared in the premultiplication cycle. Choice of the multiplicand multiple is made by examining the least significant four bits of the multiplier. The least significant bit correction may be made on the first multiplication cycle. Termination is performed by referring to the shift counter.

L. Ternary Triplets With the Carry-Save Adder

Method L operates as method K, with the exception that the adder is operated in the carry-save mode on all but the last multiplication cycle.

Cascade Carry-Save Adders Using Ternary Bit-Pair Examination

Cascade carry-save adders which use ternary bit-pair examination have a different combination of logic than we have encountered previously (Figure 11.2.2). This method actually examines the multiplier in octets; that is, four sets of pairs of multiplier bits are examined at one time. Let us number these pairs from one to four, proceeding from right to left. During multiplication one of the multiply cycles would cause the following connections to be made. The A register is connected to the right-hand input of carry-save adder 1. One of the multiplicand multiples is connected to the other adding input of carry-save adder 1, as determined by examining the first bit pair of the multiplier. A multiple of the multiplicand is connected to the carry input of the carry-save adder, as determined by examining the second pair of the bits of the multiplier. Carry-save adder 1 produces a sum-and-carry output. These are applied to the two add inputs of carry-save adder 2. The carry-input to carry-save adder 2 is one of the multiplicand multiples which is selected by examining the third bit pair of the multiplier. The carry and sum outputs of carry-save adder 2 are entered into

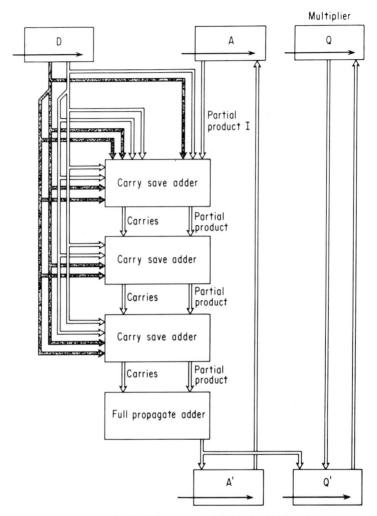

FIGURE 11.2.2   Logic for ternary multiplication in bit pairs using
cascaded multiple carry-save adders.

the two adder inputs of carry-save adder 3. The fourth pair of multiplier
bits determines which multiplicand multiple is entered into the carry input
of carry-save adder 3. Finally, the carry and sum outputs of carry-save
adder 3 are entered into the two adder inputs of the carry-propagate adder.
The sum produced by this adder is entered into the combined A′ and Q′
register, shifted eight places to be properly aligned in the A′ register and
the top eight bits of the Q′ register. This information is then returned, un-

shifted, to the A and Q registers. During this time, the Q register has been shifted eight places to the right into the Q′ register, leaving a space for the new partial product bits.

Octet cycles, as described above, are performed, and 8 is added to the shift counter until the shift counter has totaled up to N, indicating that multiplication is completed.

The initial multiplication cycle allows for correction due to a 1 in the least significant bit of the multiplier. This is done by entering the proper multiplicand multiple into carry-save adder 1.

M. Ternary Bit Pairs Shifting Over 0's Up to Four 0's

Method M allows us to perform multiplication by examining the multiplier in bit pairs using the ternary method and, in that sense, is similar to I above. In addition, we provide the capability of examining four bits of the multiplier and performing shifts of up to four bits when returning information from the prime register to the main register. This means, in addition to all bit-pair combinations, we can accommodate the combination "000" and the combination "0000." The logic for performing this is similar to that of Figure 9.4, with additional shift capability. Analysis of this method in the case of random numbers shows that it offers only a slight speed advantage over straight ternary bit-pair multiplication. However, when we consider that arithmetic frequently calls for multiplication by small numbers with many 0's in them, this method may provide a gain not apparent when examining only the random-number case.

N, O. Shifting Over 0's and 1's

Shifting over 0's and 1's is illustrated in Figure 10.4.1 and has been thoroughly discussed in Chapter 10.

P, Q. Improved Method of Shifting Over 0's and 1's

See discussion in Section 10.3.

Carry-Save Adders Applied
to Shifting Over 0's and 1's

To apply a carry-save adder to shifting over 0's and 1's would require not only two additional registers, but also a means for variable shifting between these registers and decoding networks to mechanize this shifting process. Since the number of shifts performed in each cycle is variable, the carry register must be shifted the proper number of places so that it is kept in step with the partial product. The hardware required to mechanize this process might cost more than any savings that might accrue.

11.3   TIME CONSIDERATIONS

The Most Important
Criterion—Time

The most important criterion for judging merits of a proposed multiplication procedure for a high-speed computer, where money is no object, is the amount of time that the method requires. The time factor depends upon many variables. The most significant of these is the speed of the circuitry involved in absolute terms. When we examine these circuit problems more carefully, we find that even for a given circuit, speed is determined by fan-in and fan-out; that is, the number of circuits which drive it and which it drives determines the speed at which a given circuit will operate. Another factor which determines multiplication speed is the logic used within the adder. High-speed, multi-stage adder logic can reduce the speed at which any given cycle is performed.

The third factor, and the one which interests us here, is the multiplication logic that links the registers together for the purpose of multiplication only. We would like to hold the other factors constant and make a comparison whose only variable is the multiplication logic. This would then give us the relative speed of the multiplication logic, given fixed circuit speeds and a fixed addition time.

The cost of multiplier logic is a function of the number of logical units, speed and price. This calculation should be within the capabilities of the reader should he desire to do it.

The Shift Register Chain

When we examine the time problem closer, we see that the multiplication time depends upon the configuration of circuits which connect the main

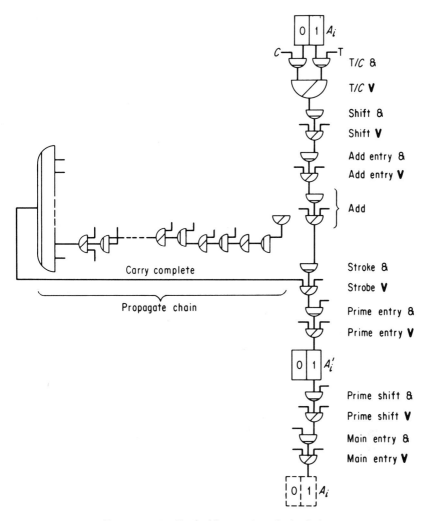

FIGURE 11.3 Typical interregister logic chain.

shift register to the prime register and the prime register back to the main register. A typical chain is illustrated in Figure 11.3.

One bit of the main shift register is labeled in this Figure, A_i. A gate is connected to each output of the bit storage device so that we can choose between true and complement. A mixer follows this. Next a shift choice is made. Now that the sign and multiple of the register have been chosen, we must provide for information to leave the register and route the information to its destination. Thus the add entry gate and mixer are required.

The output of the adder must be strobed so that it is sampled only after addition is complete. A route must be set up from the adder to a register indicated as the prime entry gate and mixer. The prime register is then set.

As information leaves the prime register, it may be shifted, requiring a gate and mixer. The route from the prime register to the main register also must be set up, which requires a gate and mixer.

Examination of Figure 11.3 shows that the path under examination consists of a series of sets of gates and mixers. As mentioned earlier, the time for information to pass through a circuit depends upon its fan-in and fan-out. However, assuming a fixed time will allow us to make at least an order-of-magnitude analysis.

Choice of Adder

The analysis made here is performed in two forms. It is done in a general algebraic way and is done for a specific adder type, making certain assumptions about the length of timing chains in order to have concrete meaning to the reader. If one of the synchronous adders was used for this analysis, the results would not show up the differences encountered in some of the methods when as asynchronous adder was used. In contrast, using an asynchronous adder will show up differences which would not exist should a synchronous adder be used. Once the reader has had a chance to see the analysis performed with an asynchronous adder, he can readily make the substitutions which will convert these equations to the synchronous case.

Paths of Input

In our analysis we are interested in three paths. The first of these is the **propagate chain**. We will say that this chain is of length π. The second chain of interest is that required for adding when propagate is not performed. The length of the **add chain** is indicated as α. The chain required for addition when propagation also takes place is then $\alpha + \pi$. The third chain of interest is the path from the main register through the prime register and back again to the main register excluding the add path. This **register chain** is of length ρ. Then the time required to perform an addition and shift is $\rho + \alpha + \pi$.

To see this relationship, examine Figure 11.3 again. Note that information from the adder is not strobed until the adder indicates that addition is complete. This means that information must travel down the propagate chain before it can come out of the adder and continue on its way to return to the main register.

Relative Times

We shall carry on our analysis in regard to a 48-bit word which is fairly typical of large high-speed computers. We must know the length of the computer word when we are dealing with the asynchronous adder, for the carry-propagate chain is dependent upon this time.

Let us now fix the time required for information to pass through a gate and a mixer. Let us call this the **stage time** and refer to it as σ. We are now able to relate the length of the chains which are of interest to us. We shall do this referring to Figure 11.3. The add chain is approximately one stage in length; thus

$$\alpha = \sigma \tag{11.3.1}$$

The propagate time for a 48-bit adder is approximately seven bits. There is one stage required for each bit; thus,

$$\pi = 7\sigma \tag{11.3.2}$$

Taking the register in Figure 11.3 as typical, we count eight stages in the loop of the main register, excluding the stage already required for adding. Then

$$\rho = 8\sigma \tag{11.3.3}$$

Typically, stage times to present stage of the art range from several nanoseconds to several microseconds. In order to place numbers in our analysis, we shall assume a stage time of one hundred nanoseconds, this furnishes us with a one-and-one-half microsecond adder. This speed is average for the fastest machines now available.

Assumption About Numbers

In the analysis, the numbers we are dealing with are assumed to be chosen so that for *any* bit position the probability of a 0 or a 1 is equal and, hence, is $\frac{1}{2}$. This is particularly appropriate as far as floating-point numbers are concerned. These are usually encountered in normalized form and, hence, the equiprobability of 0's and 1's in all *significant* bits, except the first (which is predetermined) would be difficult to disprove. The multitiude of 0's at the end of floating-point numbers of low precision makes the comments of the paragraph of this section pertinent here, too. Since new machines include floating-point hardware and old machines have software to do floating point, the day may arrive when most calculations are done in this fashion.

Fixed-point calculations are subject to scaling. This operation multiplies some of the quantities encountered by constants so that the calculations will progress without generating numbers too small or too large to be represented in the word size of the machine. This does not have much effect on the random assumption.

What does have an effect is the precision of the numbers in the problem. Quantities accurate to four places (decimal), for instance, might appear as 3571000000 or 0003571000 or 0000003571. In all these cases there is an "unrandom" predominance of 0's. This is true in binary and is always a function of the precision of measurement.

Thus the randomness assumption does not take into account the prevalence of 0's in low precision problems. This prejudices our results towards fixed-cycle operation—operations which are independent of the numbers dealt with—and against variable-cycle operation. Actually, problems of low precision would contain more 0's and longer runs of 0's and methods dependent on these run parameters would work out better for low-precision problems.

11.4 ANALYSIS

We will now begin our analysis, following the lettering used in the previous section so that the reader may relate the analysis with the description. In all cases, it will be assumed that the control operation requires less time than the arithmetic processing of the data.

A1. Bit-by-Bit, Shift-Through Adder

In multiplication by Method A, we examine only one bit of the multiplier. It may be either 0 or 1. If it is a 0, we pass the information through the adder to the prime register and then return it to the main register. The time for this is

$$Q_1 = 0: \quad t_0 = \rho + \alpha \qquad (11.4.\text{A1})$$

When examination of the multiplier bit indicates that addition is to be performed, the time required for this is the same as that for addition and, therefore, is

$$Q_1 = 1: \quad t_1 = \rho + \alpha + \pi \qquad (11.4.\text{A2})$$

t_0 in (11.4.A1) indicates the time when addition is not performed and t_1 in (11.4.A2) indicates the time when addition is performed.

The number of 0's that we can expect in the multiplier is now to be determined. To do this, we simply assume a random distribution of 0's and 1's in the multiplier word. Therefore, the average number of 0's, $\bar{N}_0$, and the number of 1's, $\bar{N}_1$, are equal, and, consequently, equal to half the total number of bits in the multiplier word,

$$\bar{N}_0 = \bar{N}_1 = \frac{N}{2} \tag{11.4.A3}$$

Since this is true, it is immaterial whether we say that 0's in the multiplier request addition or 1's in the multiplier request addition; the result will be the same,

$$T = \bar{N}_0 t_0 + \bar{N}_1 t_1 \tag{11.4.A4}$$

where T is the total time for multiplication. Substituting the value of 1's, we have,

$$T = \frac{N}{2}(\rho + \alpha) + \frac{N}{2}(\rho + \alpha + \pi) \tag{11.4.A5}$$

This reduces to

$$T = N\left(\rho + \alpha + \frac{\pi}{2}\right) \tag{11.4.A6}$$

A2. Bit-by-Bit, Shift Around the Adder

The difference between method A1 and method A2 is that information is not passed through the adder in A2 so that transit time through the adder, α, is not part of the non-add time; thus,

$$t_0 = \rho \tag{11.4.A7}$$

The add time remains

$$t_1 = \rho + \alpha + \pi \tag{11.4.A8}$$

The total time for multiplication is

$$T = \frac{N}{2}(\rho) + \frac{N}{2}(\rho + \alpha + \pi) \tag{11.4.A9}$$

which reduces to

$$T = N\left(\rho + \frac{\alpha}{2} + \frac{\pi}{2}\right) \tag{11.4.A10}$$

TABLE 11.4 Comparison of Multiplication Time for Different Methods in Terms of Carry Propagation Time, π Add Time Less Propagation Time, α, and Register Shift Time Less Add Time, ρ. Translated to Single Stage Time, σ

Entry	Type of multiplication	General equation for multiplication time	$N = 48$ $\rho = 8\sigma$ $\pi = 7\sigma$ $\alpha = 1\sigma$	Micro- seconds for $\sigma =$ 100n
A1	Bit-by-bit, shift through adder	$N\left(\rho + \alpha + \dfrac{\pi}{2}\right)$	600σ	60
A2	Bit-by-bit, shift around adder	$N\left(\rho + \dfrac{\alpha + \pi}{2}\right)$	576σ	58
B	Bit-by-bit, carry-save	$N(\rho + \alpha) + \pi$	438σ	44
C	Bit pairs, except 11	$\dfrac{4N(\rho + \alpha + \pi)}{7}$	438σ	44
D	Bit pairs with triple register	$\left(\dfrac{N}{2} + 1\right)(\rho + \alpha + \pi)$	400σ	40
E	Bit pairs, triple register, carry-save	$\left(\dfrac{N}{2} + 1\right)(\rho + \alpha) + 2\pi$	239σ	24
F	Bit triple with exceptions	$\dfrac{4N(\rho + \alpha + \pi)}{9}$	342σ	34
G	Bit triple, triple register	$\left(\dfrac{4N}{11} + 1\right)(\rho + \alpha + \pi)$	296σ	30
H	Complete bit triplet	$\left(\dfrac{N}{3} + 3\right)(\rho + \alpha + \pi)$	304σ	30
I	Ternary pairs	$\dfrac{N}{2}(\rho + \alpha + \pi)$	384σ	38
J	Ternary pairs, carry-save	$\dfrac{N}{2}(\rho + \alpha) + \pi$	216σ	22
K	Ternary triplets	$\left(\dfrac{N}{3} + 1\right)(\rho + \alpha + \pi)$	272σ	27
L	Ternary triplets, carry save	$\left(\dfrac{N}{3} + 1\right)(\rho + \alpha) + 2\pi$	167σ	17
M	Ternary pairs, shift over 4 Q's	$\dfrac{16N}{35}(\rho + \alpha + \pi)$	351σ	35

TABLE 11.4—Continued

Entry	Type of multiplication	General equation for multiplication time	$N = 48$ $\rho = 8\sigma$ $\pi = 7\sigma$ $\alpha = 1\sigma$	Micro- seconds for $\sigma =$ 100n
N	Shift over 0's and 1's, infinite shift	$\dfrac{N}{2}(\rho + \alpha + \pi)$	384σ	38
O	Shift over 0's and 1's, shift of 6	$\dfrac{16N}{31}(\rho + \alpha + \pi)$	409σ	41
P	Shift over 0's and 1's, infinite shift, improved method	$\dfrac{N}{3}(\rho + \alpha + \pi)$	256σ	26
Q	Shift over 0's and 1's, shift of 6, improved method	$\dfrac{8N}{23}(\rho + \alpha + \pi)$	279σ	28

The times for these two methods are compared in Table 11.4 on page 226. You will notice that for the constants used there, there is only a difference of two microseconds out of sixty. Henceforth, we will assume that non-add cycles are performed using the adder. This reduces the control circuitry and increases the total multiplication time only slightly.

B. Bit-by-Bit With Carry-Save

We pass information through the adder on the non-add cycles, so that the time for this process is

$$t_0 = \rho + \alpha \qquad (11.4.\text{B1})$$

When addition is called for, information is passed through the adder, but the carries are not propagated, and this time is therefore eliminated from consideration. Thus,

$$t_1 = \rho + \alpha \qquad (11.4.\text{B2})$$

The total time for multiplication is found by multiplying the average number of add cycles by the time required for each add cycle, adding this to the product of the number of non-add cycles and the time required for a non-add cycle. Finally, the time required to propagate the carries is added, for this is performed only on the last cycle. Then

$$T = \bar{N}_0 t_0 + \bar{N}_1 t_1 + \pi \tag{11.4.B3}$$

This yields

$$T = \frac{N}{2}(\rho + \alpha) + \frac{N}{2}(\rho + \alpha) + \pi \tag{11.4.B4}$$

which simplifies to

$$T = N(\rho + \alpha) + \pi \tag{11.4.B5}$$

C. Bit Pairs Except 11

To make this calculation, we determine the average shift length, $\bar{S}$. For combinations other than 11, the shift length is 2. For

$$Q_{i+1}Q_i \neq 11: \quad S = 2 \tag{11.4.C1}$$

The probability of a combination other than 11 is $\frac{3}{4}$,

$$P_{xx} = \tfrac{3}{4} \tag{11.4.C2}$$

Therefore, our shift expectation when bits other than 11 are encountered is

$$S_{xx} = \tfrac{3}{4} \cdot 2 = \tfrac{3}{2} \tag{11.4.C3}$$

When the combination 11 is encountered, we shift only one place. For

$$Q_{i+1}Q_i = 11: \quad S = 1 \tag{11.4.C4}$$

The probability of encountering 11 is

$$P_{11} = \tfrac{1}{4} \tag{11.4.C5}$$

Therefore, our expectation in number of shifts in this case is

$$S_{11} = \tfrac{1}{4} \cdot 1 = \tfrac{1}{4} \tag{11.4.C6}$$

The expected shift length is found by adding these two quantities; thus,

$$\bar{S} = S_{xx} + S_{11} = \tfrac{3}{2} + \tfrac{1}{4} = \tfrac{7}{4} \tag{11.4.C7}$$

The time for performing of a cycle, regardless of the bit pair encountered, is

$$t = (\rho + \alpha + \pi) \tag{11.4.C8}$$

The total time for multiplication by this method is found by taking the product of the number of digits and the cycle time and dividing by the average cycle length, or,

$$T = \frac{Nt}{S} \tag{11.4.C9}$$

Substituting the values for cycle time of (11.4.C8) and the average shift length of (11.4.C7),

$$T = \frac{4N}{7} (\rho + \alpha + \pi) \tag{11.4.C10}$$

D. Bit Pairs, Triple Register

The cycle time in method D is fixed,

$$t = \rho + \alpha + \pi \tag{11.4.D1}$$

We examine the multiplier bits in pairs and shift in pairs so that the number of cycles we perform is equivalent to the number of bit pairs; thus,

$$N_p = \frac{N}{2} \tag{11.4.D2}$$

The time required to perform multiplication is the time required to perform as many cycles as there are bit pairs, except that we must perform an additional cycle of addition in order to prepare the multiplicand triple. Therefore,

$$T = N_p(\rho + \alpha + \pi) + (\rho + \alpha + \pi) \tag{11.4.D3}$$

which simplifies to

$$T = \left(\frac{N}{2} + 1\right)(\rho + \alpha + \pi) \tag{11.4.D4}$$

E. Bit Pairs With Triple Register and Carry-Save

The time required for a cycle no longer includes propagation time and, therefore, is

$$t = \rho + \alpha \tag{11.4.E1}$$

The number of pairs is still

$$N_p = \frac{N}{2} \tag{11.4.E2}$$

To find the total time for multiplication, we first find the time required for as many cycles as there are bit pairs. To this must be added the propagation time which occurs on the final cycle. Also, we must consider the time required to prepare the multiplicand triple using the adder and including propagate time. The result is

$$T = N_p(\rho + \alpha) + \pi + (\rho + \alpha + \pi) \qquad (11.4.\text{E3})$$

which reduces to

$$T = \left(\frac{N}{2} + 1\right)(\rho + \alpha) + 2\pi \qquad (11.4.\text{E4})$$

F. Bit Triple With Exceptions

In method F the number of places which are shifted depends on the bit triple under examination. The expected number of shifts for various combinations is identified below. The sum of these expected values yields the average expected number of shifts:

For 000, 001, 010, 100 $\quad S = 3 \quad P_{xx} = \frac{1}{2} \quad S_3 = \frac{1}{2}\cdot 3 = \frac{3}{2}$

For 110, 101 $\qquad\qquad S = 2 \quad P_{xx} = \frac{1}{4} \quad S_2 = \frac{1}{4}\cdot 2 = \frac{1}{2}$

For 111, 011 $\qquad\qquad S = 1 \quad P_{xx} = \frac{1}{4} \quad S_1 = \frac{1}{4}\cdot 1 = \frac{1}{4}$

$$S = \frac{9}{4}$$

Then,

$$T = \frac{Nt}{S} \qquad (11.4.\text{F1})$$

which yields, on substitution,

$$T = \frac{4N}{9}(\rho + \alpha + \pi) \qquad (11.4.\text{F2})$$

G. Bit Triple with Triple Register

We can make up the following list of expected values for number of shifts with various bit-triple combinations:

For 000, 001, 010, 100, 011, 110 $\quad S = 3 \quad P_{xx} = \frac{3}{4} \quad S_3 = \frac{3}{4}\cdot 3 = \frac{9}{4}$

For 101, 111 $\qquad\qquad\qquad\qquad S = 2 \quad P_{xx} = \frac{1}{4} \quad S_2 = \frac{1}{4}\cdot 2 = \frac{1}{2}$

$$S = \frac{11}{4}$$

An extra cycle is required to prepare the multiplicand triple; thus, the total time for multiplication is

$$T = \frac{Nt}{S} + (\rho + \alpha + \pi) \qquad (11.4.\text{G}1)$$

On substituting, we have

$$T = \left(\frac{4N}{11} + 1\right)(\rho + \alpha + \pi) \qquad (11.4.\text{G}2)$$

H. Complete Bit Triplet

If all the necessary multiples of the multiplicand are available, we perform a shift of length 3 on every cycle. In determining the time for the complete multiplication process, we must also include time for preparing the three multiples of the multiplicand. Each of these can be prepared in a single addition cycle; therefore, the total time for this method is

$$T = \frac{Nt}{3} + 3t \qquad (11.4.\text{H}1)$$

Substituting the cycle time, we have

$$T = \left(\frac{N}{3} + 3\right)(\rho + \alpha + \pi) \qquad (11.4.\text{H}2)$$

I. Ternary Pairs

The number of pairs is

$$N_p = \frac{N}{2} \qquad (11.4.\text{I}1)$$

Then, the total time is

$$T = N_p t \qquad (11.4.\text{I}2)$$

On substitution, this becomes

$$T = \frac{N}{2}(\rho + \alpha + \pi) \qquad (11.4.\text{I}3)$$

J. Ternary Pairs With Carry-Save

Again there is one cycle per pair, the number of pairs being given by

$$N_p = \frac{N}{2} \tag{11.4.J1}$$

The cycle length is now reduced by the propagation time so that

$$t = (\rho + \alpha) \tag{11.4.J2}$$

The time for propagation must be added to the last cycle, so that the total time for multiplication by this method is

$$T = \frac{N}{2}(\rho + \alpha) + \pi \tag{11.4.J3}$$

K. Ternary Triplets

Cycle time, as before, is

$$t = \rho + \alpha + \pi \tag{11.4.K1}$$

The number of triplets is the number of digits divided by 3,

$$N_t = \frac{N}{3} \tag{11.4.K2}$$

The total time for multiplication is the number of cycles times the cycle time plus an additional cycle time for preparation of the multiplicand triple,

$$T = N_t t + t \tag{11.4.K3}$$

This becomes

$$T = \left(\frac{N}{3} + 1\right)(\alpha + \rho + \pi) \tag{11.4.K4}$$

L. Ternary Triplets With Carry-Save

The cycle time does not include propagation time,

$$t = \rho + \alpha \tag{11.4.L1}$$

The total time includes a term for propagation on the final cycle and a term for the preparation of the multiplicand triple,

$$T = N_t t + \pi + t \qquad (11.4.L2)$$

or

$$T = \left(\frac{N}{3} + 1\right)(\rho + \alpha) + 2\pi \qquad (11.4.L3)$$

M. Ternary Bit Pairs Shifting Over Up to Four 0's

We prepare a table which lists expected time for various bit combinations. From this we can determine the average shift length:

$$P(0000) = \tfrac{1}{16} \qquad S_{0000} = 4 \times \tfrac{1}{16} = \tfrac{4}{16}$$

$$P(1000) = \tfrac{1}{16} \qquad S_{1000} = 3 \times \tfrac{1}{16} = \tfrac{3}{16}$$

$$P(\text{others}) = \tfrac{14}{16} \qquad S_{xxxx} = 2 \times \tfrac{14}{16} = \tfrac{28}{16}$$

$$\overline{S} = \tfrac{35}{16}$$

The total multiplication time is

$$T = \frac{Nt}{S} = \frac{16N}{35}(\rho + \alpha + \pi) \qquad (11.4.M1)$$

N. Shifting Over 0's and 1's

Again we assume that the probability of a bit being a 0 or a 1 is the same; therefore, $\tfrac{1}{2}$. We wish to find the probability of a run of i 0's after a run of 1's or, similarly, a run of i 1's after a run of 0's. To begin our analysis, we assume that the arithmetic unit has infinite shift capability. We have just shifted over a series of 0's. We terminate our shift only because the bit we have just encountered is a 1. Indicating the last bit shifted over in parentheses, we say that the sequence $X0(0)$ is impossible for, since we are shifting over 0's, when we encounter a 0 we will continue to shift. Therefore, the sequence we are investigating at the moment must be in the form $X1(0)$; this sequence has a probability 1 after shifting over 0's. We can therefore make the following statement:

$$P\{\text{configuration 0, 1 after a run of 0's}\} = P\{X01(0)\} \qquad (11.4.N1)$$

$$= P_{0,1} = \tfrac{1}{2}$$

This says that the probability of the next-to-the-last digit being a 0 is $\frac{1}{2}$. This is true because the only variable in the sequence is the next-to-the-last digit and it can only be a 0 or a 1. In the statement of (11.4.N1), we may read $P_{0,1} = \frac{1}{2}$ as, "The probability of encountering 11 after a run of 0's is $\frac{1}{2}$." Similarly, we investigate the probability of the sequence $X011(0)$. In effect, we are asking for the probability of the combination 01 in the next-to-the-last position and the bit to the left of it. Since there are four combinations for these two bits, the probability for this sequence is $\frac{1}{4}$. We write this as

$$P\{X011(0)\} = P_{0,2} = \tfrac{1}{4} \tag{11.4.N2}$$

In a similar fashion we find the probability for a series of three 1's as

$$P\{X0111(0)\} = P_{0,3} = \tfrac{1}{8} \tag{11.4.N3}$$

In a general case we have the probability for a series of i 1's after a run of 0's which is given by

$$P\{X01\cdots1(0)\} = P_{0,i} = (\tfrac{1}{2})^i \tag{11.4.N4}$$

Exactly the same reasoning is used to determine the probability of a series of i 0's after a run of 1's, which is

$$P\{X10\cdots0(1)\} = P_{1,i} = (\tfrac{1}{2})^i \tag{11.4.N5}$$

Now we want to find the probability of a run of i bits, these bits being different from the preceding run of bits. This is found by adding the probabilities according to the law of conditional probabilities, so that

$$P_{X,i} = P_0 P_{0,i} + P_1 P_{1,i} \tag{11.4.N6}$$

Since a series of 0's or a series of 1's are equally likely,

$$P_{X,i} = \tfrac{1}{2} P_{0,i} + \tfrac{1}{2} P_{1,i} \tag{11.4.N7}$$
$$= (\tfrac{1}{2})^i$$

We wish to find the average expected number of shifts, $\bar{S}$. To do this we must totalize expected shifts. We must find the probability of a single shift and multiply it by 1; the probability of a double shift and multiply it by 2; and so forth; or

$$\bar{S} = 1 P_{X,1} + 2 P_{X,2} + 3 P_{X,3} + \cdots \tag{11.4.N8}$$

In summation notation, this is

$$\bar{S} = \sum_{i=1}^{\infty} i 2^{-i} \tag{11.4.N9}$$

The value of this infinite series can be shown to be equal to 2,

$$\bar{S} = 2 \qquad (11.4.\text{N10})$$

To see this, recall the series expansion

$$(1 - X)^{-2} = 1 + 2X + 3X^2 + \cdots \qquad (11.4.\text{N11})$$

Multiply both sides of this equation by X; then

$$X(1 - X)^{-2} = X + 2X^2 + 3X^3 + \cdots \qquad (11.4.\text{N12})$$

The series on the right-hand side is the same as the one in which we are interested, if $\frac{1}{2}$ is substituted for X. In so doing, we have

$$\bar{S} = \tfrac{1}{2}(1 - \tfrac{1}{2})^{-2} = 2 \qquad (11.4.\text{N13})$$

The time for multiplication by this process is determined by finding the number of cycles which is given by the number of bits in the multiplier divided by the average number of shifts per cycle. Then the total time is

$$T = \frac{N}{\bar{S}} t = \frac{N}{2} (\pi + \alpha + \rho) \qquad (11.4.\text{N14})$$

O. Shifting Over 0's and 1's With A Finite Shifter

The derivation for this formula follows the pattern above. When we reach the formula (11.4.N8) the series is no longer infinite but terminates at K, where K is the size of the maximum shift which can be performed. Then

$$\bar{S}_K = \sum_{i=1}^{K} i2^{-i} + K2^{-K} \qquad (11.4.\text{O1})$$

Hence,

$$\bar{S}_K = 2 - (\tfrac{1}{2})^{K-1} \qquad (11.4.\text{O2})$$

and, in general,

$$T = \frac{N}{\bar{S}_K} (\pi + \alpha + \rho) \qquad (11.4.\text{O3})$$

P. Shifting Over 0's and 1's, Improved Method, Infinite Shift

As before, the combination $X0(0)$ and the combination $X1(1)$ are impossible. Also, recall that we never perform a single shift in the improved method. Let us now list all the combinations of second and third bits of the multiplier which yield a shift of two places. These are

$$X01 \quad 0(1)$$
$$X10 \quad 0(1)$$
$$X01 \quad 1(0)$$
$$X10 \quad 1(0)$$

Four other combinations of second and third bits are conceivable but not permissible. From this we can say

$$P_{X2} = \tfrac{1}{2} \tag{11.4.P1}$$

Examine other cases where a shift of 3 is performed.

$$X100 \quad 1(0)$$
$$X011 \quad 0(1)$$

From this we make the statement

$$P_{X3} = \tfrac{1}{4} \tag{11.4.P2}$$

We have a similar situation for a shift of 4; these are listed as

$$1000 \quad 1(0)$$
$$0111 \quad 0(1)$$

This yields

$$P_{X4} = \tfrac{1}{8} \tag{11.4.P3}$$

Finally, let us list the occasions where we will shift i places; these are

$$\underbrace{10\cdots0}_{i-1} \quad 1(0)$$

$$\underbrace{01\cdots1}_{i-1} \quad 0(1)$$

Therefore, the probability of these situations arising is

$$P_{Xi} = (\tfrac{1}{2})^{i-1} \qquad (11.4.\text{P4})$$

The average number of shifts performed is

$$\bar{S} = 1P_{X,1} + 2P_{X,2} + \cdots + iP_{Xi} + \cdots \qquad (11.4.\text{P5})$$

This is put into summation notation as

$$\bar{S} = \sum_{i=2}^{\infty} i2^{-(i-1)} \qquad (11.4.\text{P6})$$

Note that when $i = 1$ the term to the right of the summation sign would be equal to 1. It is therefore permissible that we decrease the lower index of the summation by 1 and subtract 1 from the result. This may be written as

$$\bar{S} = \sum_{i=1}^{\infty} i2^{-(i-1)} - 1 \qquad (11.4.\text{P7})$$

To evaluate this series, we recall that

$$(1 - X)^{-2} = 1 + 2X + 3X^2 + \cdots \qquad (11.4.\text{P8})$$

When this is evaluated, the result is

$$\bar{S} = 4 - 1 = 3 \qquad (11.4.\text{P9})$$

The total multiplication time is

$$T = \frac{N}{\bar{S}} (\rho + \alpha + \pi) \qquad (11.4.\text{P10})$$

If the average shift length is substituted in this operation, we have

$$T = \frac{N}{3} (\rho + \alpha + \pi) \qquad (11.4.\text{P11})$$

Q. Shift Over 0's and 1's, Improved Method, Finite Shift

The expression found in (11.4.P6) is converted for use with a finite shifter by setting the upper limit of the summation sign equal to K. This yields

$$\bar{S}_K = \sum_{2}^{K} i2^{-(i-1)} + K2^{-K+1} \qquad (11.4.\text{Q1})$$

$$= 3 - (\tfrac{1}{2})^{K-2} \qquad (11.4.\text{Q2})$$

The time for multiplication by this method is then evaluated by

$$T = \frac{N}{\bar{S}_K} (\rho + \alpha + \pi) \qquad (11.4.\text{Q3})$$

11.5   FURTHER COMMENTS ON MULTIPLICATION

Introduction

This section takes up some of the problems of multiplication which have been neglected in order to give greater consideration to hardware and timing for the most general cases. One of these problems is the allocation of the register when a multiplicand of maximum size is being used to form a product. Double-length multiplication is contrasted with single-length multiplication. For the first time, we discuss rounding, an important consideration in numerical analysis. Here we will expect the computer to do the rounding instead of having it built into the program. Another thing we can ask the computer to do is to accumulate products; that is, to add the desired product to a quantity stored in one of the registers. Negative product accumulation is mentioned.

Two complete chapters, 15 and 16, are devoted to floating-point multiplication and division, so this topic is not discussed here.

Multiplication Cycle Using the Maximum Size Multiplicand

Let us begin our discussion considering positive numbers; then the largest number which can be used as a multiplicand is $0.11\cdots111$. We wish to consider what happens in one of the intermediate cycles. We expect that at some intermediate point the A register stores a quantity greater than 0. The D register contains the multiplicand whose numerical portion consists of a series of 1's. When the contents of the A and D registers are added in the adder, the number produced will be greater than 1. That is to say, this sum will overflow into the sign position. Overflow is really not the correct term to apply here, since a respectable partial product is in the process of being formed.

In any case, the point of this discussion is to indicate that we will commandeer the sign position of the A' register. Only one extra bit is required in forming proper partial products. Even if the impossible case should arise where all 1's are stored in both the A and D registers, this sum will not exceed the space provided by the extra bit, the sign bit of the A' register, since our addition does not affect the sign portion of the numbers.

When the partial product is returned from the A' register to the A register, it is shifted at least one position to the right. This restores the partial product so that this number occupies only the numerical portion of the A register.

If you think about it, you will see that using the sign position of the A' register for numerical information will suffice for not only positive numbers but for signed numbers.

When dealing with signed numbers, previously, we have indicated that the sign of the product is determined at the beginning of multiplication and stored in an auxiliary bit storage device. This permits the bit positions A_s and A_s' to take part in arithmetic.

When multi-bit multiplication is performed, the D register may be multiplied by a constant before it is added to the partial product. So doing may create left-hand bits for which a provision must be made in the prime register. In other words, if we are doing 3-bit multiplication, not only will the sign position of the A' register take part in the multiplication, but we must provide two extra bits to the left of the sign position to accommodate the large partial products formed when maximum or near maximum multiplicands are used.

Double-Length Multiplication

In our discussion of multiplication, three registers usually take part. At the end of multiplication the product is found spread across two registers. Both of the two words produced by multiplication are rarely required in a scientific problem; the least significant word is usually discarded. This is so for two reasons. First the lower word does not have significance, as a study of numerical analysis will show. Second, a problem is usually set up to use single words. If the product produced by multiplication is to be augmented in later processing, only one word of this product, the upper word, will be carried along.

The reader may wonder if it might not be handy to have these two words when performing double-precision arithmetic. However, in order to maintain the accuracy required, one needs at least a 3-word product instead of two. Therefore, even double-precision arithmetic does not have its requirement satisfied by the double-length word.

We might note in passing that the two words developed by our left-to-right examination of multiplier bits are differently situated at the end of multiplication than for the right-to-left multiplication. In the present case, the lower word is found in the A register and the upper word in the Q register.

Single-Length Multiplication

The first question which is to be answered is which word do we wish to keep in single-length multiplication. If you experiment with multiplication using both integral and fractional numbers, you find that for the latter, the most significant portion of the product is always contained in the upper word. Therefore, it would seem that single-length multiplication should conserve the left word and round off the second word for fractional numbers. For small integers, the result is always in the lower word, but large integers may produce a result spread over both words. An integer multiply command, as in the CDC 3600, must take this into account.

Is there a need for a special command which performs single-length multiplication? Only if it is required to conserve the multiplier or if rounding is to be performed. Since the multiplier is always conserved in computer memory as long as a functionally non-destructive memory is employed in the computer, there is no justification in this request for maintianing the multiplier in a register. However, rounding will require extra program steps if it is not performed automatically and, therefore, a special command for multiply and round is advantageous.

When single-length multiplication is provided, often the multiplier is retained in the Q register. It may be destroyed if the Q register is used in the rounding process. Let us see what happens if we wish to keep the multiplier in the Q register. Consider right-to-left examination of the multiplier digits. As the partial product is prepared, it is passed over to the A' register; it is returned to the A register afterward. In double-length multiplication, the least significant bit or bits are passed over to the most significant bits of the Q register. During single-length multiplication, these bits are discarded (into our fictitious wastebasket). The first bit which is to be saved is passed over to the A register in the least significant bit position. This causes the proper alignment of the partial product in the A register for the next cycle.

In the meantime, Q-register bits must be shifted from the left end of the register to the right end. In so doing, an end-around shift is performed. To outline this more specifically, the Q register is transferred directly to the Q' register. For bit-at-a-time multiplication, in general, we transfer the bit Q_i' to Q_{i-1}. This is true except for the right-hand bit Q_1', which is transferred to the other end of the register to position Q_N. During this process, the sign bit may or may not be shuffled back and forth between Q_s' and Q_s according to the design requirements.

Rounding

This discussion will begin with what rounding is and then continue with how and when it is done for multiplication.

what is it?

Let us start by examining rounding for decimal numbers. If we are going to round a number, whether it is integral or fractional, and we wish to round it to, say the ith digit, then we examine the digit directly to the right of it [the $(i - 1)$th digit]. The rule for performing this rounding is that if this $(i - 1)$th digit is 4 or less, we keep the ith digit unchanged and drop all the digits to the right of it; if the $(i - 1)$th digit is 5 or greater, we add 1 to the ith digit and discard everything to the right of it.

We are interested in seeing the error which may arise in rounding. Let us call E the exponent of the base which applies to the $(i - 1)$th position. Then the maximum error we might anticipate due to rounding for decimal numbers is $10^E/2$. Notice that if our approximating were done simply by dropping the right-hand digits from the $(i - 1)$th place on, then our maximum error would approach 10^E. The rounding procedure, on the average, cuts the error in half.

The same situation is approximately true for binary numbers. Now we have only two alternatives for the right-hand digit. If it is 0, we leave the ith position unchanged and drop the other bits; if it is 1, we add 1 to the ith position and drop the other right-hand digits. The maximum error due to rounding is therefore $2^E/2 = 2^{E-1}$. This is contrasted in the case where all the right-hand digits are dropped, whereby the resulting maximum error is simply 2^E.

how?

To perform rounding, we must add 1 to the right-hand digit of the upper word of the product in certain cases. The difficulty which arises is the ripple carry. This is true in both the binary and decimal machine, although here we restrict our attention to the binary machine. Carries may occur all the way down the line. Therefore, it would seem that we can perform our rounding only by doing a bona fide addition. However, as we will see, depending on when we perform the rounding, our requirements may be modified. We can do the rounding before multiplication, during multiplication, or after multiplication.

after

If we are going to round the product after it has been formed, and rounding is to be done so as to keep the upper word and dispose of the lower word, then we must first examine the lower word. Rounding is done by adding 1 to the most significant bit of the lower word. If this bit is a 1, it will cause a carry into the upper word. Actually, as you can see, addition need not be performed with the lower word. We merely need to examine the most significant bit of the lower word to determine if it is a 1. Thus, in half the cases, we can simply discard the lower word. In the remaining cases, 1 must be added to the *least* significant bit of the *upper* word. If this is done after forming the product, there is no choice but to pass the upper word into the adder, adding 1 to it there, transferring it to the prime register, and, finally, returning it to the main register, all of which takes an extra cycle. By the way, this addition may be done by inhibiting the other entry to the adder but energizing ${}^1C_0$.

before

Except in accumulating multiplication which is discussed later, the A register is cleared to 0 before multiplication begins. At this time, we can perform a modification which will automatically do the rounding for us. To see this, note that anything which is presently contained in the A register will be added to the lower word of the product when multiplication is complete. We are interested in rounding the upper word. From the earlier discussion, you see that this could be done by adding 1 to the most significant position of the lower word. If the 1 is stored at A_N while the A register is being cleared, rounding will automatically take place because, in right-to-left multiplication, that bit will occupy Q_N when we are done.

during

Rounding can be performed *on the run*, if we observe that on the final cycle of multiplication, what will be the most significant bit of the lower word is passing between A and A' as the least significant bit of the upper word. To do our rounding, we want to add 1 to this position as it passes by. There is a simple expedient for doing this. If the numbers being manipulated are positive, that is, if the partial product and multiplicand are both positive numbers, normally the carry entry to the adder would be $^0C_0$. Changing this to $^1C_0$ affects the addition of a single 1 to the product at the proper position in the total product word.

negative products

How do we perform the rounding when dealing with negative numbers? If we are accumulating a negative partial product, we are using complementary notation. Increasing the absolute value of the number we are dealing with corresponds to reducing the complement. When we are subtracting the multiplicand, we energize the $^1C_0$ input; reversing this so as to energize the $^0C_0$ input effects the addition required for rounding.

Both the *Before* and *During* methods of rounding can be done on the fly; they are done without increasing the number of cycles required to perform multiplication.

Simultaneous Multiplication and Accumulation

Simultaneous multiplication and accumulation is a very convenient facility to have in forming the sum of products. It also finds use in innumerable programming problems. What we wish to do here is to take a number, store it in one of the registers, and add the product now being formed to this number. This is most useful when the number being added to is stored in the accumulator, the A register. After memory reference, we can say that we desire to perform

$$(A) + (Q)(D) \longrightarrow A \cup Q.$$

We have two alternatives: we may add the proposed number to the lower or upper word of the product. Adding this amount to the lower word is very easy to perform. The number is simply left in the A register and as multiplication takes place, this number is automatically added to the product.

Although adding to the lower word is easier, it is not very useful. We usually wish to accumulate on the upper word. To do this we must store the contents of the A register temporarily while multiplication is taking place. Since the D′ register is not used during multiplication, this is a handy place to put the augend during multiplication. When multiplication is complete we can simply return the information from the D′ register to the D register and then do addition.

In both cases of accumulating multiplication, overflow can occur. It cannot occur in normal multiplication, as the reader should verify. Therefore, accumulating multiplication requires alarm provision not normally made in non-accumulating multiplication.

Occasionally we have to subtract the product from a number which is stored in the accumulator. Although this may be implemented in hardware, it is much less expensive to do by programming it directly. There is never any need to provide for negative accumulation as a special order, although certain rare computers may do so.

Truncation

Multiplication is said to be truncated when not all of the bits of the multiplier word are used. This is a way to gain speed, especially when calculations are known to be of low precision.

how?

In binary machines the computer detects the equivalent for truncation only from the command code. This code must also indicate the amount of truncation—on what bit to stop multiplication. Here decimal manipulation offers an advantage. If the multiplier digit turns out to be a particular one of the forbidden code, this can indicate *where* truncation is to take place.

why?

When calculations of known, low precision are scheduled, this will cause a definite acceleration. However, strict attention must be paid to scaling or misinterpretation of the answers might ensue.

A Problem Product

It is possible to request (1.0) (1.0). Recall that in 2's complement notation $1.00\cdots00$ is the representation for $-1.00 - 0$. Therefore the request above is for (-1) (-1) $= +1.0$. However, $+1.0$ is *not representable*. Machines may detect this before, during or after a solution is attempted; they must recognize it and indicate a fault so that a correction can be made before the problem is continued. Detection of this difficulty appears as one of the problems at the end of this chapter.

Method 1 Multiplication

Method 1 multiplication, though explained in Section 3.3, has not been applied in high-speed multiplication. This is because it requires an *extra* cycle which slows down performance. So far, no technique has derived enough speed to compensate for the extra cycle; hence, this method was ignored.

PROBLEMS

11.1 For each method in Table 11.4 determine how large an extension of the A' register is required.

11.2 Could you indicate how the carry-save adder might be incorporated in shifting over 0's and 1's by time-sharing the shifter.

11.3 Develop a rule-of-thumb for the time saving by the incorporation of a carry-save adder into a given multiplication scheme.

11.4 For Table 11.4 estimate the hardware for each method. Develop a figure of merit for each.

11.5 Review all the methods and discuss how each may be applied for multiplication with a high-speed parallel decimal adder.

11.6 Referring to (8.6.1) through (8.6.3), for $k = 6$ what is the time required for multiplication by methods A1, B, C, D, E, F, G, H, I, J, K, and L?

12

DIVISION I

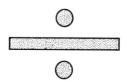

12.1 INTRODUCTION

General Method of Performing Division

Division, whether preformed manually or by machine, requires an examination of the divisor with relation to the dividend or partial remainder. We try to determine precisely as many digits of the quotient as possible. Having done this, we may guess one more digit of the quotient. Then we verify this guess by performing arithmetic on the dividend or partial remainder. In dealing with positive numbers, reduction is performed by subtracting the divisor from the dividend. We term this reduction *successful* if the result is of the same sign as the partial remainder; it is called *unsuccessful* if a sign change occurs. When we are unsuccessful, our guess was wrong; we must then make a new guess and verify it. In dealing with binary digits a bit at a time, our second guess need not be verified, since we have only two alternatives. If one of these is wrong, the other must be correct.

In this chapter we concern ourselves with methods for speeding up the division process and limit our scope to binary numbers. To facilitate discussion, we use the term "remainder" instead of the longer phrase "partial remainder" when no misunderstanding could arise.

Methods For Increasing Speed

There are only four basic methods known to this author for increasing the speed of division. There are variations and modifications of these methods, but these do not alter the general principles. We preview these methods now and expand upon them in this chapter and chapters 13 and 14.

early termination of arithmetic

After we make a guess for a quotient digit, we usually verify this by performing arithmetic. All we need to do is to determine whether our guess is right or wrong. If we find it is wrong, we can terminate arithmetic and do something else. The correctness of our guess depends on whether a change in sign takes place in the remainder. We may determine the correctness of our guess by monitoring the sign bit of the sum produced by arithmetic. If sign information is produced before the complete sum, we have sufficient information to terminate arithmetic before it is completed.

no restoration

When arithmetic is unsuccessful, the remainder has changed sign. If we can handle the remainder in this new form without restoring it to its original condition, we can save a subcycle.

several divisor multiples

If we provide several multiples of the divisor, we can make a guess as to several bits of the quotient rather than one. We then verify our guess using the appropriate multiple of the divisor. The guess is corrected by using the next lower multiple.

normalization

Maintaining the divisor and remainder in normalized form allows us to determine when the remainder becomes very small on a given cycle. This may allow us to determine several quotient bits without performing arithmetic, which definitely accelerates division.

Things To Come

We will discuss many variations of performing division arithmetic. The next section will review the very simple single-bit methods. These consist of restoring, non-restoring, and non-performing division. Shifting over 0's is examined next. This is applied to quotient lookahead. The rest of the chapter is devoted to various lookahead quotient development methods.

In the next chapter we discuss normalization as it applies to positive numbers using a restoring method. Shifting over 1's, then shifting over 0's and 1's is looked into. This is then combined with lookahead using divisor multiples are investigated in the sections that follow. Then normalization is combined with the non-restoring arithmetic to provide a method faster than either of the two.

Finally, in Chapter 14, all three tools are combined so that we have normalizing non-restoring division using divisor multiples and, therefore, multiple-bit quotient lookahead. Two choices of multiples are investigated for this purpose. Hardware is then considered. Finally, two sections are devoted to comparing the division methods in much the same fashion as was used with multiplication.

12.2   SINGLE-BIT DIVISION

This section discusses three kinds of division: restoring, non-performing and non-restoring. No difficulty is encountered with signed numbers for restoring or non-performing division. Only when a sign reversal occurs do we encounter some difficulty.

The methods of this section are easy to implement; however, they yield only slight gains in speed. They are used by most of the general-purpose computers on the market.

Restoring Division

We define a cycle as the processing required to generate at least a single bit of the quotient. In restoring division, a cycle may consist of two or three subcycles. For positive numbers the first subcycle always consists of subtracting the divisor from the remainder. If the result is positive, the second subcycle is omitted; if it is negative, the original remainder is to be placed into the prime register. Although subtraction has been performed, the minuend is still intact in the main register. It is now passed over to the prime register. In any case, the third subcycle consists of entering the quotient bit and of shifting the quotient and remainder with respect to the divisor.

When the subtraction is successful, the quotient bit is 1; when it is unsuccessful, the quotient bit is 0. The remainder and the quotient are shifted one place leftward, which is equivalent to multiplying each by 2. When dealing with signed numbers, we change the sign of the divisor, if necessary, so that it will correspond to the sign of the remainder and then subtract it from the remainder. Otherwise, our processing remains the same.

The assignment of the quotient bit depends upon the quotient sign. When we are developing a positive quotient, successful arithmetic enters a quotient bit of 1; an unsuccessful arithmetic enters a quotient bit of 0. When developing a negative quotient, successful arithmetic develops a quotient bit of 0; unsuccessful arithmetic develops a quotient bit of 1.

When sufficient quotient bits have been determined, division terminates. The remainder does not require any correction, since its sign has never been permanently changed. The quotient is correct except when it is a negative number and we are using 2's complement notation. In that case, 1 must be added to the least significant bit of the quotient.

Non-Performing Division

Division is performed in exactly the same manner described above, with one exception: an asynchronous adder is used and the sign bit of this unit is constantly monitored. When this bit indicates that the result has the same sign as the present remainder, we allow arithmetic to continue to completion and enter a quotient bit of 1 for a positive quotient or 0 for a negative quotient. When monitoring of the sign bit indicates a sign reversal, arithmetic is abandoned and a shift of the remainder is initiated. By this means, the remainder is preserved unaltered, since no arithmetic is taking place. Hence, it need not be restored; it can be shifted immediately. At the same time, a 0 quotient bit is entered for a positive quotient or a 1 quotient bit is entered for a negative quotient. The hardware for performing this arithmetic was described in detail in Section 7.6. Additionally, an example of non-performing division is presented in Figure 12.2.1.

Non-Restoring Division

The cycle for non-restoring division consists of two subcycles. The first subcycle performs arithmetic—no restoration is required; the second subcycle enters the quotient bit and does a single shift of the remainder and quotient.

First examine how we deal with positive numbers. Assume that we are somewhere in the middle of division and the present remainder is positive. We subtract the divisor from the remainder and test the result. As in the other two methods, if the result is positive, the quotient bit is 1; if negative,

Line	D Divisor	A Dividend (Remainder)	Q Dividend	Do
1	1.10011	0.00100	10001/	
2		1.10011		Start to add (D)
3		0◄⏌		^0C_s; terminate add
4		0.01001	0001/1	$A \leftarrow Q \leftarrow 1$
5		1.10011		Start to add (D)
6		0◄⏌		^0C_s; terminate add
7		0.10010	001/11	$A \leftarrow Q \leftarrow 1$
8		1.10011		Start to add (D)
9		10.00101		^1C_s; complete add
10		0.01010	01/110	$A \leftarrow Q \leftarrow 0$
11		1.10011		Start to add (D)
12		0◄⏌		^0C_s; terminate add
13		0.10100	1/1101	$A \leftarrow Q \leftarrow 1$
14		1.10011		Start to add (D)
15		10.00111		^1C_s; complete add
16		0.01111	/11010	$A \leftarrow Q \leftarrow 0$
17		1.10011		Start to add (D)
18		10.00010		^1C_s; complete add
			/110100	$A \leftarrow Q \leftarrow 0$
			1	add e
		0.00010	1.10101	
		Remainder	Quotient	

FIGURE 12.2.1 $(145 \times 2^{-10})/(-13 \times 2^{-5}) = (-11 \times 2^{-5}) + (2 \times 2^{-10})$
using non-performing division

the quotient bit is 0. Also if the result is positive, the next cycle will be the same as this one.

Now suppose we have a negative remainder. We complete the cycle as though nothing had happened. The next cycle, however, requires that we add instead of subtract the divisor from the remainder. Again this is followed by a test of the new remainder. If it is positive, we enter a 1 as the quotient bit; if negative, a 0. Other cycles continue in this fashion.

The rule for *non-restoring division of positive numbers* is very simple: whether doing addition or subtraction, if the result is positive, the quotient bit is 1, if negative, the quotient bit is 0.

The example of Figure 12.2.1 is reworked by the non-restoring method and is illustrated in Figure 12.2.2.

Let us investigate the rationale for this procedure. Suppose we start

D	A		Q
1.10011	0.00100	10001/	
	1.10011		
	———		
	1.10111		
	1.01111	0001/1	
	01101		
	———		
	1.11100		
	1.11000	001/11	
	01101		
	———		
	0.00101		
	0.01010	01/110	
	1.10011		
	———		
	1.11101		
	1.11010	1/1101	
	01101		
	———		
	0.00111		
	0.01111	/11010	
	1.10011		
	———		

complete remainder → 0.00010

                                        1.10100 ← complete quotient
                                             1
                                         ———

corrected remainder → 0.00010   1.10101 ← corrected quotient

FIGURE 12.2.2 $(145 \times 2^{-10})/(-13 \times 2^{-5}) + (-11 \times 2^{-5}) + (2 \times 2^{-10})$
using non-restoring division

with a positive remainder, perform a subtraction, and get a negative remainder, then perform an addition and get a positive remainder. If we call the divisor D, then the total change in the remainder is $-D + (D/2)$. This is the same as $-D/2$. In other words, we would have gotten this result if we had not performed arithmetic on the first cycle, merely shifting instead, and then subtracted the divisor, yielding a positive remainder. The quotient bits which we would have entered in that case would have been 01. This makes sense.

Next, suppose that we have a positive remainder, we subtract the divisor and get a negative remainder; we add the divisor and get the negative remainder again. Finally, we add the divisor and get a positive remainder. The total change in the remainder is $-D + (D/2) + (D/4) = -D/4$. This is the same as though we had performed no arithmetic for two cycles and then performed a subtraction which was successful. That would have been recorded as 001. Again, our method holds up.

Suppose, in general, that we subtract the divisor from a positive remainder and get a negative result. Further, suppose that we perform a series of additions of the divisor and shifts, each time yielding a negative remainder. Finally, suppose that we perform one more addition and the result goes positive. The total change in the remainder is given by $-D + (D/2) + \cdots + (D/2)^k = (-D/2)^k$. This would be recorded as a series of 0's followed by a final 1. Again, the general case checks out against our method.

Division is complete when we have developed a sufficient number of quotient bits. For positive numbers the quotient is correct; however, the remainder may be either positive or negative. It should only be positive. Therefore, when a negative remainder occurs, it is necessary to restore it by adding the divisor to it.

Non-Restoring Division, Signed Numbers

Dealing with signed numbers presents no problem; we proceed exactly as before. We only have to slightly change the statement of our rule. We sign the divisor so as to be opposite to the remainder and then add it to the remainder.

The rules for developing the quotient bit depend upon the sign of the quotient. In developing a positive quotient, a 1 is entered when the remainder is of the same sign as the dividend; a 0 is entered when the remainder is a different sign from the dividend. When developing a negative quotient, the rule is reversed: a 0 is entered if the remainder is the same sign as the dividend, a 1 is entered if the remainder is a different sign from the dividend.

We terminate division after having developed sufficient quotient bits. A positive quotient is always correct; a negative quotient requires correction when using 2's complement notation, in which case we add a 1 to the least significant bit of the quotient. The remainder is correct if it has the same sign as the dividend. Otherwise, we must complement the remainder so that the sign of the remainder will change and become that of the original dividend.

Comparison

Obviously, restoring division takes longer than the other two methods since half the time an extra cycle is required for restoration. Little extra register hardware and some little control hardware is required to eliminate this restoring cycle. Non-performing division is the fastest of the three when an *asynchronous adder is used*, since then the sign of the remainder is available usually quite a bit earlier than the entire remainder.

Non-performance accrues another advantage—the sign and format of the partial remainder is always correct. Thus, after the last cycle, no correction of the remainder is required.

A more specific comparison of all the methods is made in Section 14.7 and is summarized in Table 14.7 (see page 334).

12.3 SHIFTING OVER 0's

We can gain speed in division in a manner very similar to that used in multiplication. Recall the method whereby we shifted over 0's and 1's in the multiplier up to the maximum shift length of the computer. There is a similar method for division, but explanations are usually more successful when they start with the simplest and proceed to the most difficult. For that reason, we shall first discuss the method of shifting over 0's only. In addition, we shall restrict our explanation to positive divisors and dividends.

It is less important to extend this method, per se, to negative numbers. Therefore, in Chapter 13 we will take up the process of division by shifting over 0's and 1's. In that section, we will extend the method to negative numbers.

Positioning the Numbers

Legal division in most machines requires only that the divisor is larger than the dividend. As in earlier discussions, we store the divisor in the D register and the dividend in the A register. At the start of division, positive numbers will be oriented in the registers something like this.

$$A: \quad 0.00 \cdots 01XX$$

$$D: \quad 0.00 \cdots 01XX$$

where X represents either 0 or 1, we cannot say anything about the number of 0's following the binary point in either register; we only know that since it is the smaller, there are the same number or more 0's after the binary point in the A quantity than in the D quantity.

The first step of this process is to align the numbers so that the sign bit in the D register and the bit to the right of the binary point are different. Since we have restricted the discussion to positive numbers, this requires that we shift the D register until a 1 appears in the most significant bit position. This means that the number in the D register is now less than 1 but greater than or equal to $\frac{1}{2}$, or

$$1 > (D) \geq \tfrac{1}{2}$$

In discussing floating-point numbers, we say that a number is normalized when it is shifted within a register so that it meets the condition quoted above. Since what we are doing here is similar, we say that we have normalized (D).

As we normalize (D) we shift the contents of the A register the same number of positions to the left. At the end of this positioning process, the two registers will look something like

$$\overbrace{Z_1}$$
$$A: \quad 0.0 \cdots 01XX$$

$$D: \quad 0.1XXX$$

where Z_1 is the number of 0's between the first 1 in the A register and the binary point. Z_1 is a positive integer which ranges from 0 to the numerical capacity of the register, N. The numbers are now properly positioned in the register so that we may start to shift over 0's.

Shifting Over 0's

Next, we shift the A register to the left until the 1 is oriented immediately to the right of the binary point. We may say that we are normalizing A. From our discussion above the number of shifts required to normalize A is exactly Z_1. This can be indicated symbolically as

$$A \xleftarrow{z_1} 0$$

For each shift of the A register, we enter a 0 into the Q register, the register which will store the quotient. We indicate this by

$$Q \xleftarrow{z_1} 0$$

Let us now see the rationale for entering 0 bits into the quotient. As long as there is a 0 to the right of the binary point in the A register, we know that that register contains a quantity less than $\frac{1}{2}$. Also, since D has already been normalized, it contains a quantity greater than or equal to $\frac{1}{2}$. The division process seeks to reduce the dividend by an amount equivalent to that of the divisor, if this can be done. Otherwise the two quantities are shifted with respect to one another and a 0 is the quotient bit which has just been developed. If we try to subtract the quantity in the D register from that in the A register before the A register is normalized, we will certainly produce a number which is less than 0. Therefore, we are certain that as long as the D register is normalized and the A register is not normalized, subtraction will not be successful, a 0 should be entered into the quotient register, and the A register should be shifted.

After both A and D have been normalized, these registers look something like this:

$$A: \quad 0.1XX \cdots$$

$$D: \quad 0.1XX \cdots$$

We can no longer form a quotient bit without performing a test requiring arithmetic.

Comparing A and D by Subtraction

The way the numbers are now sitting in the A and D register, it is impossible to tell which is larger without the capability of comparing the numbers bit by bit from one end of the register to the other. For certainly, the numbers may be identical right up to the very last, the right-most bit.

The method which we are going to use here is one which keeps the dividend or partial remainder in a positive form. This dictates a restoring or non-performing method. That is, either we subtract and, if unsuccessful, add, or else we test to see if subtraction will be successful and perform it only in that case.

If subtraction is unsuccessful *this* time, it has to be successful *next* time. To see this, note that both numbers are greater than $\frac{1}{2}$. After attempting an unsuccessful subtraction, we perform a shift of the A register equivalent to multiplying (A) by 2. At that time the number contained in A will be larger than 1 and smaller than 2. Since (D) is less than 1, subtracting the contents of the D register from that of the A register will produce a positive number.

Whenever the subtraction is completed, it is followed by a shift left of A corresponding to a multiplication of (A) *by 2.*

For an initially successful subtraction, we enter a 1 into the A register.

$$Q \longleftarrow 1$$

When subtraction is initially unsuccessful, it will be successful after a shift of A so that we enter a 0 followed by a 1 into the Q register

$$Q \longleftarrow 01$$

After subtraction and shift left of A is over with, the condition of the registers is

$$\overset{Z_2}{\overbrace{}}$$

A: $0.00 \cdots 001$

D: $0.1X \cdots X$

Again the A register contains a number of 0's, this time designated as Z_2, between the binary point and the first 1 in the register. Now we are able to shift over these 0's, as previously, and enter corresponding 0's in the Q register. After shifting over 0's, the Q register contents is indicated by one of these expressions,

$$\overset{Z_1}{\overbrace{}} \quad \overset{Z_2}{\overbrace{}}$$

Q: $0 \cdots 01\ 0 \cdots 0$

$$\overset{Z_1}{\overbrace{}} \quad \overset{Z_2}{\overbrace{}}$$

Q: $0 \cdots 001\ 0 \cdots 0$

The first appears after an initially successful subtraction; the second for an initially unsuccessful subtraction. Here both of the Z's are positive integers or 0.

About Shifts

It is possible that in examining A we may encounter *no* strings of 0's; the most obvious case where this can occur is where we are developing a quotient consisting entirely of 1's. Also, with the proper combination of events, this can occur in developing a quotient consisting of runs of 1's with single 0's interspersed, such as,

Q: $1011010110 \cdots$

In this case, shifting over 0 provides no speedup over the method used for performing a subtraction.

The shift ability for this method is limited by the hardware provided. In describing multiplication, we said that the hardware provided a shift capable of length K. If we make this assumption here, we require that strings of 0's of length greater than K must be made in two or more steps. We perform a shift of length K on the A register and note that 0's still exist to the right of the binary point. The length of the next shift is then decoded and mechanized.

Termination

Finishing up the division process is almost always a problem. In the case of shifting over 0's, it is simpler than usual. The first case we encounter is when we decode a request for a shift of 0's which is larger than the room left in the quotient we are developing. In that case, we perform the number of shifts left in the shift counter and insert the same number of 0's in the quotient, thus filling the quotient sum. As you can see, this provides both a correct quotient and remainder.

If the numbers in the A and D registers are both normalized, then subtraction must be attempted. Its success is used to set the last quotient bit. Either subtraction is successful and the remainder is correct or it is unsuccessful and the remainder is restored and is therefore again correct.

12.4   QUOTIENT LOOKAHEAD PRINCIPLES

Introduction

The method described in this section is one which presumes the use of shifting over 0's. It then seeks to develop two or more quotient bits at one time. This method carries the shifting-over-0's method one step further in a system which does not provide the facility for shifting over 1's. This latter method is discussed in Chapter 13. The principles which are developed in this section are those which will be used in Chapter 14 to make a further speedup of the already rapid method of shifting over 0's and 1's. Therefore, although useful in itself as a fast method for division where limited hardware is available, it is also useful in presenting the principles required to develop a near-optimum, high-speed division method.

The work presented in this section is believed to be, at least to some degree, original. The author does not know of any machines which use the exact method described here. A method which may start out in a similar vein has been described by the Russian author, Burtsev.*

The Decision Point

Let us restrict our present discussion to positive dividends and divisors. In the previous section, we noted that shifting over 0's is performed until a 1 appears just to the right of the binary point. At that time, both the divisor and remainder are normalized. They appear as below,

$$A: \quad 0.1X \cdots X$$

$$D: \quad 0.1X \cdots X$$

where, as before, the remainder is in the A register and the divisor is contained in the D register. We are now at a decision point.

When the condition above arises, we cannot proceed without performing arithmetic. It may be conjectured that the two numbers could be compared to determine which is larger. The difficulty is that, when the numbers are equal or almost equal, every bit of both must be examined. This comparison would require as much hardware and would take as long as if a trial subtraction took place.

The above is certainly true if we want to do a complete and thorough job of the comparison, but there is no reason why we cannot abide a half-way measure. Maybe we can examine sufficient bits of both numbers so as to reach a decision in a majority of the cases. Certainly this will expedite division to some extent.

Now we will examine the improvement which may be gained by comparing a limited number of corresponding bits of the partial remainder and divisor. First, we will compare only the $(N - 1)$th bits, A_{N-1} and D_{N-1}; there are four such combinations. These are comparisons of the second bit to the right of the binary point. Next, we will examine what happens when we compare the second and third bit of each number. This presents sixteen combinations. Finally, we will examine what happens when the second through fifth bits of each number are compared. This presents a total of 256 combinations.

The methods above present multiple decision alternatives. To make use of these alternatives requires that we have a similar number of action alternatives. There is no sense in making a decision if there is no capability for taking action on the decision. We will consider two action capabilities

---

* V. S. Burtsev, "Accelerating multiple and division operations in high speed digital computers," *The Institute of Exact Mechanics and Computing Technique* (Moscow: Academy of Sciences of the U.S.S.R., 1958).

and modifications thereof. The first capability is referred to as a two-bit capability. It allows us to perform the following arithmetic on the remainder and requires that we enter the correspondingly indicated bits of the quotient,

$$Q \longleftarrow 01; \qquad 4[(A) - \tfrac{1}{2}(D)] \longrightarrow A$$

$$Q \longleftarrow 10; \qquad 4[(A) - (D)] \longrightarrow A$$

$$Q \longleftarrow 11; \qquad 4[(A) - \tfrac{3}{2}(D)] \longrightarrow A$$

As you can see, this permits us to develop two bits of the quotient in one operation. We omitted the following capability from the list above

$$Q \longleftarrow 00; \qquad\qquad 4(A) \longrightarrow A$$

because it is implicit in the capability of shifting over 0's. Besides that, supposedly it will never be required at a decision point since we could never develop two 0 quotient bits at such a time (this was discussed in detail in the last section).

A three-bit capability is similarly described in the following form.

$$Q \longleftarrow q_3 q_2 q_1; \qquad 8\left[(A) - \frac{k}{4}(D)\right] \longrightarrow A$$

$$k = q_3 q_2 q_1 \qquad 7 \geq k \geq 1$$

Here we develop three bits of the quotient at one time. This requires the capability of subtracting from the remainder multiples of one-quarter of the divisor ranging from 1 to 7. The bits of the quotient that are developed correspond to the binary representation of the number k.

It is possible to conjecture about the efficiency of a capability of more than three bits. However, the efficiency of the unmodified three-bit capability is comparatively low so that it is unwarranted to go beyond this point.

Measure of Doubt

The systems that we are talking about which compare bits of the remainder and divisor will always have some doubt connected with them. The only way that we can be absolutely sure that we are doing the right arithmetic is when we take into account, at one time, all the bits of both the remainder and the divisor. Thus, when we know that the first and second bits of both the divisor and the remainder are the same, we still can only guess which of these two is the larger. We can settle this doubt only by making a complete comparison or by performing a trial arithmetic. The methodology we shall use is (1) to do trial arithmetic or (2) to do arithmetic and when it is unsuccessful we restore the remainder. Thus, we may say that this method requires restoring or non-performing arithmetic.

When we are dealing with several multiples of a fraction of the divisor, our non-performing arithmetic requires one or more stages. Simple non-performing subtraction examined the result of the subtraction, and if it was unsuccessful, subtraction was abandoned and a shift performed. In the present instance, we perform a subtraction of one multiple of half the divisor; if it is unsuccessful, we try a subtraction of the next smaller multiple of half the divisor. Supposedly, our system will be good enough so that if the first multiple fails, the second will always be successful. We continue now by examining several possible systems.

12.5 LOOKAHEAD, POSITIVE REMAINDERS

Two-Bit Lookahead, One-Bit Comparison

This system requires the capability of subtracting one, two, or three halves of the divisor from the remainder. A decision table is presented as Table 12.5.1; it presents the four combinations for the second bit of the

TABLE 12.5.1 Success of Processing in Leaving Positive Remainder for Permissible Combinations of Positive Dividend and Divisor, Two-Bit Lookahead, One-Bit Compare Division Method

	Partial remainder (A)		
(D) Divisor	$0.11X$	$0.10X$	Process
$0.11X$	Yes ? No	Yes No No	$(A) - \frac{1}{2}(D) \rightarrow A$ $(A) - (D) \rightarrow A$ $(A) - \frac{3}{2}(D) \rightarrow A$
$0.10X$	Yes Yes ?	Yes ? No	$(A) - \frac{1}{2}(D) \rightarrow A$ $(A) - (D) \rightarrow A$ $(A) - \frac{3}{2}(D) \rightarrow A$

divisor and the dividend. Each box contains the results of performing the processes indicated at the right. Thus, when the remainder and the divisor both take the form $0.11X$, we know that we can successfully subtract half the divisor from the remainder; we know that we cannot subtract three-halves the divisor from the remainder; we are not sure whether we can subtract the full divisor from the remainder. The other boxes are similarly arranged.

Notice that we can make a definite decision only in one case; the other cases require a trial subtraction. Can we therefore expect any improvement in using this method? One-fourth of the time we definitely develop two bits of the quotient at one shot. Three-fourths of the time we may or may not. The randomness of the numbers dealt with suggests that, on the average, in these cases, we expect that half the time we will be successful in developing two quotient bits by obtaining a difference of the right sign. Therefore, if we multiply three-fourths by one-half, we see that in these doubtful cases three-eighths of the time we develop two bits at one shot. Adding one-quarter and three-eighths together, we find that the method will yield two bits at one shot five-eighths of the time. The rest of the time (three-eighths) it requires two shots to develop two bits of the quotient. Therefore, we may say that five-eighths of the time an improvement occurs.

TABLE 12.5.2 Multiples of Half the Divisor, D/2, which can be Subtracted from
(A) Leaving a Positive Remainder for Permissible Combinations of Positive
Dividend and Divisor, Two-Bit Lookahead, Two-Bit Compare Division
Method. Parenthetical Multiples of Divisor Halves May or May Not
Be Successful

(D) Divisor	Partial remainder (A)			
	$0.111X$	$0.110X$	$0.101X$	$0.100X$
$0.111X$	1 (2)	1	1	1
$0.110X$	2	1 (2)	1	1
$0.101X$	2 (3)	2	1 (2)	1
$0.100X$	3	2 (3)	2	1 (2)

TABLE 12.5.3   Four × Four Decode for Division by the Method of Four-Bit Compare, Two-Bit Lookahead. Entries Are the Number of Divisor Halves which Will Be Successful; When Parenthesized this Number May Be Successful

	0.10000X	0.10001X	0.10010X	0.10011X	0.10100X	0.10101X	0.10110X	0.10111X	0.11000X	0.11001X	0.11010X	0.11011X	0.11100X	0.11101X	0.11110X	0.11111X
0.11111X	1	1	1	1	1	1	1	1	1	1	1	1	1	1	1	1 (2)
0.11110X	1	1	1	1	1	1	1	1	1	1	1	1	1	1	1 (2)	2
0.11101X	1	1	1	1	1	1	1	1	1	1	1	1	1	1 (2)	2	2
0.11100X	1	1	1	1	1	1	1	1	1	1	1	1	1 (2)	2	2	2
0.11011X	1	1	1	1	1	1	1	1	1	1	1	1 (2)	2	2	2	2
0.11010X	1	1	1	1	1	1	1	1	1	1	1 (2)	2	2	2	2	2
0.11001X	1	1	1	1	1	1	1	1	1	1 (2)	2	2	2	2	2	2
0.11000X	1	1	1	1	1	1	1	1	1 (2)	2	2	2	2	2	2	2
0.10111X	1	1	1	1	1	1	1	1 (2)	2	2	2	2	2	2	2	2
0.10110X	1	1	1	1	1	1	1 (2)	2	2	2	2	2	2	2	2	2
0.10101X	1	1	1	1	1	1 (2)	2	2	2	2	2	2	2	2	2	2 (3)
0.10100X	1	1	1	1	1 (2)	2	2	2	2	2	2 (3)	2	2	2	2 (3)	3

0.10011X	1	1	1	1 (2)	2	2	2	2	2	2	2	2	2 (3)	2 (3)	3	3
0.10010X	1	1	1 (3)	2	2	2	2	2	2	2	2 (3)	2 (3)	3	3	3	3
0.10001X	1	1 (2)	2	2	2	2	2	2	2	2 (3)	2 (3)	2	3	3	3	3
0.10000X	1 (2)	2	2	2	2	2	2	2	2 (3)	3	3	3	3	3	3	3

Two-Bit Lookahead, Two-Bit Comparison

This system requires the same two bit action capability as a one-bit comparison but compares two remainder bits with the corresponding two divisor bits. Table 12.5.2 is the decision table for this process. Each box contains the number of multiples of half the divisor which can definitely be subtracted from the remainder. The parentheses in the box contain the number of divisor halves which *may or may not* be subtracted successfully from the remainder. From this table, we see that ten out of the sixteen entries are definite—we know positively the results in these ten cases. This leaves six doubtful cases—six for which trial subtraction must be made. Assuming that the success probability for these six cases is one-half, a simple calculation shows that thirteen-sixteenths of the time we can develop two quotient bits at one shot. This seems to be a substantial improvement for the additional hardware required.

Two-Bit Lookahead, Four-Bit Compare

This method requires that the five most significant bits of the divisor and remainder be available for comparison. The right-most four of each of these are actually compared. For each of these sets of four bits there are sixteen possibilities. These have been arranged in table form and appear as Table 12.5.3. Each entry in the table contains one or two numbers. The entry in parentheses indicates the multiple of the divisor halves which *may* be subtracted from the remainder. A number which is not in parentheses indicates a multiple of the divisor which undoubtedly can be subtracted from the remainder. Examining the chart, notice that there are only 24 entries that contain parenthetical items. The proportion of the entries which are doubtful is then $\frac{3}{32}$. Since only half of these items will require repeat arithmetic, we can say that we can generate two bits at one try $\frac{61}{64}$ths of the time.

The decoding required to attain this figure is of no small magnitude. It requires the mixing of many eight-input gates. The reader may try to obtain a simple expression for Table 12.5.3, but it is doubtful that he would be successful. The amount of hardware for such a decoding table must be seriously weighed against the additional hardware required for the method of shifting over 0's and 1's described in Chapter 13.

The heavy outlines in Table 12.5.3 indicate the results that would be obtained from a two-bit comparison. As can be seen, the results of two-bit decoding which are much simpler hardware-wise, provide a fair gain for a low cost.

Three-Bit Lookahead

To perform a three-bit lookahead requires that several multiples of the divisor be available. We need three, five, and seven times the divisor immediately available in register form. The other multiples less than seven can be formed by shifting the divisor or the triple of the divisor.

Do we need all these multiples? Suppose we were requested to subtract five times the divisor from the present remainder. Certainly six times the divisor would cause a sign reversal. If we subtract only four times the divisor, we find that the remainder in subsequent cycles will always be too big—we can never reduce it enough. As a consequence, we must have all multiples of the divisor available. If we go to a non-restoring method, we find that we are approaching the method of shifting over 0's and 1's which turns out to be more economical in hardware because extra registers are not required.

12.6 HARDWARE FOR THE LOOKAHEAD WITH POSITIVE REMAINDER

Configuration

Using the lookahead with a positive remainder seems to offer some economical advantage. It can be used with hardware providing a shift network of only two places; it requires only one auxiliary register to hold the divisor half triple. An example of the hardware for this process is found in Figure 12.6.

The register configuration in Figure 12.6 is fairly familiar except for the presence of the T register. This is to hold the triple of half the divisor. Notice several inputs to the adder. These will be explained in conjunction with their use later in this subsection. Notice also that shift ability is provided for the D register. This is required when the divisor is normalized.

Forming Half the Divisor Triple

The first cycle of division by this method is used only to prepare half the divisor triple. Since it will always be used that way it is prepared in complement form. Notice that the divisor complement, shifted one posi-

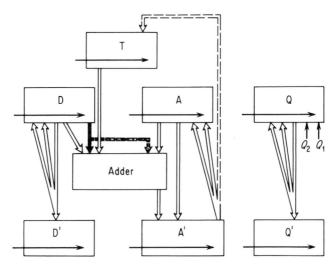

FIGURE 12.6   Register configuration for division by two-bit lookahead, two-bit decode method.

tion to the right, is available at the left-hand adder input. Also notice the dashed solid line leading from the D register to the right-hand input of the adder. This presents the divisor complement to the adder. On the first cycle, these two quantities are entered into the adder and the result is passed into A'. The second half of that cycle enters the contents of A' into the T register without shifting it. The T register now contains $\frac{3}{2}$ the divisor.

Shift Capability

In order to make this process economically complete, we have only provided shift capability of two places. If further shift capability were provided, the method of shifting over 0's and 1's would prove superior. It would be nice if a shift of one place were not required—if only shifts of two places could be used throughout the processing. Such an arrangement is feasible and is explored in detail in the next sections. Since single shifts are required in other arithmetic processes, let us content ourselves with providing both a single- and double-shift capability.

Normalizing the Divisor

Before forming half the divisor triple, the first step, naturally, is to normalize the divisor. This requires shifting the divisor to the left until the sign bit and the most significant bit disagree. This is done by shifting the divisor left two bits at a time, although the last shift may be single or double depending on whether the number of normalized shifts required is odd or even. Of course, as the divisor is shifted, the dividend is shifted correspondingly.

Shifting Over 0's

Shifting over 0's is performed by passing the remainder from the A register to the A' register directly and then returning it to the A register, shifted left by one or two places according to the number of remaining right-hand numerical 0's in the partial remainder. The quotient in the Q register is similarly shifted and one or two 0's are entered at the right-hand end of the Q register as the quantity in Q' is returned to the Q register.

Decision Point

To determine the number of multiples of the divisor which are to be used, we set up a decode matrix. Table 12.6 is to be used to make this determination when dealing with positive numbers. This table is similar to Table 12.5.2, except that this table always contains the higher multiple of the divisor. In the upper right-hand corner of each entry is included a boxed number so that easy reference may be made to each entry.

We now derive logic equations for the functions which may be done. The choice of three times half the divisor is indicated by T, since this is the register which contains that multiple; Dcr indicates a right shift of the divisor which yields half the complemented divisor; for one times the divisor we simply complement the contents of D, calling this Dc.

To find the logical function for each of these multiples, we simply logically add the function corresponding to the similarly numbered entries in Table 12.6. For instance, to find the function for three times the divisor, we add boxes 9, 13, and 14. Notice, however, that it is more convenient to add and subtract box 10. Then we have boxes 9, 10, 13, and 14 which form a function of two variables. We subtract box 10 by negating a function of four variables.

Let us indicate the D bits proceeding to the right from the binary point as D_N, D_{N-1}, D_{N-2}, and so forth; the A bits are similarly labeled. Then from the discussion above, we find that the expression for T is

$$T = (\bar{D}_{N-1}A_{N-1})(\bar{D}_{N-1}D_{N-2}A_{N-1}\bar{A}_{N-2}) \qquad (12.6.1)$$

TABLE 12.6 Number of Multiples of Half the Divisor Used for Combinations of Divisor
and Dividend Bits, Positive Numbers, Two Bit Decode, Two-Bit Lookahead

		A			
		$0.111X$	$0.110X$	$0.101X$	$0.100X$
	$0.111X$	1 2	2 1	3 1	4 1
D	$0.110X$	5 2	6 2	7 1	8 1
	$0.101X$	9 3	10 2	11 2	12 1
	$0.100X$	13 3	14 3	15 2	16 2

The reader may derive the equations for the other multiples of the
divisor.

$$\text{Dcr} = D_{N-1}\bar{A}_{N-1} + \overline{D_{N-1}D_{N-2}A_{N-1}\bar{A}_{N-2}} + \bar{D}_{N-1}D_{N-2}\bar{A}_{N-1}\bar{A}_{N-2} \quad (12.6.2)$$

$$\text{Dc} = (D_{N-1}A_{N-1})(D_{N-1}D_{N-2}A_{N-1}\bar{A}_{N-2})$$
$$+ (\bar{D}_{N-1}\bar{A}_{N-1})(\bar{D}_{N-1}D_{N-2}\bar{A}_{N-1}\bar{A}_{N-2})$$
$$+ \bar{D}_{N-1}D_{N-2}A_{N-1}\bar{A}_{N-2} \quad (12.6.3)$$

Now, in performing the addition of the divisor half-multiple to the
remainder, we anticipate that occasionally our guess may be incorrect and
our remainder will become negative instead of positive. For instance, when
we subtract three times half the divisor from the remainder, we determine
that a negative number results by observing the carryout of the sign bit
of the adder. Such a carry should be produced if subtraction yields a positive number. If, instead, a 0 carry from the sign bit is sensed, we must try
our subtraction with a multiple one smaller than our last try. Therefore,

sensing a 0 carry while using half the divisor triple requires that we replace the triple divisor half entry into the adder by the divisor entry and redo the subtraction. Similarly, sensing a 0 carry when adding the divisor requires that we replace the divisor entry into the adder by half the divisor. Notice that it is supposedly impossible for half the single divisor to produce an unsuccessful subtraction.

Shifts and Entries

A double shift of both the A and Q registers is performed after arithmetic is fully completed. During this process, two bits are entered into the Q register. These are

$$T\ ^1C_s: \quad Q \longleftarrow 11 \tag{12.6.4}$$

$$Dc\ ^1C_s: \quad Q \longleftarrow 10 \tag{12.6.5}$$

$$Dcr\ ^1C_s: \quad Q \longleftarrow 01 \tag{12.6.6}$$

Consequently, we will enter 11 into the Q register if half the divisor triple is successfully subtracted, etc.

New Cycle

The next cycle to be performed is determined by decoding the bits to the right of the decimal point in the A register. If 0's are sensed, then we shift over two 0's; if one 0, we call for a *single* shift over 0; if a 1 is found in the most significant position, arithmetic is to be performed. This is referred, as previously, to the logic matrix to determine the proper multiple of half the divisor for subtraction.

Counter

A counter is used to perform two functions: it keeps track of the quotient bits generated; it protects against a 0 divisor. During the first phase of division the divisor is normalized. In this phase, the divisor and dividend are shifted to the left in synchronism. The counter is used to determine how many shifts are performed. If we find that the number of shifts is greater than N, we are dealing with a 0 (or almost 0) divisor and we are entitled to quit. Otherwise, when the divisor is normalized, we reset the counter and adapt it to its other use.

We begin to count quotient bits as we normalize the dividend. For each normalized shift of the dividend, we also enter a 0 into the quotient register.

During subtraction of the divisor from the remainder, we accumulate two bits of the quotient at a time and therefore add two to the counter. As each cycle is begun, the counter is checked to determine if we have accumulated enough quotient bits. We must take familiar precautions to be sure that only one quotient bit is generated when there is only room for one in the quotient bit counter. Thus, termination of division is similar to other methods discussed.

The Q Register

The Q register is set up to provide room to store the quotient bits and to provide a second word for double-length division.

12.7 LOOKAHEAD USING MULTIPLE ADDERS

Principle

We can cut down the time required for subtraction if we prepare the results of subtraction of two multiples of the divisor at one time. In other words, if we have several adders and prepare several results at once, we can compare these results, choose the best one, and enter it as the partial remainder for the next cycle. Reference to Table 12.5.2 shows that for any given entry only two possibilities need be explored. This means that only two adders are required to give us definite results in one try. We examine the result of subtracting three or two times half the divisor or the result of subtracting two or one times half the divisor.

Two-Bit Lookahead, Two-Bit Decode, Two Adders

The hardware required for two-bit, lookahead, two-bit decode, using two adders, is shown in Figure 12.7. The preliminary cycle prepares the divisor half triple using Adder 1 and entering the result into the T register. This is done *only* when the divisor is less than or equal to 0.101. Adder 2 is used for subtracting the divisor from the remainder. This is always one of the choices. The other adder uses either one or three times half the divisor.

The decode network merely decides whether Adder 1 is supplied with half the divisor triple or the divisor half. In the case of divisors as large as 0.110, Adder 1 always gets the divisor half. The higher multiple yielding a

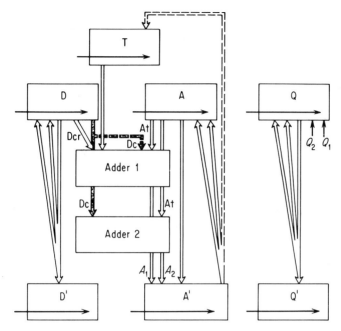

FIGURE 12.7 Register configuration for division by two-bit lookahead two-bit decode method where two adders are used.

positive remainder is then entered into the A' register. This is passed back to the A register, shifted two places to the left in preparation for the next decode examination. The logic functions in a manner similar to that of Figure 12.6, except as it involves the two adders.

12.8 TWO-BIT LOOKAHEAD NON-RESTORING DIVISION, PRINCIPLE

Introduction

The lookahead systems of the previous sections cannot correctly anticipate each maximum divisor multiple by which the remainder may be reduced and still remain positive. Their main disadvantage then is that occasionally two cycles may be required to develop two quotient bits.

The non-restoring method overcomes this difficulty. It depends on our ability to make a good guess, but it allows us to be wrong sometimes. The decoder's obligation is to provide either the correct divisor multiple or the one just larger. Then, if it turns out to be the wrong multiple, it causes the remainder to change sign. In so doing, the proper remainder value is obtained, although its sign is wrong.

The lookahead method requires normalization of both the divisor and remainder, as do most accelerated methods. This is expedited by multiple shift ability. However, such ability is expensive in hardware. Where a cost comprise is mandatory, *this* method offers emphatic advantages. Uniform quotient development at the rate of two bits per cycle is guaranteed. This double shift ability is used during normalization so that it transpires at a reasonable, though not maximum, rate.

Two-bit lookahead, non-restoring division is applicable to large general-purpose scientific computers in the million-dollar class. It does not apply to those where money is not a prime object, such as the Larc-Stretch class.

The Decoder

To see how easy it is to make an unequivocal judgment of which multiple of the divisor half will yield the desired result for both positive divisor and dividend, we refer to Table 12.5.1. We can always choose the entries with the question mark or the correct entry in the case of the upper right-hand entry square and be sure to get the desired result. Thus, for instance, when the divisor is $0.10X$ and the remainder $0.11X$, we subtract the divisor half triple. Sometimes a positive remainder occurs and we are, without doubt, okay. If the remainder becomes negative, at least its magnitude is correct. This negative remainder is handled by proper quotient development machinery.

If the remainder bits encountered are 0.00, it is clear that nothing is to be subtracted. But what about the remainder 0.01? Previously we would use one cycle of normalization which would perform a single left shift and

TABLE 12.8.1 Multiples of Half the Divisor Used to Reduce the Remainder for Division by the Two-Bit Lookahead, Non-Restoring Method

Divisor magnitude	Remainder magnitude			
	$0.11X$	$0.10X$	$0.01X$	$0.00X$
$0.11X$	2	1	1	0
$0.10X$	3	2	1	0

enter 0 into the quotient; then we would make a comparison for lookahead arithmetic. Since we are using a non-restoring method, we have another alternative. The divisor half may or may not work here. It is worth a try, for even if it does not, the correct value of the remainder is maintained, though the remainder becomes negative.

Table 12.8.1 presents the decisions to be made by our decoder. Since the devisor is always normalized, only two entries appear for it. The right-hand column requests shifting over two 0's when normalizing for at least two bits is to be done. Notice that for large divisors, half the divisor triple is never used! This is a saving, for the extra cycle required to prepare this half triple may then be eliminated.

To build a full decoder to handle signed numbers only requires a 2×3 matrix. The divisor need only be examined for *sign* and second numerical bit. The remainder must be scanned for *sign* and the first two bits.

Quotient Bit Development

Now that the method has been presented, we must determine how to establish the quotient bits according to the possible eventualities. Two bits to be inserted, and there will always be two of them, will be determined by

1. The divisor half multiple used.
2. The old remainder sign.
3. The new remainder sign.

We now develop the rules for quotient bit pair determination, the results of which are presented in Table 12.8.2.

0 multiple—no addition

When the two numerical bits of the positive remainder are 00, we do not add; we simply shift two places. This is the same as shifting over 0's and hence 00 is recorded. A negative remainder, 1.11, calls for a shift over 1's and so 11 is the bit pair developed. The reasoning for this is demonstrated in Chapter 13. Since no arithmetic takes place, the sign of the remainder *cannot change*; hence, two entries are impossible and we find dashes in Table 12.8.2.

half divisor

Simple non-restoring division is stated in our terms as subtracting the divisor. The decoder tells us that, for this case, the full divisor subtraction

TABLE 12.8.2 Quotient Hits Developed for Reduction of the Remainder by Multiples of Half the Divisor in Terms of Old and New Remainder Signs for Two-Bit Lookahead, Non-Restoring Division

Old remainder sign		$+$		$-$	
New remainder sign		$+$	$-$	$+$	$-$
Multiple	0	00	—	—	11
	1	01	00	11	10
	2	10	01	10	01
	3	11	10	01	00

NOTE. For signed numbers the labels at top left should read, respectively, "Sign of old remainder with respect to dividend," "Sign of new remainder with respect to dividend." Then "$+$" and "$-$" are replaced by "same" and "different" respectively. When developing a negative quotient the 1's complement of the bit pair is entered into the quotient.

will be unsuccessful. If the divisor half, when subtracted, leaves the positive remainder positive, it is equivalent to two cycles of the simple method; the remainder goes negative on the first of these cycles; it goes positive on the second cycle. Hence, 01 is developed.

If the positive remainder goes negative with half the divisor, then it is obvious that neither the full nor half divisor is successful and 00 are the proper quotient bits.

Similarly, if we cannot add the divisor half to the negative remainder without it going positive, 11 is to be entered. Suppose that on the previous cycle, the equivalent, after shifting, of $2D$ was subtracted. Now $-2D + D/2 = -D - D/2$, which is recorded, when a positive remainder results, as (0)11. This says if we had not subtracted $2D$ then both D and $D/2$ could now be subtracted successfully.

When a negative remainder stays negative for the single multiple addition, we enter 10. We know that it would go positive if we *add* the *full* divisor, for if there were any doubt, the decoder would then choose the full divisor. Now $-2D + D/2$ is negative, but $-2D + D$ would be positive. Hence, $-D - D/2$ is unsuccessful whereas $-D - 0$ is successful and 10 is the proper entry.

full divisor

A positive remainder which stays positive on reduction by the full divisor is recorded as 10. We rely upon the decoder to tell if there is any possibility of using three-halves the divisor; since it says there is none, 10 must be right. Should the remainder go negative, we have assurance from the decoder that the single half of the divisor would have been successful and can record 01.

A negative remainder may go positive when the full divisor is added. We rely on the decoder to assure us that it would not also go positive for half the divisor. The result is plus for $-2D + D + 0$ or $0 - D - 0$ but not for $-2D + 0 + D/2$ or $-D - D/2$. Hence, (0)10 is correct and not (0)11.

When the new remainder is also negative, we rely on the decoder to assure us that three-halves the divisor would be successful. Hence, we know $-2D + D + D/2$ or $-0 - D/2$ is positive. But $-2D + D$ or $-D - 0$ is negative. Thus we record quotient bits corresponding to the former, 01.

three-halves divisor

When the positive remainder is unchanged sign-wise, we immediately record 11. A remainder which stays negative on addition of three-halves the divisor calls for recording 00 because $-2D + D + D/2$ is $0 + 0 - D/2$—this combination would also prove unsuccessful. Hence, the remainder could not be reduced by a multiple of $D/2$, leading to (0)00.

If the positive remainder goes negative on subtracting three-halves the divisor, we rely on the decoder and presume that the divisor would have been successful, and so record 10.

Similarly, when the negative remainder goes positive, we can be sure it would have stayed negative if we had added the full divisor. Thus $-2D + D + D/2$ is $+0 + 0 - D/2$ or (0)01. It could not be (0)10, for then $-2D + D + 0$ would be positive in contradiction to the directions of the decoder that it would be negative.

Signed Numbers

This system works well for signed numbers. In case the divisor and dividend are not both positive on all occasions, we must change the labels of Table 12.8.2. We refer the sign of the remainders to the original dividend. If the present remainder has the same sign as the dividend, the two left columns of the table are used; otherwise the two right columns are used. If the remainder after arithmetic has the same sign as the dividend, the left column of the column pair is referred to; otherwise the right column of the column pair is used.

This change takes care of division with two negative quantities. The reader should check the various combinations of events to satisfy himself that this works. When developing a negative quotient, it is stored in complement form. Hence, the entries in the table must be complemented to suit this arrangement for a negative quotient. So doing covers all alternatives.

Example

An annotated example of division by this method is presented in Figure 12.8.

Entry		
1	0.00001000110111110	Dividend
2	1.101101	Divisor
3	1.01101	Normalized divisor
4	0.10011	Normalized divisor magnitude
5	0.0001000110111110	Dividend alligned to match divisor
6	0.01000110111110/11	Shift left twice and enter comp (00)
7	1.101101	Add half normalized divisor
8	1.11111010111110	New remainder is negative
9	1.111010111110/1111	Enter comp (00), shift twice
10	1.1010111110/111100	Shift twice over 1's enter comp (11)
11	0.010011	Add half divisor magnitude
12	1.1111101110	Still negative
13	1.11101110/11110001	Shift twice, enter comp (10)
14	1.101110/1111000100	Shift twice over 1's enter comp (11)
15	0.010011	Add half divisor magnitude
16	0.000001	Positive remainder
17	0.0001/111100010000	Shift twice enter comp (11)
18	1	Adjust quotient for 2's complement
19	1.11100010001	
20	1.1111	Complement positive remainder

FIGURE 12.8 Division of (4542×2^{-17}) by $(19 \times 2^{-6}) = (239 \times 2^{-11}) +$
(1×2^{-17}) using the two-bit lookahead, non-restoring method

12.9   TWO-BIT LOOKAHEAD,
NON-RESTORING HARDWARE

The configuration of Figure 12.6 is used for reference. The need for each connection should be obvious as the discussion of each phase proceeds.

Division Cycle

Discussed in succession are the following phases:

1. Divisor normalization.
2. Triple preparation.
3. Connection of registers for arithmetic.
4. Quotient bit pair recording.
5. Termination.
6. Quotient correction.
7. Remainder correction.

Divisor Normalization

Before division can begin, the divisor must be properly aligned. It is passed over to the D' and returned to D shifted two places to the left. Such cycles continue until the sign and most significant numerical bit or the sign bit and the most significant bit are the same but the next-to-the-most-significant bit is different. Of course, the dividend must be shifted correspondingly.

Preparation of Three-Halves
the Divisor

Three-halves the divisor is required only for divisors of absolute value less than $\frac{3}{4}$. In those cases, it is formed by entering (D) and (D)/2 into the two adder inputs, placing the sum in A' and passing it over to T.

Register Connection for
Arithmetic

The proper bits of (A) and (D) are scanned by the decode matrix. It connects one of six sources to one input of the adder: three-halves the divisor or its complement; the divisor or its complement; half the divisor or its complement. The remainder from A is entered into the other input.

Of course, the quotient bit counter must be monitored to prevent incorrect connection when termination is called for.

Quotient Bit Pair Recording

The quotient is passed from Q to Q′ as arithmetic is being done. It is returned to Q shifted two places to the left. At this time, the quotient entry unit furnishes the two new quotient bits. To do so, it must know the following things:

1. The sign of the quotient being developed.
2. The multiple of the divisor used.
3. The sign of the new remainder.
4. The sign of the old remainder.
5. The sign of the divisor.

Then it inserts these bits as determined by Table 12.8.2.

Termination

The quotient bit counter stores the number of bits developed. This count is always even, since *pairs* of bits are always furnished. Therefore, no split cycle is required for termination as long as an even number of quotient bits (exclusive of sign) is specified. When the last quotient cycle is complete, we must determine if correction cycles are needed.

Quotient Correction

For the negative quotient, 1 is *always* added into the least significant bit position of the quotient on a separate cycle. The Q register is entered into one side of the adder; the other side is inhibited; a carryin of 1 is called for; the result is passed into Q′; it is returned to Q unshifted.

Remainder Correction

Whenever the final remainder is different in sign from the original dividend, it is replaced by the 1's complement. Whether this is necessary, is determined by examining the quotient and divisor sign and that of the present remainder.

PROBLEMS

12.1 Describe restoring decimal division.

12.2 How could the nonrestoring principle be used with decimal division?

12.3 Could decimal division incorporate nonperforming division?

12.4 Examine normalization for decimal division.

12.5 How could decimal division be expedited by providing divisor multiples? Suggest a way to provide only a few multiples instead of all.

12.6 With the above method devise a table of divisor versus remainder digit to choose the proper multiple of the divisor for subtraction for $3D$, $6D$, and $9D$. Do the same for $2D$, $4D$, and $8D$.

12.7 For making the Table above, how much improvement is made by considering two digits (eight bits) of the divisor or dividend or both.

12.8 Examine the hardware requirements for nonrestoring decimal division with one-digit lookahead and divisor multiples 2, 4, and 8. How does the time for this decimal division compare with that for high-speed binary division? Include time for multiple preparation. See Table 14.7.

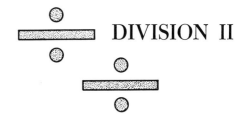

13

DIVISION II

13.1 THE NORMALIZING PRINCIPLE

This section describes a powerful shortcut for division. It provides a speedup over the methods described in Chapter 12 and over the conventional method of non-restoring division. It uses shifting over 0's when strings of 0's appear and shifting over 1's when strings of 1's appear. There are intermediate cases which have to be treated by actual subtraction or addition, but this is done in a non-restoring fashion, and the result is examined for strings of 0's and 1's. Because of the complexity of the concept, we start by describing the method as it is used for finding the quotient of two positive numbers without any rationale for what is going on. Then, to clarify the procedure, an example is presented step by step. The reasoning for shifting over 1's is explained. Then division of signed numbers is described and the principles are discussed in detail. Finally, the considerations for termination are discussed. The sections that follow consider a variation of this procedure.

Positive Divisor and Dividend

A normalized divisor and dividend are essential, so we start by normalizing the divisor, equalizing the dividend as we do so. Next, we shift over 0's and enter 0's into the quotient register corresponding to that shift. When this is finished, we find the registers in the following state:

$$A: \quad 0.1X \cdots$$
$$D: \quad 0.1X \cdots$$
$$Q: \quad \underbrace{0.0 \cdots 0}_{Z_1}$$

where there were Z_1 zeros left in (A) to be normalized and where X's are either 0's or 1's. Next, we compare the aligned dividend and divisor by performing a subtraction of the divisor from the dividend. This is carried to completion whether or not it is "successful."

Of course, a positive or negative remainder may result; each is handled differently. If subtraction is successful, the A register now contains a positive quantity; enter a quotient bit of 1 and shift, then shift over 0's and test as described earlier.

In the case where subtraction is unsuccessful, where the quantity in the A register is a negative number, we have the following register contents:

$$A: \quad 1.1 \cdots 10X$$
$$D: \quad 0.1X \cdots X$$
$$Q: \quad \underbrace{0.0 \cdots 0}_{Z_1 + 1}$$

The extra 0 was put in because the new remainder is negative. Next *we shift over 1's in the A register until there is a 0 in the place to the right of the binary point.* The number of 1's contained in the A register at the beginning of this process is indicated above as U_1. For each position of the A register that is shifted over, a 1 is entered at the right-hand position of the quotient. This process can be symbolized by,

$$A \xleftarrow{U_1} 0 \qquad Q \xleftarrow{U_1} 1$$

At the end of the process we have a normalized negative number in the A register, a normalized positive divisor in the D register, and the Q register contains $(Z_1 + 1)$ 0's followed by U_1 1's; thus,

$$A: \quad 1.0X$$
$$D: \quad 0.1X$$
$$Q: \quad \underbrace{0.0 \cdots 0}_{Z_1 + 1} \quad \underbrace{1 \cdots 1}_{U_1}$$

Next we perform an *addition* of the divisor to the remainder. *Addition* is required after we shift over 1's. This may yield either a positive or negative number. In both cases it is carried through to completion. Thus,

$$2[(A) + (D)] \longrightarrow A$$

When the result is *positive*, we enter a 1 at the right of the Q register; when it is *negative*, we enter a 0 at the right of the Q register. When there is a *positive* number in the A register, we shift over 0's and enter 0's into the Q register, following this by *subtraction*. When there is a *negative* number in the A register, we shift over 1's, enter 1's in the Q register, and follow this by an *addition* when both registers are normalized. Termination of division is discussed and explained in a later subsection.

An Example

Figure 13.1 shows how a division is performed using the method of shifitng over 0's and 1's. Entry 1 shows the dividend. Entry 2 shows the divisor. These are both positive numbers with the divisor larger than the dividend. The divisor is not normalized; it is shifted left once to normalize it, Entry 3. At the same time, the dividend is shifted a corresponding number of places to the left. At the end of this initial process, the adjusted dividend appears as in Entry 4. We now normalize the dividend by shifting over 0's three positions. This simply amounts to shifitng the A register three bits to the left so that it appears as Entry 5. We keep count of these three shifts by entering three 0's into the Q register, Entry 6.

Now both divisor and dividend are normalized, and we cannot determine the next bit without performing arithmetic. Since the two are of similar sign, subtraction is performed. Naturally it is done in the computer by complement addition; using 2's complements for brevity, this is shown as Entry 7. Notice that as complement addition is performed, a shift of the A register one position to the left is associated with it. The result in this instance is a negative number.

Since the subtraction has produced a negative result, a 0 is entered into the Q register, Entry 8. This negative remainder is not normalized and contains three 1's to the right of the binary point. We perform the shift over 1's in Entry 9. For each 1 that we shift over, a 1 is entered into the Q register, Entry 10. Now we have both a normalized divisor and remainder. Since they are opposite in sign, we add them performing a single shift to the left upon completion of addition, Entry 11.

Notice that the result is negative. This requires entering a 0 into the Q register, Entry 12. We shift over 1's three times, line 13, and enter three 1's

			Entry
0.00001000110111110		Dividend $= 4542 \times 2^{-17}$	1
0.010011		Divisor $=\quad 19 \times 2^{-6}$	2
0.10011		Normalized divisor $= 19 \times 2^{-5}$	3

(A)	(Q)		
0.0001000110111110		Dividend aligned to match divisor	4
0.1000110111110		Shift over 0's, dividend	5
	000	Enter 0's into Q	6
1.01101			
‾‾‾‾‾‾‾‾‾‾‾		Add complement of normalized	
1.111101011110		divisor and shift	7
1.11101011110			
	0000	Enter 0 into Q for arithmetic	8
1.010111110		Shift over 1's	9
	0000111	Enter 1's into Q	10
0.10011			
‾‾‾‾‾‾‾			
1.111101110		Add normalized divisor and shift	11
1.11101110			
	00001110	Enter 0 into Q	12
1.01110		Shift over 1's	13
	00001110111	Enter 1's into Q	14
0.10011			
‾‾‾‾‾		Add normalized divisor and shift	15
0.00001			
0.0001		*Remainder* $= 1 \times 2^{-17}$	16
	0.00011101111	Enter 1 into Q	17
		Quotient $= 239 \times 2^{-11}$	18

FIGURE 13.1   Performing $(4542 \times 2^{-17}) \div (19 \times 2^{-6}) = (239 \times 2^{-11}) + (1 \times 2^{-17})$
using the method of shifting over 0's and 1's

into the Q register, line 14. Now the remainder and divisor are opposite in sign and normalized which dictates an addition and shift, line 15. This result is a positive number and requires that a 1 be put into the Q register, line 17.

At this point the reader will have benefited as much as he ever will from the example; therefore, it would be of no avail to develop more quotient bits. In the computer, a counter holds the number of bits of the quotient that are to be developed and tests it at each cycle against the number of bits developed so far, as we will see in the later development.

The quotient now stored in the Q register is indicated on line 18. The relative position of the binary point is directly related to the present position of the quotient in the quotient register. The remainder, which is found on line 16, will usually have a least significant bit corresponding to the least significant bit of the dividend. This factor is fixed by the designer of the machine.

13.2 SHIFTING OVER 1's AND ARITHMETIC

The rationale for shifting over 0's was discussed in Section 12.3. The reasoning involved in shifting over 1's is more involved. Let us begin just after arithmetic, where the remainder and divisor look like

$$A: \quad 1.1X\cdots$$

$$D: \quad 0.1X\cdots$$

The number in the A register is negative, but it is larger than $-\frac{1}{2}$—it is between 0 and $-\frac{1}{2}$; the contents of the D register is a number which is equal to or larger than $\frac{1}{2}$ but less than 1. When these two numbers are added together, the sum must be a number greater than 0. We do not need to perform addition to verify this!

We would like to know what would happen if we doubled the remainder and then tried to perform addition. Doubling this number does not destroy any information. To put this another way, shifting a number to the left which is not normalized does not destroy any information. Even though we are throwing away left-hand 1's, these 1's only carry positional information. This is because the number is in 2's complement form, therefore, these 1's represent 0's which have been complemented. Therefore, shifting an unnormalized remainder to the left doubles it and conserves its value in the register. Also, we are free to enter a 1 into the Q register when dealing with positive numbers since we can say that addition would have been successful if it had been performed. The reasoning for each normalizing shift of the remainder is as above, and a 1 is entered into Q at each shift.

Look at it another way. We have just added $-2D$ to get the negative remainder. Next we would try $+D$, then $+D/2$, then $+D/4$, and so forth, as long as we knew the remainder would go positive. As long as the negative remainder is unnormalized, we *know* it *will go positive*. For the $U1$'s, we know $-2D + (D/2)^U$ is positive; this represents $-D - D/2 - D/4\cdots$ $-(D/2)^U$ corresponding to the quotient bits $011\underbrace{\cdots11}_{U}X$, where the X must be determined by arithmetic.

In other words, if we had not done $-2D$ then we could do $-D$, then $-D/2$, then $-D/4$, etc., and each time the remainder would be positive. This corresponds to quotient bits $011\cdots$, etc.

When both the divisor and remainder are normalized, we cannot make a decision without performing arithmetic. We now know that a normalized negative remainder is less than $-\frac{1}{2}$. Yet we cannot predict whether the sum of the remainder and divisor will be greater or less than zero when addition is performed. Therefore, we must actually do the addition. We consider two cases, since the new sum may be greater than or less than zero.

New Remainder Greater Than or Equal to Zero

Let us call the remainder positive when *subtraction* was just successful, (A'). The events leading up to this moment are this. We subtracted the divisor from the remainder and got a negative number,

$$(A) = (A') - (D) \tag{13.2.1}$$

The shift associated with this subtraction was performed,

$$(A) = 2[(A') - (D)] \tag{13.2.2}$$

Then we shifted over 1's until the partial remainder was normalized,

$$(A) = 2^{U+1}[(A') - (D)] \tag{13.2.3}$$

It was then necessary to add the divisor to the remainder to determine the next quotient bit,

$$(A) = 2^{U+1}[(A') - (D)] + (D) \tag{13.2.4}$$

As a result, the present remainder is a positive number.
Expanding (13.2.4),

$$(A) = 2^{U+1}(A') - 2^{U+1}(D) + (D) \tag{13.2.5}$$

This may be rewritten as

$$(A) = 2^{U+1}(A') - 2^{U}(D) - 2^{U-1}(D) - \cdots - (D) \tag{13.2.6}$$

using a substitution we have encountered before. To put this another way, we would have gotten the same result using a restoring or non-performing division method if we had not performed the subtraction indicated in (13.2.1) and had performed the $U + 1$ subtractions corresponding to the shifts over 1 and the final addition performed here. If we had done that, obviously we would have inserted a 0 followed by $(U + 1)$ 1's into the Q register; thus,

$$Q \leftarrow 0\underbrace{1\cdots1}_{U+1}$$

Since this is in essence what has been performed here, we are entitled to do the same thing now; we may insert $(U + 1)$ 1's into the Q register. The first U of these is associated with shifting over 1's. The last one results when addition causes the remainder to become positive.

New Remainder Less Than Zero

After performing our addition and determining that the remainder went negative, let us look back to the last previous shift over 1. We know that if we had performed addition at that point, the sum would have been greater than zero—the remainder would have been positive,

$$2^U[(A') - (D)] + (D) \geq 0 \tag{13.2.7}$$

We also know that

$$2^{U+1}[(A') - (D)] + (D) < 0 \tag{13.2.8}$$

If we had stopped before this last step, using only the knowledge conveyed in (13.2.7), we could expand it to yield

$$(A) = 2^U(A') - 2^U(D) + (D) \tag{13.2.9}$$

or using our substitution,

$$(A) = 2^U(A') - 2^{U-1}(D) - 2^{U-2}(D) - \cdots - (D) \tag{13.2.10}$$

This would call for an insertion of U 1's into the Q register, thus,

$$Q \leftarrow \underbrace{01 \cdots 1}_{U}$$

This would have been the result using restoring or non-performing division.

The next thing that we would do in one of those processes would be to double this result and try to subtract the dividend again. In restoring division, this would produce, before restoring, the exact same result we have at this moment, which is given as,

$$(A) = 2[2^U(A') - 2^U(D) + (D)] - (D) \tag{13.2.11}$$

We would also insert a 0 into the Q register,

$$Q \leftarrow 0$$

Hence, from our starting point, we would have placed U 1's and one 0 into the Q register; thus,

$$Q: \quad \underbrace{01\cdots10}_{U}$$

13.3 SIGNED NUMBERS

Normalizing

The principles developed above can be applied to signed numbers without any difficulty. Again, the first step is to normalize the divisor, adjusting the dividend at the same time. The next step is to normalize the adjusted dividend. This is shifting over 0's for positive dividends and shifting over 1's for negative dividends. Notice that this has the same effect, regardless of the sign of the dividend; these 0's or 1's only carry positional information and not significant numerical information.

When dealing with positive numbers, the initial normalization of the dividend required that we place 0's in the Q register. Now the bits which we place in the Q register depend upon the sign of the quotient we are developing. For positive quotients, 0's are entered into the Q register; for negative quotients, 1's are entered into the Q register. In fact, throughout division, when normalizing by shifting over 0's, 0's are entered in the positive quotient and 1's in a negative quotient; shifts over 1's enters 1's in a positive quotient, 0's in a negative one.

Arithmetic

When both the divisor and dividend have been normalized, we cannot determine the next quotient bit without performing arithmetic. Therefore, add a quantity to the dividend corresponding to the divisor and of sign opposite to the dividend.

Next we enter a bit into the Q register, according to the sign of the remainder. This bit is a 1 if the remainder and the divisor have the same signs; it is a 0 if the signs of the remainder and divisor are different. The reasons for this are discussed later. At this point, we can see that if we started with a dividend and divisor of the same sign and they are now of the same sign, then the addition which was performed was "successful" and we may rightfully enter a 1 into the Q register. If they are of different signs, we were "unsuccessful" and we enter a 0. If we started with a dividend and divisor of different signs and they are still of different signs, again we are successful. However, since we are developing a negative quotient, a 0 is entered into the Q register. If the remainder and divisor are now of the same sign, our addition was unsuccessful; but this requires an entry of 1 into the Q register.

The method continues as outlined above. After an addition, we shift over 0's or 1's, as required to normalize the remainder. For each shift, a bit determined by the quotient being developed is entered into the Q register; 0's and 1's are entered directly for positive quotients but reversed for

				Entry
0.00001000110111110			Dividend	1
1.101101			Divisor	2
1.01101			Normalized divisor	3
0.0001000110111110			Align dividend to match divisor	4
0.1000110111110			Shift over 0's	5
		111	Enter 1 into Q for each 0 above	6
1.01101			Add divisor	7
1.1111010111110				
1.111010111110			Shift sum	8
		1111	Enter 1 for negative partial remainder	9
1.010111110			Shift over 1's	10
		1111000	Enter 0 into Q for each 1 above	11
0.10011			Add divisor complement	12
1.111101110				
1.11101110			Shift sum	13
		11110001	Enter 1 for negative partial remainder	14
1.01110			Shift over 1's	15
		11110001000	Enter 0 into Q for each 1 above	16
0.10011			Add divisor complement	17
0.00001			Shift sum	18
		111100010000	Enter 0 for positive partial remainder	19
0.0001		1	Adjust 2's comp. quotient: add e	20
1.1111		1.11100010001	Complement positive remainder	21

FIGURE 13.3 Performing $(4542 \times 2^{-17}) \div (-19 \times 2^{-6}) = (-239 \times 2^{-11}) + (-1 \times 2^{-17})$ using the method of shifting over 0's and 1's

negative quotients. When the remainder is normalized, an addition is performed. The quantity added is opposite in sign to the present remainder and of the same magnitude as the divisor. The result of this addition reflected in another rule determines the bit to be entered into the Q register. Then shifting over 0's or 1's is performed again, normalizing the remainder.

Example

An example of signed division by shifting over 0's and 1's is presented without explanation in Figure 13.3.

Why Normalize?

The first step that we take in this method is to normalize the divisor. The necessity for this step may not be clear. It is to permit a fixed reference point for comparing the divisor and remainder. It would be possible to develop a method which used a variable reference point in the divisor and compared it with that position in the remainder. This would present obstacles to implementation that would be hard to overcome. In normalizing the divisor, the reference point always corresponds to the binary point and, therefore, becomes a fixed point of reference in both registers. When we wish to test the alignment of the remainder with respect to the divisor, we refer it to the binary point in the remainder register.

Another point which needs emphasis is that 1's to the right of the binary point in negative quantities do not carry numerical information but, rather, indicate the position of the binary point in a normalized number. Therefore, they serve the same function as 0's to the right of the binary point in positive numbers. This permits us to double the number by shifting left until the number has been normalized.

Diminishing the Remainder

During the processing when both the divisor and the remainder are normalized, there comes a time when we must diminish the remainder in order to determine the proper quotient bit. It is obvious that to diminish the remainder a number opposite in sign to it must be added to it. We wish to bring the magnitude of the remainder toward 0. If we add a number with the same sign as the remainder, this sum will go away from 0 rather than toward 0. To determine the success of this operation and at the same time to find out how we should set Q, we make up a table.

TABLE 13.3.1   Determination of Setting of Q_1 after Diminishing the Partial Remainder.
Division by Shifting over 0's and 1's

	Original		Present	
Entry	A_s	D_s	A_s	Set Q_1
1	0	0	0	1
2	0	0	1	0
3	1	1	1	1
4	1	1	0	0
5	0	1	0	0 ⎫
6	0	1	1	1 ⎬ Develop
7	1	0	1	0 ⎬ complement
8	1	0	0	1 ⎭ quotient

Table 13.3.1 lists the original sign of the dividend, of the divisor, of the present remainder, and the proper setting of the quotient bit. In Entry 1 we see that if we start with positive numbers and now have a positive remainder, we set the quotient bit to 1; if the remainder is now negative, we set the quotient bit to 0, Entry 2. A similar situation is found when both divisor and dividend are negative. When the remainder which results from diminishing the previous remainder is negative, we set the quotient bit to 1, Entry 3; when the present remainder is positive, we set the quotient bit to 0. Entries 5 through 8 occur when the dividend and divisor have opposite signs, and, hence, we are developing a negative quotient. When the present remainder has the same sign as the dividend, the quotient bit is 0, Entries 5 and 7, when they are opposite in sign, a 1 is entered into the quotient bit, Entries 6 and 8.

We can summarize the entire table if we observe how the setting of Q is related to the remainder and divisor sign. We see that when the sign of the resulting remainder and the divisor are the same, the quotient bit is set to 1; when they are different, the quotient bit is set to 0.

Quotient Bit Entry

As we shift the remainder to the left when shifting over 0's or 1's, we make entries into the Q register. How do we know what this entry should be for all possible cases? Table 13.3.2 is made up of entries for the dividend sign, the divisor sign and the remainder sign. The proper quotient bit is then noted for each combination of these entries.

TABLE 13.3.2 Determination of Setting of Q Bits for Shifting over 0's or 1's for Division by That Method

Entry	A_s	D_s	A_s at start of shift	Set Q for each bit shifted
1	0	0	0	0
2	0	0	1	1
3	1	1	1	0
4	1	1	0	1
5	0	1	0	1 ⎫
6	0	1	1	0 ⎬ Develop complement
7	1	0	1	1 ⎬ quotient
8	1	0	0	0 ⎭

Entry 1 shows that starting with a positive dividend and divisor, 0's are entered into the quotient whenever shifting over 0's; 1's are entered into the quotient whenever shifting over 1's, Entry 2. The same would be true for a negative divisor except that we develop a negative quotient and must complement the quotient entries. This accounts for lines 5 and 6. Lines 3 and 4 show that an original negative dividend requires that 0's are entered in the quotient bit when shifting over 1's; 1's are entered into the quotient bit when shifting over 0's.

To see this, suppose that we have a normalized negative dividend. If we add a large positive number to it, this will make the remainder become positive. We describe this situation by a 0 in the quotient bit. By similar reasoning, Entries 7 and 8 can be accounted for.

Table 13.3.2 can be summarized by noting that 0's are entered into the quotient register at the right for a normalized shift performed when the signs of the remainder and the divisor are the same; a 1 is entered when the signs of these quantities are different.

The case may arise where the run of 0's or 1's encountered is greater than the shift capacity of the hardware. It would be foolhardy to let the hardware try to do it in one shot, so the control logic must intervene. In reviewing the formulas, it is recalled that the greatest shift which is decoded is that of the capacity of the shift network, K. In other words, when more than K shifts are to be performed, the hardware executes a shift of K places and then examines the result to determine the next request. Thus, large shifts are performed in two or more steps.

13.4   TERMINATION

In concluding the division process, four things must be considered:

1. Has the last bit of the quotient been determined?
2. Does the quotient require correction?
3. Has the remainder been completely formed?
4. Does the remainder require correction?

To determine when the last quotient bit generation cycle is being performed, we refer to the shift counter. Near the last stage it will contain some quantity $N - j$. This counter is tallying the number of bits of the quotient which we have formed. After N bits of the quotient are available, division is complete. The counter now indicates that j bits have yet to be formed. As long as the number j is greater than the number K, we know that we cannot determine enough bits in this stage to complete the division process. In other words, we surely will not terminate in this cycle.

Shifting into Termination

Now, consider if the counter contains $N - j$, where j is less than or equal to K. We look at the run of 0's or 1's now present in the partial remainder. If this number, Z or U respectively, in the two cases cited is less than j, this cycle will not cause us to terminate.

Termination will occur when we encounter a run of 0's or 1's greater than or equal to the number of quotient bits which are yet to be formed, provided this is within the capacity of the shift hardware. In other words, we have j less than or equal to K and U or Z greater than or equal to j.

Once we have determined that this is a termination cycle, how do we effect the termination? Obviously the limiting factor is j. We are going to perform a shift of j places and accumulate j quotient bits. The bits to be accumulated are determined in a normal fashion. Thus, if we are shifting over 0's, 0's or reversed 0's are entered into the right end of the Q register; shifting over 1's causes us to enter 1's or reversed 1's into the Q register. When this is performed, the remainder is kept in the A register and the quotient is kept in the Q register. Only corrections may be required to complete division.

Adding into Termination

If the counter has not yet reached $N - 1$ when a subtraction is called for, this will not be a termination cycle. Consider now when the counter is set to $N - 1$ and there is a request for a subtraction. When recording $N - 1$,

the counter indicates that only one more bit of the quotient is to be prepared and we can assume that the present cycle will terminate quotient-bit
preparation. We perform the requested subtraction (or addition, as the
case may be). We record the result of the arithmetic and set the last
quotient bit into the Q register. Now both the quotient and the remainder
are complete. Only corrections may be required.

From the discussion above, it can be seen that termination can be approached in two ways: we can determine the last quotient bits by shifting
over 0's or 1's; we can determine the last bit of the quotient by performing
arithmetic. There are no other alternatives.

Quotient Correction

Positive quotients are always found in correct form. Negative quotients
require the correction discussed in detail in Section 3.6. Any 2's complement division method accumulates a quotient in 1's complement form. To
put it into 2's complement form requires that a 1 be added to the least
significant bit position of the quotient. In Chapter 3, we called the 1 in
that notation e. We then require, when accumulating a negative quotient,
that a last correction step stated as

$$(Q) + e \longrightarrow Q$$

The criterion for performing the correction is the sign of the quotient.

Remainder Correction

This method of division may leave us, after the termination cycle, with
a remainder signed similarly or differently to the original dividend. In
order for the remainder to be considered correct, it must agree in sign with
the original dividend. In order to determine whether the remainder is in
the correct form, we have made up Table 13.4. This table compares the
present signs of the quotient, remainder, and divisor and states whether
the remainder is presently correct. Entry 1 shows that if all quantities are
positive, the remainder is correct. Entry 2 says that if we now have a
negative remainder and a positive divisor, and we have been developing a
positive quotient, then these conditions are inconsistent and our remainder
must be corrected. The reader should examine the remaining entries to
check his understanding of the presentation.

From Table 13.4 we can now set up an equation which tells us when a
remainder correction cycle, Re, is required,

$$\mathrm{Re} = Q_s(\bar{A}_s\bar{D}_s + A_sD_s) + \bar{Q}_s(A_s\bar{D}_s + \bar{A}_sD_s) \qquad (13.4.1)$$

TABLE 13.4   Remainder Condition for Various Register Sign Conditions. Division by Shifting over 0's and 1's

	Present			
Entry	A_s	D_s	Q_s	Correct remainder
1	0	0	0	Yes
2	1	0	0	No
3	0	1	0	No
4	1	1	0	Yes
5	0	0	1	No
6	1	0	1	Yes
7	0	1	1	Yes
8	1	1	1	No

which is correct when the signs of the remainder and divisor disagree for a positive quotient or agree for a negative quotient.

The remainder, if it requires correction, is of the wrong sign. If it is negative, the last thing we did was to subtract the divisor when we should not have. To correct this remainder, we now add the divisor. We are sure from the processing above that the remainder is less than the divisor. Therefore, when we add the divisor, the final remainder will be positive. Of course, we have assumed that the divisor is positive; if it is negative, then we must subtract it in order to make the remainder become positive.

If the remainder is positive, whereas it should be negative, we subtract the absolute value of the divisor from it. Again we are sure that the absolute value of the divisor is larger than that of the remainder so that the subtraction will yield a negative number.

13.5   SHIFTING OVER 0's AND 1's COMBINED WITH LOOKAHEAD

Discussion

Let us recall the lookahead method discussed in Section 12.5. This method requires that we examine the remainder and the divisor at the beginning of any given cycle. This examination reveals the probable quotient bits and determines one of several multiples used to diminish the partial remainder. The selected multiple is such as to assure that if it does not work, the next lower multiple surely will. The remainder is then diminished and the results are checked. If they are not satisfactory, the next lower divisor multiple is used. At the end of the first or second trials, accordingly, the proper pair of quotient bits is set. A cycle is completed when the quotient and remainder are shifted two places in accordance with the two bits just set into the quotient register.

We now seek to incorporate this procedure into the method of shifting over 0's and 1's. After each cycle wherein the remainder is diminished, normalization of the remainder is provided. In other words, we shift over 0's and 1's, entering quotient bits accordingly until we can no longer do so. At that point, we examine the remainder and divisor in a fashion similar to that used in the two- or three-bit lookahead. Our objective now is to subtract a multiple of the divisor such that the result will produce the *greatest number of quotient bits as we next shift over either 0's or 1's*, as the case may be.

Two Adders

The simplest approach to this is for the examination of the remainder and the divisor to determine two multiples, one of which will surely be the best of the lot. Then two separate adders are used, one for each multiple proposed. One adder subtracts one divisor multiple from the present remainder. Decoding networks are attached to the output of each adder so that the better result may be chosen—the one providing more shifts of 0's or 1's. Quotient bits are recorded corresponding to this divisor multiple and the division proceeds by completing the shift of 0's or 1's, continuing to another comparison of remainder and divisor.

One Adder

The other alternative is to use a single adder. A certain percentage of the comparisons of remainder and divisor will yield definitive results. We know that a given multiple or the divisor will yield the best results when subtracted from the remainder. The rest of the time we have two possibilities. If we use the larger multiple sometimes our results will be incorrect; if we use the smaller multiple our results will *always* be correct but they will not always be optimum. We are forced to use the second alternative, but we can produce near-optimum results by increasing the number of remainder and divisor bits which determine the divisor multiple used.

Line	Dividend		Quotient
1	0.10111111110111001111000100100/		
2	1.001010		*Entry*
3	1.111001	Remainder/Quotient	
4	1.00111110	/*0*11	1
5	0.110110		
6	0.00010110	Remainder/Quotient	
7	0.101101110	/011*1*00	2
8	1.001010		
9	1.110111110		
10	1.011111001	/01110*0*01	3
11	0.110110		
12	0.010101001		
13	0.10101001	/011100*1*	4
14	1.001010		
15	1.11010001		
16	1.0100011110	/0111000110*1*	5
17	0.110110		
18	0.0001111110		
19	0.1111110	/01110001101*1*00	6
20	1.001010		
21	0.0010010		
22	0.1001000100100/0111000110110010		7
23	1.001010		
24	1.1011100100100		
25	1.011100100100/01110001101100100		8
26	0.110110		
27	0.010010100100		
28	0.10010100100/011100011011001001		9
29	1.001010		
30	1.10111100100		
31	1.0111100100/0111000110110010010		10
32	0.110110		
33	0.0101000100		
34	0.101000100/01110001101100100101		11
35	1.001010		

36	1.110010100	
37	1.0010100/011100011011001001010101	12
38	0.110110	
	—————————	
39	0.0000000	
40	0.00000/0111000110110010010101*0*	13
	Remainder Quotient	

FIGURE 13.6.1   Divide 402,398,759 $\times$ 2^{-29} by 54 $\times$ 2^{-6} using method of shifting over 0's and 1's

Explanation Procedure

The explanation of this process presents difficulties. The reader is advised to study carefully the method of division by shifting over 0's and 1's and to practice his binary arithmetic! Our plan of action for the rest of the chapter is to examine exhaustively an example using the method of shifting over 0's and 1's. A graph of the remainder during each cycle is then presented. Next, we discuss the cases where use of a double divisor produces better results and the reasons for this. The half divisor is discussed in a similar fashion. Next, the criterion used for selecting the proper multiple is examined. We are ready to pursue in detail the original example now performed using the divisor multiples method. The explanation is aided by the use of a graph of the remainder.

13.6   VISUAL DEMONSTRATION

Shifting Over 0's and 1's

Figure 13.6.1 presents a sizeable example of division by the method discussed in Sections 13.1 through 13.4. Such a lengthy example is necessary in order to demonstrate the usefulness of both the method under discussion and the method discussed in the following section. By becoming familiar with demonstration of Figure 13.6.1 and 13.6.2, the explanation of the more complicated method will be expedited.

The illustration uses numbers which have already been normalized, so as to remove from consideration this matter with which the reader should now be familiar. Also, the example uses positive numbers only, because the explanation is then simpler.

We find the dividend on line 1. Since both numbers are normalized, we can reduce the dividend only by subtracting the divisor. The complemented divisor is shown on line 2. The result of subtraction appears on line 3. It is a negative number with three 1's to the right of the decimal point. Thus, we can shift over 1's three times. However, the first bit of the quotient is reserved for the result of the subtraction. Since our remainder has become negative, the first bit of the quotient developed here is a 0; the other two bits are the ones corresponding to the other two places in our shift over 1's. The "0" is set in bold italics in the figure to show that it is the result of arithmetic, not shifting. To reiterate, the first bit of the quotient is 0 because our remainder is negative; the next two bits are 1's because we were able to perform a three-place shift over 1's in normalizing the remainder. After we shift, the remainder is found on the left side of line 4; the quotient bits are the three bits to the right of the slash on line 4.

The slash is our visual aid for discriminating between remainder and quotient bits in the Q register. The computer contains a counter to keep track of this *dividing line*.

To diminish our present negative remainder of line 4, we must add the true divisor which appears in line 5. The result is found on line 6. It contains three 0's to the right of the binary point. Therefore, on line 7 we shift three places to the left. First we enter a 1 into the quotient, since the new remainder is positive. The two 0's which follow correspond to a three-place shift over 0's.

As we continue the example, notice that the remainder produced on line 12 is a positive number with only one 0 to the right of the binary point. When this is normalized in line 13, only one bit can be entered into the quotient. This must be a 1, because we have created a positive remainder.

Please follow all thirteen cycles of the division presented in Figure 13.6.1 and become thoroughly familiar with this method.

Graphical Presentation of the Division Example

To aid the explanation of this kind of division, graphical presentation is used. The graph of division of Figure 13.6.1 appears as Figure 13.6.2. There are several points of significance on this graph. The two dashed lines corresponding to $+\frac{1}{2}$ and $-\frac{1}{2}$ on the chart are the criterion lines. We continue to shift over 0's or 1's until the partial remainder is above the $+\frac{1}{2}$ line in the case of positive numbers or below the $-\frac{1}{2}$ line in the case of negative numbers. The verticals on the chart are identified by numbers which appear at the top of the chart. We use them to facilitate our discussion.

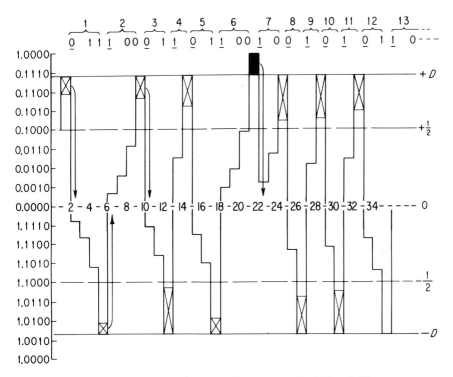

FIGURE 13.6.2 Graph of division $(402, 398, 759 \times 2^{-29}) \div$ (54×2^{-6}) using method of shifting over 0's and 1's.

The beginning of division is at Vertical 1. The remainder is greater than $\frac{1}{2}$ but less than the divisor. The difference of these two is the shaded rectangle. After subtraction, this is the amount by which the remainder has gone negative. Thus, the amount below the 0-line at Vertical 2 corresponds to the difference between the remainder and the divisor at Vertical 1.

We now perform normalized shifts until the remainder becomes less than $-\frac{1}{2}$. Each normalizing cycle corresponds to doubling the remainder. Thus, Vertical 3 represents an amount twice that of Vertical 2. Notice that Vertical 4 finally shows a quantity which has become less than $-\frac{1}{2}$ (greater in absolute value than $\frac{1}{2}$). This requires a subtraction of minus the divisor from the present remainder. The solid rectangle at Vertical 5 is the amount by which the remainder goes positive after subtraction. This is the value of Vertical 6.

Here are some further features of note. At Vertical 19, unlike the other entries, the remainder has now become *greater* than the divisor. When the divisor is subtracted from this remainder, the result is the solid rectangle *above* the divisor line. This is the amount by which the remainder remains *positive*, as found in Vertical 21. At Vertical 33, in normalizing the remainder, it becomes exactly equal to the negative divisor. Therefore, when subtraction takes place, the result is 0. This is what happens in exact division where no remainder occurs. The verticals in Figure 13.6.2 do not correspond to the line numbers of Figure 13.6.1, but this should not cause confusion.

Here would be a good time to peek ahead and see the advantage gained by using half and double divisors in this same example. This is worked out in Figure 13.9.1, the graph of which appears as Figure 13.9.2. Only ten cycles are required to complete division formerly requiring thirteen cycles. Before that example is explained, we investigate the rationale and the criterion.

13.7 WHY MULTIPLES HELP

Large Remainder, Small Divisor

Now we will put to use the graphical method described above. Consider a large remainder, one which is almost equal to 1. Consider also, a small normalized divisor, one which is almost as small as $\frac{1}{2}$. This case is presented as Figure 13.7.1. The divisor and its complement are indicated by straight black lines. The normalization crtierion, $+\frac{1}{2}$ and $-\frac{1}{2}$, appear as dashed lines. The double of the divisor appears on the graph as a dotted line.

Recall that we continue to normalize a remainder until it becomes greater than $+\frac{1}{2}$ or less than $-\frac{1}{2}$. First, let us see what happens to our cast of characters as we apply the familiar method of shifting over 0's and 1's to it, Vertical 1. The long black column to the left of Figure 13.7.1 (see the center of the figure for vertical numbers) is the difference between the divisor and the remainder: it is a positive number. After subtraction, we are left with the positive number almost equal to $\frac{1}{2}$, Vertical 2. When we double it, we have a large positive number again, Vertical 3. Again, we subtract the divisor and are left with a number not quite as close almost equal to $\frac{1}{2}$, Vertical 4. Shifting one place produces another large positive number, Vertical 5. This continues until the result of subtraction is small enough (Vertical 8) so that when it is doubled (Vertical 9) it does not exceed $\frac{1}{2}$.

In this fashion, each cycle produces only one quotient bit because of

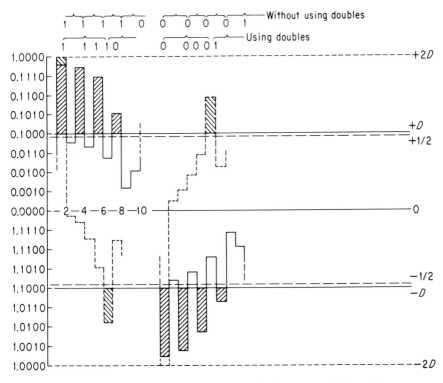

FIGURE 13.7.1   Contrasting division for large remainder and
small divisor shifting over 0's and 1's *with* versus *without* divisor
doubles.

the nature of the numbers with which we are dealing. For these kinds of
numbers, we will see that it would have been better to subtract twice the
divisor at the first step.

Double Divisor

We now follow this procedure in the dotted lines using the divisor
double. The remainder differs from twice the divisor by an amount sectioned in dotted lines in Vertical 1 in Figure 13.7.1. This is a small quantity
and is the amount by which the remainder goes negative in Vertical 2.
Since this is a small amount, it takes a number of shifts to normalize it,
Verticals 3, 4, 5, 6. This increases our efficiency, since now we develop one
quotient bit for each normalizing shift position—each time we shift over 1's.

We must change the rules so that the quotient developed by this method corresponds exactly to that developed by the first method. Thus, when using twice the divisor, we record a 1 regardless of the sign of the remainder. The remaining bits are developed and recorded as previously. Shifting over 1's causes us to record 1-bits for the quotient. Notice that to generate five bits of the quotient by the old method required four cycles; to generate the same number of bits using the divisor double requires only two cycles (since the shift over 1's is part of the cycle). Note that the *number of cycles* (or reversals of direction) determines the time consumed, not the length of the line or the number of verticals required in Figure 13.7.1.

Of course the gain is not always as substantial as shown in the Figure 13.7.1. This particular case is presented to show dramatically how the advantage is gained.

Small Negative Remainder

The right-hand half of Figure 13.7.1 illustrates how a similar principle is applied to a very small negative remainder—one almost as small as -1—used with a normalized divisor almost equal to $\frac{1}{2}$. It is approximately the mirror image of the case just cited. The similarity existing between the two sides of Figure 13.7.1 and the rationale for the process should be obvious after a careful examination of the figure.

Half Divisor

When dealing with a small divisor, the alternatives for the subtrahend or addend are either the divisor double or the divisor itself. In dealing with a large divisor, we find that there are cases where it is advantageous to use half the divisor instead of the divisor itself. Such a case is presented in Figure 13.7.2. Here we have a small partial remainder and a large divisor. In subtracting the latter from the former, the result is a number close to $-\frac{1}{2}$. When it is doubled, we get a small negative number, and so forth. In the figure, the half divisor is indicated by the dotted lines just below the $+\frac{1}{2}$ dashed line and just above the $-\frac{1}{2}$ dashed line. If we use this multiple in this case the dotted graph results. As you can readily see, we develop five quotient bits in two cycles using the $\frac{1}{2}$ divisor, contrasted against three cycles using the full divisor.

Having demonstrated the advantage of the multiple divisor system, it remains to develop a criterion for determining when the multiple should be invoked.

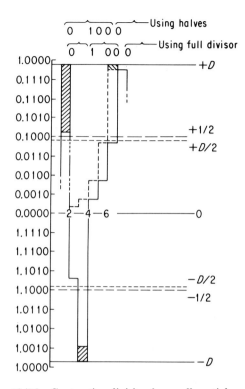

FIGURE 13.7.2   Contrasting division for small partial remainder
and large divisor, shifting over 0's and 1's with versus without
using divisor halves.

The Quotient Bit

Whenever a divisor multiple is used, the quotient bit is set without
regard to the sign of the new remainder. This can be done as long as the
criterion for using the multiple provides sufficient selectivity to assure
that the sign of the remainder could be predicted *if* the divisor itself had
been used. This is feasible and the design of the criterion is the subject of
Section 13.8.

Effectiveness

The effectiveness of this method depends on the machine definition of
the cycle which consists of arithmetic and normalization. Either may be
first, but the sequence is fixed for a given design. The multiples method

allows, in some cases, more bits of normalization for a cycle and thus develops, on the average, more bits per cycle.

In comparing two methods, *the number of cycles* to prepare a quotient, on the average, is a measure of the effectiveness of the method.

13.8   CHOOSE THE DIVISOR OR
THE MULTIPLE?

Examining the Possibilities

To determine when it would be best to use one of the multiples of the divisor, $\frac{1}{2}$, 1, or 2, let us enumerate what happens in each of the cases for various combinations of divisor and remainder bits. The number of bits to be examined is, as always, a compromise. The more bits we wish to investigate, the better will be our answer; but, similarly, the more bits we investigate, the more hardware required to make our judgment.

Single Divisor

This analysis is based on the first five bits to the right of the binary point in both the remainder and divisor. Since both of these quantities are assumed to be normalized, the first bit to the right of the decimal point in each does not bear important information; it is the other four bits that are of importance. Thus, we have sixteen combinations of divisor bits and sixteen combinations of remainder bits or a total of 256 combinations to be investigated. Luckily, the results are the same whether the remainder is in true or complement form so that a single table will suffice for both of these conditions. First, we make up Table 13.8.1. This gives the number of shifts that will result from subtracting one times the divisor from the remainder. For instance, the bottom entry in the second column from the left is a 4. This means that when the divisor, 0.10000, is subtracted from the partial remainder, 0.10001, the result can be shifted four places to the left. The difference between these two quantities is 0.00001 and this quantity can be shifted over 0's four positions to the left.

Notice for this same entry, when a negative remainder is used, a similar result occurs. When we *add* the divisor, 0.10000, to the remainder, 1.01110, the result is 1.11110 and we may shift over 1's a total of four places.

TABLE 13.8.1 Number of Shifts Resulting from Reducing the Partial Remainder by the Properly Signed Divisor for Five-Bit Combinations of the Most Significant Bits of the Divisor and Dividend for Division by Shifting over 0's and 1's

absolute value of divisor	True partial remainder (0.)															
	10000	10001	10010	10011	10100	10101	10110	10111	11000	11001	11010	11011	11100	11101	11110	11111
	Complement partial remainder (1.)															
	00000	00001	00010	00011	00100	00101	00110	00111	01000	01001	01010	01011	01100	01101	01110	01111
0.11111	1	1	1	1	1	1	1	2	2	2	2	3	3	4	5	5
0.11110	1	1	1	1	1	1	2	2	2	2	3	3	4	5	5	4
0.11101	1	1	1	1	1	2	2	2	2	3	3	4	5	5	4	3
0.11100	1	1	1	1	2	2	2	2	3	3	4	5	5	4	3	3
0.11011	1	1	1	2	2	2	2	3	3	4	5	5	4	3	3	2
0.11010	1	1	2	2	2	2	3	3	4	5	5	4	3	3	2	2
0.11001	1	2	2	2	2	3	3	4	5	5	4	3	3	2	2	2
0.11000	2	2	2	2	3	3	4	5	5	4	3	3	2	2	2	2
0.10111	2	2	2	3	3	4	5	5	4	3	3	2	2	2	2	1
0.10110	2	2	3	3	4	5	5	4	3	3	2	2	2	2	1	1
0.10101	2	3	3	4	5	5	4	3	3	2	2	2	2	1	1	1
0.10100	3	3	4	5	5	4	3	3	2	2	2	2	1	1	1	1
0.10011	3	4	5	5	4	3	3	2	2	2	2	1	1	1	1	1
0.10010	4	5	5	4	3	3	2	2	2	2	1	1	1	1	1	1
0.10001	5	5	4	3	3	2	2	2	2	1	1	1	1	1	1	1
0.10000	5	4	3	3	2	2	2	2	1	1	1	1	1	1	1	1

Double and Half Divisor

Now we must make up similar tables for half and twice the divisor. These have been combined into one table, Table 13.8.2. They may be combined in this way because, in some of the cases where half the divisor is completely unuseable, twice the divisor may be used, and vice versa. Notice that there are cases where both half the divisor and twice the divisor yield the incorrect result. These lay close to the diagonal of the table. This is convenient because the highest values of Table 13.8.1 also lie along the diagonal. Therefore, a first step toward obtaining a criterion might be that when entries in the Table lie along the diagonal or close to it, use one times the divisor; for upper left-hand entries use half the divisor; for lower right-hand entries use twice the divisor.

Now we will combine these tables so that we can extract the greatest advantage in our choice of the divisor multiple, Table 13.8.3.

Combined Table

The upper stepped dashed line in Figure 13.8.3 separates the area of the Table for which half the divisor is appropriate from that for which the full divisor is used. Similarly, the lower stepped dashed line separates the choice of the full divisor from the cases where the double divisor proves better. The stepped lines are optimum choices. To implement them requires logic which considers every bit in both the remainder and the divisor. We might say that such a process produces a 4×4 logical matrix. This is a lot of hardware.

We have a fairly good alternative indicated in Figure 13.8.3 by the dashed lines in the upper left-hand corner and lower right-hand corner of the table. This requires only the examination in both the divisor and remainder of the second and third bits to the right of the binary point. Thus we use half the divisor when the divisor is $0.111XX$ and when the remainder is either $0.100XX$ or $1.011XX$. The logical equations required to implement this near-optimum solution are of a simple 2×2 form.

Analysis of the efficiency of the two methods is found in Section 14.6. A means for evaluating division methods of this kind is to indicate the average number of bits shifted across per shift cycle. In the optimum coded case, this is 2.94; in the 2×2 coded method (the dashed lines) the number of bits shifted across is 2.86. This is contrasted with 2.66 bits per cycle using *only* the value of the divisor.

TABLE 13.8.2   Number of Shifts Resulting from Reducing the Partial Remainder by the Properly Signed Double Divisor or Half Divisor for Five-Bit Combinations of the Most Significant Bits of the Divisor and Dividend for Division by Shifting over 0's and 1's

Absolute value of divisor	True dividend 0.															
	Complement dividend 1.															
	10000 / 01111	10001 / 01110	10010 / 01101	10011 / 01100	10100 / 01011	10101 / 01010	10110 / 01001	10111 / 01000	11000 / 00111	11001 / 00110	11010 / 00101	11011 / 00100	11100 / 00011	11101 / 00010	11110 / 00001	11111 / 00000
0.11111	4	3	3	2	2	2	2	1	1	1	1	1	1	1	1	1
0.11110	4	3	2	2	2	2	2	1	1	1	1	1	1	1	1	1
0.11101	3	3	2	2	2	1	1	1	1	1	1	1	1	1	1	1
0.11100	3	3	2	2	2	1	1	1	1	1	1	1	1	1	1	1
0.11011	3	3	2	2	2	1	1	1	1	1	1	1	1	1	1	1
0.11010	3	2	2	2	1	1	1	1	1	1	1	1	1	1	1	1
0.11001	2	2	2	2	1	1	1	1	1	1	1	1	1	1	1	1
0.11000	2	2	2	1	1	1	1	1	1	1	1	1	1	1	1	1
0.10111	2	2	2	1	1	1	1	1	1	1	1	1	1	1	1	1
0.10110	2	2	2	1	1	1		1	1	1	1	1	1	1	1	1
0.10101	2	2	1	1		1			1	1	1	1	1	1	1	1
0.10100	2	1	1	1						1	1	1	1	1	1	1
0.10011	2	1	1								2	1	1	2	2	2
0.10010	1											2	2	2	2	3
0.10001	1												2	2	3	3
0.10000	1													3	4	5

Region labels within the table: "half divisor", "twice divisor", "Neither (wrong result)".

TABLE 13.8.3 Number of Shifts Resulting from Reducing the Partial Remainder by a Properly Signed Choice of Multiples ($\tfrac{1}{2}$, 1, 2) of the Divisor for Five-Bit Combinations of the Most Significant Bits of the Divisor and Dividend for Division by Shifting over 0's and 1's. Two-Bit Decode (Dashed Corners) and Optimum Decode (Stepped Corners)

Column-group headers (left to right): *Half divisor* · *Half divisor* · *Full divisor*

Right-hand annotations (top to bottom): *True partial remainder* / *Complement partial remainder* · Full divisor · Double divisor · Double divisor

Absolute value of divisor	0.10000	10001	10010	10011	10100	10101	10110	10111	11000	11001	11010	11011	11100	11101	11110	11111	1.01111	01110	01101	01100	01011	01010	01001	01000	00111	00110	00101	00100	00011	00010	00001	00000
0.11111	4	3	3	2	2	2	2	2	2	2	2	3	3	4	5	5	5	4	3	3	3	3	3	3	4	5	5	4	3	3	3	2
0.11110	3	3	2	2	2	2	2	2	2	2	3	3	5	5	4	3	3	3	3	3	3	4	5	5	4	3	3	2	2	2	2	2
0.11101	3	3	2	2	2	2	2	2	2	3	3	4	5	5	4	3	3	2	2	2	2	3	4	5	5	4	3	3	2	2	2	2
0.11100	3	2	2	2	2	2	2	2	3	3	4	5	5	4	3	3	2	2	2	2	3	4	5	5	4	3	3	2	2	2	2	2
0.11011	3	2	2	2	2	2	2	3	3	4	5	5	4	3	3	2	2	2	2	3	4	5	5	4	3	3	2	2	2	2	2	2
0.11010	3	2	2	2	2	2	3	3	4	5	5	4	3	3	2	2	2	2	3	4	5	5	4	3	3	2	2	2	2	2	2	2
0.11001	2	2	2	2	2	3	3	4	5	5	4	3	3	2	2	2	2	3	4	5	5	4	3	3	2	2	2	2	2	2	2	2
0.11000	2	2	2	2	3	3	4	5	5	4	3	3	2	2	2	2	3	4	5	5	4	3	3	2	2	2	2	2	2	2	2	2
0.10111	2	2	2	3	3	4	5	5	4	3	3	2	2	2	2	3	4	5	5	4	3	3	2	2	2	2	2	2	2	2	2	2
0.10110	2	2	3	3	4	5	5	4	3	3	2	2	2	2	3	4	5	5	4	3	3	2	2	2	2	2	2	2	2	2	2	2
0.10101	2	3	3	4	5	5	4	3	3	2	2	2	2	3	4	5	5	4	3	3	2	2	2	2	2	2	2	2	2	2	2	2
0.10100	3	3	4	5	5	4	3	3	2	2	2	2	3	4	5	5	4	3	3	2	2	2	2	2	2	2	2	2	2	2	2	3
0.10011	3	4	5	5	4	3	3	2	2	2	2	3	4	5	5	4	3	3	2	2	2	2	2	2	2	2	2	2	2	2	3	3
0.10010	4	5	5	4	3	3	2	2	2	2	3	4	5	5	4	3	3	2	2	2	2	2	2	2	2	2	2	2	2	3	3	4
0.10001	5	5	4	3	3	2	2	2	2	3	4	5	5	4	3	3	2	2	2	2	2	2	2	2	2	2	2	2	3	3	4	5
0.10000	5	4	3	3	2	2	2	2	3	4	5	5	4	3	3	2	2	2	2	2	2	2	2	2	2	2	2	3	3	4	5	5

13.9 HOW THE METHOD WORKS

An Example

Let us see how the method we have just developed applies to the division illustrated in Figure 13.6.1. The value of the divisor, 54×2^{-6}, does not change throughout the example. Therefore, the row corresponding to the first five numerical bits of this divisor in Table 13.8.3 has been sectioned by dotted lines. We use the optimum choice for the example. This row is our criterion for determining whether we shall use one-half the divisor or the full divisor. Only two choices are possible once a divisor is fixed; that is, no divisor will ever require both half and double multiples during the division process.

The example of Figure 13.6.1 is now repeated as Figure 13.9.1 using the newly developed multiples method. On line 1, the first five bits of the dividend have been sectioned by dashed lines. We look for the column headed by 0.10111 of Table 13.8.3 and follow it down until it intersects the dot-sectioned portion of the chart. We notice that this calls for using the full divisor. Therefore, on line 2 the full divisor complement is added to the dividend. Division proceeds as previously until we reach line 10. Here we see an entry for the partial remainder which begins with 1.01111. This corresponds to the first column in Table 13.8.3. As we scan down that column, we notice that it intersects the dot-sectioned row at a point which calls for half the divisor. In line 11, half the divisor is added to the partial remainder. The result produced on line 12 contains three 1's which may be shifted over. Now, however, in entering the quotient bits, two of these bits correspond to the arithmetic process performed. The first two bits entered into the quotient must be 10 in the case under consideration, since we are *adding* the divisor. If we were *subtracting* one-half the divisor, we would enter 01. Each time a half divisor is used, two bits of the quotient are developed (lines 13, 22, and 25).

There are three occasions in the example where one-half the divisor can be used instead of the full divisor. This produces a complete quotient in ten cycles instead of the thirteen cycles required in Figure 13.6.1.

Graph

The method described is presented a little more vividly in the graph of Figure 13.9.2. Notice the dashed lines above $+\frac{1}{2}$ and below $-\frac{1}{2}$. The dashed-sectioned area between $+\frac{1}{2}$ and the dashed line is the criterion

Line		Entry

Line	Entry
1	0.*10111*111110111001111000100100/
2	1.001010
	―――――
3	1.111001 Remainder/Quotient
4	1.*00111*110 /*0*11 1
5	0.110110
	―――――
6	0.00010110 Remainder/Quotient
7	0.*101101*110 /011*1*00 2
8	1.001010
	―――――
9	1.110111110
10	1.*0111*110 /01110001 3
11	0.011011 (half)
	―――――
12	1.1110100
13	1.*0100*011110 /0111000*1*0*1* 4
14	0.110110
	―――――
15	0.0001111110
16	0.*1111*110 /01110001101*1*00 5
17	1.001010
	―――――
18	0.0010010
19	0.*100100*0100100/0111000110110*0*1*0* 6
20	1.100101 (half)
	―――――
21	0.0010010100100
22	0.*10010*100100/01110001101100100*1* 7
23	1.100101 (half)
	―――――
24	0.00101000100
25	0.*10100*0100/0111000110110010010*1* 8
26	1.001010
	―――――
27	1.110010100
28	1.*0010*100/011100011011001001010*1* 9
29	0.110110
	―――――
30	0.0000000
31	0.00000/0111000110110010010101*1*0 10

FIGURE 13.9.1   (402,398,759 × 2⁻²⁹) ÷ (54 × 2⁻⁶) using shifting over 0's and 1's with halves and doubles of division Bold remainder bits determine divisor multiple; bold quotient bits are determined by divisor multiple and the result of arithmetic

area. There is a similar area in the lower half of the graph. When the partial remainder lies in this criterion area, half the divisor is used instead of the full divisor.

Notice there are four dotted lines in Figure 13.9.2: the upper-most and lower-most lines correspond to the positive and negative divisor; the inner dotted lines correspond to half of the positive and negative divisor.

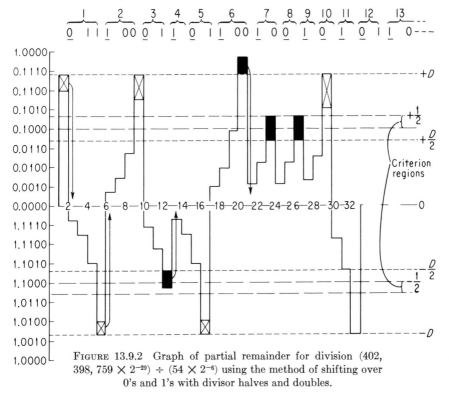

FIGURE 13.9.2 Graph of partial remainder for division (402, 398, 759 $\times$ 2^{-29}) $\div$ (54 $\times$ 2^{-6}) using the method of shifting over 0's and 1's with divisor halves and doubles.

The bracketed entries at the bottom of the figure correspond to the entries of Figure 13.9.1. Figure 13.9.2 is similar to Figure 13.6.2. Notice that the difference between the divisor and the dividend is the dotted area at the extreme left of the figure. When a subtraction is performed, this area represents the amount by which the remainder goes negative. The entries with asterisks use one-half the divisor instead of the full divisor.

Notice that in Entry 4 the remainder, after having been shifted, lies in the dashed criterion region. This says that it is more advantageous to use half the divisor rather than the full divisor. Therefore, the remainder is referred to the dotted line directly above it corresponding to $-\frac{1}{2}$ the divisor. The dotted area is the amount by which the new remainder remains negative.

Follow Figure 13.9.2, in conjunction with Figure 13.9.1 to which it is cross referenced, to see how the criterion is used in determining which multiple of the divisor is to be used, how the new remainder is formed, and why the use of multiples produces faster division than using the divisor alone in shifting over 0's and 1's.

13.10 QUOTIENT BIT DEVELOPMENT

As observed earlier, when the half or double divisor is used to diminish the remainder, as many as two bits of the quotient may be developed. As long as we set up our decoding scheme so as to be sure that two shifts are possible after using a divisor multiple, we can use simple rules to determine what the quotient bits should be. We develop these rules now, assuming that a positive quotient is being developed; a negative quotient merely requires bit reversal as discussed later.

Half Divisor, Present Remainder Positive

First, suppose the remainder is now positive. The divisor must be normalized when we start; the remainder is also normalized, for if it were not, we would continue to shift over 0's instead of starting arithmetic. Since they are normalized, arithmetic can yield, as the two quotient bits only 01. If the result might be $1X$, then our criterion table would request that we subtract the *whole* divisor. Thus, if we are requested to use the half divisor, we know we will shift at least two places and that, in this case, the first two bits are 01.

For a slightly different interpretation, examine Table 13.8.3. All the entries where half the divisor is used require that the full divisor be greater than the present remainder. This guarantees that the first new bit for the positive quotient is 0. Next, recall that the divisor is less than one. Half the divisor is less than $+\frac{1}{2}$ which, in turn, is less than the present remainder (it is greater than $+\frac{1}{2}$). Hence, a new positive remainder results, calling for the second new quotient bit of 1.

Now the new remainder might be very small for some combinations of remainder and divisor. The number of 0's to the right of the binary point determine the shift over 0's and the additional 0's placed in the quotient. Thus, for a new remainder of $0.00001X$, the total quotient bits developed are $\underline{01}00$. The $\underline{01}$ is from arithmetic as reasoned above; the 00 is from shifting over 0's.

Half Divisor, Negative Remainder

When adding the full divisor successfully to a negative remainder, we generate 00 or 01. Decoding tells us that this is not possible and that the half divisor is in order. By reasoning similar to the above, half the divisor cannot make the remainder go positive. Also, we cannot generate 11 because the remainder is already normalized. Therefore, the bits generated must be 10.

To look at it a different way, suppose that subtracting $2D$ on the previous cycle caused the remainder to become negative. This generates 0 for a quotient bit. Relative to the remainder, the divisor is now D, due to a shift to the left of the remainder. Table 13.8.3 guarantees that when $D/2$ is to be used it is only because the divisor is greater than the present remainder magnitude. At this point, we know that $-2D$ (from before) $+D$ (from now) is positive leading to $(0)1$. Next we can predict what happens when $D/2$ is added to this present negative remainder. As above, since $D < 1$ we know $D/2 < \frac{1}{2}$ so that when it is added to the negative remainder, it is insufficient to cause it to go positive. Then $-2D + D + D/2$ is negative or $-0 - D - D/2$ is negative, and what should have been done to keep a positive remainder over three bits is $-0 \times 2D - D - 0 \times D/2$. Hence, the proper quotient bits are $(0)10$.

Of course, the new remainder might be a very small negative number like $1.11110X$. In that case, we develop the quotient bits $\underline{10}11$. The first two are due to arithmetic (underlined); the next two are from shifting over 1's.

Double Divisor, Positive Remainder

Starting with a positive remainder, subtracting the divisor double must leave a negative remainder, for the divisor is greater than $\frac{1}{2}$ and the divisor double is greater than 1. We are sure the remainder is less than 1 because it was normalized. This does not upset us though, because we know that using the full divisor leaves a positive remainder; we rely on the decoder to use the full divisor if there is any chance that it might make the remainder go negative, since the full divisor *could have been* subtracted. Hence, we know the first quotient bit is 1 and we enter $1X$; the other bit is determined during normalization.

Double Divisor, Negative Remainder

When the divisor double is called for in Table 13.8.3, it is because the divisor is so small (bit $> \frac{1}{2}$) that when it is added to the negative remainder, that remainder remains negative. This requires that a 0 quotient bit be entered.

What do we have after adding the divisor double? If we suppose a 0 was developed last, we have $-2D$; now we request $+2D$. This brings us back to the status of the previous cycle. What sense is that? None! In fact, that situation does not arise. The double would be requested only after developing a 1-bit.

For instance, suppose we have just developed (011). Suppose we designate the first 0 as due to $-8D$ which takes us negative. As we shift over the first 1, we note that $-8D + 4D$ would bring us positive, but we do not do it; we note $-8D + 2D$ would bring us positive but do not do it. Now we note $-8D + D$ leaves us negative, but we do not do it. Instead, we do $-8D + 2D$ which takes us positive *and* we record a 0 for the predicted result, $-8D + D$ negative; thus, $(011)0$.

If the new remainder from $-8D + 2D$ is very small, say $0.0001X$, we develop new 0's by shifting over 0's; thus, $(011)000$, where the first 0 is from arithmetic.

Negative Quotient

Where the divisor and dividend are of different sign, we develop a negative quotient. It is usually formed as a complement for such machines as use the 2's complement notation. When shifting over 0's or 1's to normalize the remainder, these bits are entered reversed as 1's and 0's respectively. To maintain the complement notation, the bits developed by arithmetic as described above, whether using the half, full, or double divisor, are also recorded reversed in the quotient register.

Thus the development of a negative quotient calls for the reversal of recording of bits, whether due to normalizing shifts or arithmetic. A negative quotient must also be corrected, upon completion, by adding 1 into the least significant bit for 2's complement notation.

Hardware

Hardware for this method is not discussed here for two reasons: the hardware is almost identical to that used for shifting over 0's and 1's using $\frac{3}{4}$, 1, $\frac{3}{2}$ divisor multiples and is discussed in detail in Section 14.5; further, this latter method is much more efficient and effective than the one just considered.

PROBLEMS

13.1 Why does normalization facilitate division?

13.2 How can we account for the extra time to
    a. Align the divisor.

    b. Normalize the dividend or remainder.

13.3 Do $(3456 \times 2^{-17}) \div (-21 \times 2^{-6})$ by
    a. Restoring division.
    b. Nonrestoring division.
    c. Two-bit lookahead, nonrestoring.
    d. Shifting over 0's and 1's.

13.4 When and why is
    a. Quotient correction
    b. Remainder correction
    necessary? Consider
     i. Representation.
    ii. Sign of operands.
    iii. Sign of results.
    iv. Phase of division.

13.5 How are shifting over 0's and shifting over 1's related?

13.6 How is lookahead combined with shifts over 0's and 1's?

13.7 Contrast the criterion for divisor multiple choice or straight lookahead with that associated with shifts over 0's and 1's.

14

DIVISION

III

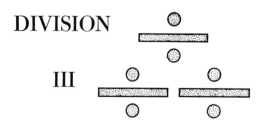

Choice of Multiples

We want to make the best choice of a multiple of the divisor for reducing the remainder. Of course, the very best choice for such a multiple would be one which, when reducing the remainder, yielded 0 as a result. The name for such a multiple is the quotient! That is, if we found this number which, when multiplied by the divisor, was equal to the dividend, we would find the quotient. There is no cheap and dirty method of getting all these bits in one operation. Therefore, we want to find multiples of the divisor which will be best in terms of facilitating our division process while not asking too much of the hardware.

We are looking for multiples for performing division by the method of shifting over 0's and 1's. We can therefore set up the following criteria for judging the qualities of multiples of the divisor:

1. Use of one of the sets of multiples should yield a large number of shifts over 0's or 1's.
2. The multiple should be easily preparable by performing addition.
3. The criterion for determining which multiple is used should be easy to apply.
4. The quotient bit assignment after arithmetic should be made with simple rules.

Various multiples of the divisor which met only the objective (1) above were investigated by Freiman.* He found that the very best triplet of multiples was given as $\frac{77}{128}$, 1, $\frac{53}{32}$. These multiples would be more difficult to prepare than the complete division process! Therefore, we may ignore them. Freiman found a near-best triplet was $\frac{3}{4}$, 1, $\frac{5}{4}$. These multiples did not offer much of an advantage over the triplet of $\frac{3}{4}$, 1, $\frac{3}{2}$. In addition, not only the triple but the quintuple is required. Though easy to prepare, *two* cycles of multiple preparation are needed. Therefore, the candidate which we investigate presently is the triplet $\frac{3}{4}$, 1, $\frac{3}{2}$.

Preference for $\frac{3}{2}$ over 2

Before plunging in, let us examine intuitively the preference of $\frac{3}{2}$ over 2 as a multiple of the divisor for reducing the remainder. We use the large multiple ($\frac{3}{2}$ or 2) when we have a small divisor and a large remainder. Twice a small divisor will always be greater than 1, since the normalized divisor is always greater than $\frac{1}{2}$. However, we can expect that in most cases $\frac{3}{2}$ times a small divisor is less than 1. Therefore, we can undoubtedly set up a criterion table so that $\frac{3}{2}$ the divisor is closer in value to the remainder than twice the divisor would be. The reason for using a multiple of the divisor is so that we can produce a very small new remainder when we reduce the present remainder by this divisor multiple and thus many normalizing shifts result. Therefore, a multiple which produces a number close in size to the remainder is one which is of most use to us.

The same argument may be used in contrasting $\frac{3}{4}$ against $\frac{1}{2}$.

14.2 WHEN DO WE USE A MULTIPLE?

A Table for Multiples

The usefulness of the $\frac{3}{4}$ and $\frac{3}{2}$ multiple of the divisor is most vividly seen when a table of the number of shifts resulting from the use of these multiples is constructed, Table 14.2.1. In constructing this table we have to use three times the appropriately shifted divisor. In practice, this may require additional register length. If such length is not available, the multiple is said to be truncated. In this case, the speedup of division is not

* C. V. Freiman, "Statistical Analysis of Certain Binary Division Algorithms," *Proc. IRE*, V. 49, No. 1, (Jan., 1961), pp. 91–103.

TABLE 14.2.1 Number of Shifts Resulting from Reducing the Partial Remainder by the Properly Signed $\frac{3}{4}$ Divisor or $\frac{2}{3}$ Divisor for Five-bit Combinations of the Most Significant Bits of the Divisor and Dividend for Division by Shifting over 0's and 1's

Absolute value of divisor	0. 10000 / 1. 01111	10001 / 01110	10010 / 01101	10011 / 01100	10100 / 01011	10101 / 01010	10110 / 01001	10111 / 01000	11000 / 00111	11001 / 00110	11010 / 00101	11011 / 00100	11100 / 00011	11101 / 00010	11110 / 00001	11111 / 00000
0.11111	2	2	2	3	3	4	5	5	4	3	3	2	2	1	1	
0.11110	2	2	3	3	4	5	5	4	3	3	2	2	1	1	1	1
0.11101	2	3	3	4	5	5	4	3	3	2	2	1	1	1	2	1
0.11100	2	3	3	4	5	5	4	3	3	2	2	1	1	2	2	1
0.11011	3	3	4	5	5	4	3	3	2	2	1	1	1	2	2	1
0.11010	3	4	5	5	4	3	3	2	2	1	1	1	2	2	3	2
0.11001	4	5	5	5	3	3	2	2	2	1	1	2	2	3	3	2
0.11000	4	5	5	4	3	3	2	2	1	1	1	2	2	3	3	2
0.10111	5	5	4	3	3	2	2	2	1	1	2	2	2	3	5	3
0.10110	5	4	3	3	2	2	2	2	1	1	2	2	3	3	5	4
0.10101	4	3	3	3	2	2	2	1	1	1	2	2	3	4	4	5
0.10100	3	3	3	2	2	2	2	1	1	1	2	3	3	4	5	4
0.10011	3	3	2	2	2	2	2	1	1	2	2	3	3	5	4	3
0.10010	3	2	2	2	2	2	1	1	1	2	2	3	4	5	3	3
0.10001	2	2	2	2	2	2	1	1	1	2	3	3	4	5	3	2
0.10000	2	2	2	2	2	1	1	1	1	2	3	3	4	4	3	2

Annotations: *True partial remainder* (00000 side); *Complement partial remainder* (01111 side); arrow to *Three-quarter divisor*; *One and one-half divisor*.

quite as great as if truncation had not taken place. The difference, however, is only a matter of a few per cent.

Examine Table 14.2.1. The highest values of shifts are found to lie between the diagonal, the corner on each side; this is as we would expect. Thus, when we have a divisor which is close to $\frac{1}{2}$, the $\frac{3}{2}$ multiple of this divisor is close to $\frac{3}{4}$. Therefore, we will develop the maximum number of shifts when the remainder is close to the value $\frac{3}{4}$.

A Combined Table

To form our criterion table, we combine Table 14.2.1 with Table 13.8.1. Using for our new table the higher of the two values, the combined table is shown in Table 14.2.2. Note that several of the possibilities in this table have two entries. This is because different decoding methods may recommend one or another multiple of the divisor.

Optimum Decoding

Optimum decoding requires a 4×4 decoding matrix, as seen by observing the stepped lines in Table 14.2.2. When an entry lies above the upper dashed-stepped line in Table 14.2.2, we use the $\frac{3}{4}$ multiple of the divisor; an entry which lies within the two dash-stepped lines uses one times the divisor; an entry which is below the lower dash-stepped line uses $\frac{3}{2}$ the divisor.

Near-Optimum Decoding

A near-optimum solution can be found using a 2×3 decoding matrix. Such a solution follows the heavy black bounding lines in Table 14.2.2. Entries above the upper line use the $\frac{3}{4}$ multiple, and so forth.

Observe the shift size for the entries in Table 14.2.2. All of them provide a shift of at least two places; most of the shifts are three or more places. Notice also that there are divisors for which, depending on the remainder, either multiple or the full divisor may produce an optimum result. This presents a difficulty if we wish to use only two adders *and* a reduced decision criterion.

Multiple Adders

The only way to use multiple adders in a *fully optimum* fashion would be to provide three adders, one for each multiple of the divisor. Then we

TABLE 14.2.2 Number of Shifts Resulting from Reducing the Partial Remainder by the Properly Signed Choice of Multiples ($\frac{3}{4}$, 1, $\frac{3}{2}$) of the Divisor for Five-Bit Combinations of the Most Significant Bits of the Divisor and Dividend for Division by Shifting over 0's and 1's. Two Four Decode (Heavy Lines) and Optimum Decode (Dashed Lines). Bold Numbers Are from $\frac{3}{4}$ or $\frac{3}{2}$ Multiples.

Absolute value of divisor	Three-quarter divisor								Three-quarter	Full divisor							True partial remainder / Complement partial remainder
0.	10000	10001	10010	10011	10100	10101	10110	10111	11000 11001	11010 11011	11100	11101	11110	11111			
1.	01111	01110	01101	01100	01011	01010	01001	01000	00111 00110	00101 00100	00011	00010	00001	00000			
0.11111	2	2	3	3	3	4	5	5	4 3	3 23	3	3	4	5	5		Full divisor
0.11110	2	2	3	3	4	5	5	4	3 3	3 23	4	5	5	4			
0.11101	2	3	4	4	5	5	4	3	3 32	3 3	3	4	5	5			
0.11100	2	3	4	4	5	5	4	3	33 3	3 4	5	5	4	3			
0.11011	**3**	**3**	**4**	**5**	**5**	**4**	**3**	**33**	**4 5**	**5 5**	**4**	**3**	**3**	**2**			Three-halves
0.11010	3	4	5	5	4	3	3 33	23	4 5	5 4	3	3	**22**				
0.11001	4	5	5	4	3	3 32	3	4	5 5	4 3	3 22	2	2				
0.11000	4	5	5	4	33 3	3 3	4	5	5 4	3 3 22	3	3					
0.10111	5	4 33	33	3	4	5	5	4	3 3	22 2	2	3	3				
0.10110	5	4 33	33	4	5	5	4	3	3 22	2 2	3	4	5				
0.10101	**42**	33 3	4	5	5	4	3	3 23	2 3	4 5	5						
0.10100	**43**	3 3	4	5	5	4	3	3 2	2 3	4 5	5						Three-halves Divisor
0.10011	3	3 4	5	5	4	3	3 22	3	3 4	5 5	4	3	2				
0.10010	4	5 5	4	3	3 32	3	4	5	4 3	3 2	2						
0.10001	5	5 4	3	3 23	3	4	5	4	3 3	2 2	2						
0.10000	5	4 3	3	3 4	5	5	4	3	3 2	2 2	2						

could examine the three sum outputs and use the one which provided the largest shift.

If we were to use two adders, we would find that a large decoding matrix would be required to approach optimum performance. Thus, if we use the simple approach of two adders as used in the last section, whereby divisors of at least $\frac{3}{4}$ called for divisor multiples 1 and $\frac{3}{4}$ and divisors less than $\frac{3}{4}$ called for multiples of 1 and $\frac{3}{2}$, we would find that the area bounded with x's in Table 14.2.2 would not give optimum performance. This method is contrasted with the decoder procedure in the analysis section. Let us say at this point that the two-adder solution is not as good as the 3 × 2 decoder matrix.

14.3   DEMONSTRATION OF THE MULTIPLES METHOD

Using the same example as appeared in Figure 13.6.1, but done using $\frac{3}{4}$, 1, and $\frac{3}{2}$ multiples, we produce Figure 14.3.1. We use Table 14.2.2 as our criterion table for this example. The row for the divisor 0.11011 is outlined and sectioned by dotted lines on Table 14.2.2.

We use the optimum decoding method calling for the $\frac{3}{4}$ divisor when entries to the left of the jagged dashed line are encountered. That is, the remainder is found at the head of a column. Where this column intersects, the dash-sectioned row will determine whether we use the full divisor or $\frac{3}{4}$ divisor.

Numerical Example

In Figure 14.3.1, the portion of the remainder, or dividend in the case of the first entry, which is used to determine what divisor multiple is to be used, is in bold italics. On line 1 you notice that the original dividend begins with 0.10111. When we look this up in the criterion table, we find that the entry is to the left of the dashed line. Therefore, we use the $\frac{3}{4}$ multiple of the divisor, line 2. The result on line 3 requires three shifts to be normalized. In so doing on line 4, all three bits to be entered into the quotient are predetermined by the addition and its result. That is to say, when using the $\frac{3}{4}$ multiple, as many as three bits of the quotient will be predetermined by the addition performed. Quotient bits developed by arithmetic are shown in bold italics.

On line 4, the beginning of the partial remainder 0.11101 requests that the full divisor be used, line 5. The result on line 6 permits a shift of three

Line		Entry
1	0.*10111*11111011100111100010010 0/	
2	1.0101111 (three-quarters)	
3	0.0001110	
4	0.*111011*110 *011* 1	
5	1.001010	
6	0.00010110	
7	0.*101101*110 /011*1*00 2	
8	1.0101111 (three-quarters)	
9	0.000101010	
10	0.*101010*011110 /011100*011* 3	
11	1.0101111 (three-quarters)	
12	0.000001111110	
13	0.*11111*1000100100/0111000110*1*100 4	
14	1.001010	
15	0.001001000100100	
16	0.*100100*0100100/0111000110110010*1*0 5	
17	1.0101111 (three-quarters)	
18	1.1110111100100	
19	1.*0111*100100/01110001101100100*10* 6	
20	0.1010001 (three-quarters)	
21	0.0001101100	
22	0.*1101*100/011100011011001001*010 1* 7	
23	1.001010	
24	0.0000000	
25	0.00000/01110001101100100101011*1*0 8	

FIGURE 14.3.1 ($402{,}398{,}759 \times 2^{-29}$) $\div$ (54×2^{-6}) by shifting over 0's and 1's with ($\frac{3}{4}$, 1, $\frac{3}{2}$) multiples of the divisor Bold remainder bits determine divisor multiple; bold quotient bits are determined by divisor multiple and the result of arithmetic

places. However, since the whole divisor was used in this case, only one quotient bit is determined by addition, line 7, bold italic.

The reader may follow the example as found in Figure 14.3.1, encountering only the difficulty that we have not yet discussed how to determine the three quotient bits in reducing the remainder by the $\frac{3}{4}$ multiple of the divisor. This point is covered in detail in the next section.

Observe that the full quotient is developed in eight cycles in Figure 14.3.1. Contrast this with the thirteen cycles required for the straightforward method illustrated in Figure 13.6.1.

Graph of the Example

A visual appreciation of what transpires by this method of performing division is found by consulting Figure 14.3.2. The first step to orientation

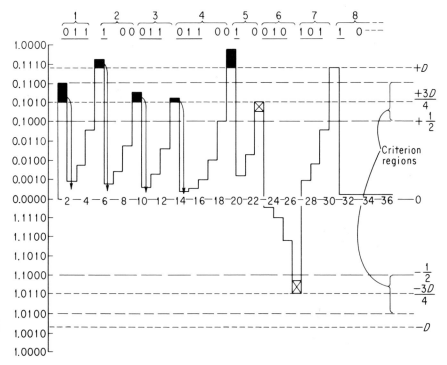

FIGURE 14.3.2 Graph of remainder for division of $(402, 398, 759 \times 2^{-29}) \div (54 \times 2^{-6})$ using the method of shifting over 0's and 1's with divisor multiples $\frac{3}{4}$, 1, $\frac{3}{4}$.

is to find the 0 center line and the two dashed lines which indicate $+\frac{1}{2}$ and $-\frac{1}{2}$. There are four dotted lines. From top to bottom these dotted lines represent the divisor, $\frac{3}{4}$ the divisor, $-\frac{3}{4}$ the divisor, and the negative divisor. One of these will be referenced for subtraction. The criterion regions are bounded by the upper and lower dashed line and lie, for the positive case, between the upper dashed line and $+\frac{1}{2}$ and, in the negative case, between $-\frac{1}{2}$ and the lower dashed line.

In Figure 14.3.2, on the first cycle the remainder is found in the upper criterion region. Therefore, the difference between the partial remainder and $\frac{3}{4}$ the divisor is found indicated by the left-most dotted square. This is the amount by which the new remainder will lie *above the 0 line*. We must double this quantity three times in order to normalize it, in order to make it exceed $+\frac{1}{2}$. The three bits of the quotient developed are found at the top of the chart within the brace labeled 1. These bits were found using the $\frac{3}{4}$ divisor and, therefore, the first three (in this case, all) bits are fixed by the result of the reduction.

On the second cycle, the remainder lies outside of the criterion region which means that we use the complete divisor for reducing the remainder. Therefore, the new remainder is the second dotted square from the left laying wholly above the top dotted line.

On the sixth cycle, the remainder lies within the positive criterion region. However, it is smaller than the $\frac{3}{4}$ divisor, which is indicated by the fact that the partial remainder line lies below the $\frac{3}{4}$ divisor line. Therefore, the result of reduction causes a *negative* remainder, and we find the new entries to be in the *negative* region of the graph.

Similarly, for the seventh cycle the partial remainder lies in the *negative* criterion region. Now the remainder is larger than the $\frac{3}{4}$ multiple of the divisor and, therefore, reduction causes us to re-enter the positive remainder region.

Observe the last, or eighth, cycle of division where the remainder and divisor are *equal*. Since these quantities lie outside the criterion region, using the full divisor results in a 0 remainder and completion of the division.

14.4 QUOTIENT BIT DEVELOPMENT

In using the $\frac{3}{4}$ divisor, three quotient bits are developed and, for the $\frac{3}{2}$ multiple, two quotient bits are developed. Unlike the case of halves and doubles, the bits developed depend upon the sign of the new remainder. We now discuss the cases in terms of the sign of the *remainder before arithmetic* and the *multiple used*.

Positive Remainder, $\frac{3}{4}$ Divisor

From Table 14.2.2 we note that the $\frac{3}{4}$ divisor is recommended only when the divisor is larger than the remainder. Thus, we must develop

$(X)0$. Also, we recall that no matter how large the normalized divisor, the normalized remainder is larger than *half* the divisor. Then $(X)01$ is developed.

However, we subtract the $\frac{3}{4}$ divisor. If this leaves a positive remainder, we know $-0 \times D - D/2 - D/4$ is successful and this calls for $(X)011$.

If the remainder is negative, the quotient is not as great as $(X)011$, but since it is at least $(X)01$, it is $(X)010$.

As before, further quotient 1's are developed for each extra 1 over three in the negative remainder; 0's are developed in the quotient for more than three 0's in the positive remainder. Thus, a remainder of $1.111110X$, after subtraction of $\frac{3}{4}$ of the divisor from the previous positive remainder, develops the quotient bits $01011 : 010$ is from arithmetic reasoned as above; the last two 1's are from shifting over 1's.

Positive Remainder, $\frac{3}{2}$ Divisor

We have a small divisor, and Table 14.2.2 assures that when $\frac{3}{2}$ is used it is smaller than the remainder. Hence, $(X)1$ is developed in the quotient. If, in addition, the new remainder is positive, it is obvious that $(X)11$ is to be placed in the quotient.

In contrast, for a new negative remainder, while $-D$ is known to be positive, $-D - D/2$ is negative; hence, $(X)10$ is the proper quotient development. As usual, shifts over 0's or 1's are appropriate. Thus, a remainder of $0.00001X$ develops quotient bits $1100 : 11$ due to arithmetic and 00 due to shifts over D's.

Negative Remainder, $\frac{3}{4}$ Divisor

The case appears on Table 14.2.2 only when the divisor is larger than the remainder magnitude. Then $+D$ causes a positive remainder. Also, since $D/2$ is less than $\frac{1}{2}$, $+D/2$ causes a negative remainder. Hence, the first two bits developed are 1 and 0. There is doubt, of course, of the effect of $+D/2 + D/4$. Judge this only on the basis of the effect of $D/4$, since we already know the effects of $0 \cdot D + D/2$. When the new remainder is positive, this leads to $(X)101$; when it is negative, this leads to $(X)100$.

Shifting over 0's or 1's is as before, Thus the remainder $0.000001X$ leads to the quotient bits $(X)10100$.

Negative Remainder, $\frac{3}{2}$ Divisor

In Table 14.2.2, these instances arise when the divisor is smaller than the remainder magnitude. Hence, adding the divisor cannot make the remainder go positive and the first bit is 0. Since this is the effect of $+D$, the effect of $+D + D/2$ determines the second bit. For a positive remainder, $(X)01$ is developed; for a negative one, $(X)00$ is produced.

The example for shifting over 1's is for when the new remainder is $1.1110X$; the quotient bits are then $(X)\underline{001}$.

TABLE 14.4   Quotient Bits Developed by Arithmetic for Multiples of the Divisor in Terms of the Signs of the Old and New Remainder for Division by Shifting over 0's and 1's with $\frac{3}{4}$, 1, $\frac{3}{2}$ Divisor Multiples

Old remainder		+		−	
New remainder		+	−	+	−
Multiple	$\frac{3}{4}$	011	010	101	100
	$\frac{3}{2}$	11X	10X	01X	00X

The quotient bits developed by arithmetic for all cases of $\frac{3}{2}$ and $\frac{3}{4}$ in terms of the signs of old and new remainder are summarized in Table 14.4. Table 14.4 holds true for developing *any positive quotient*, even when the divisor and dividend were both negative to begin with.

Negative Quotients

The development of a negative quotient calls for bit reversal in recording the quotient, whether the bits originate from normalization or arithmetic. Thus, shifting over 0's or 1's calls for recording of 1's and 0's respectively; using a $\frac{3}{4}$ divisor with both positive old and new remainders as remainders is recorded as 100 instead of 011; etc. Thus Table 14.4 is equally applicable in *all* cases. For negative quotients the complement of the appropriate entry is used to record the first few bits of the quotient.

14.5   HARDWARE, SHIFTING OVER
0's AND 1's WITH $\frac{3}{2}$, 1, $\frac{3}{4}$ DIVISOR
MULTIPLES

Register Configuration

Figure 14.5 shows the register configuration which may be used to implement the method of division by shifting over 0's and 1's with the $\frac{3}{4}$, 1, $\frac{3}{2}$ multiples of the divisor (or for $\frac{1}{2}$, 1, 2 multiples, for that matter). The

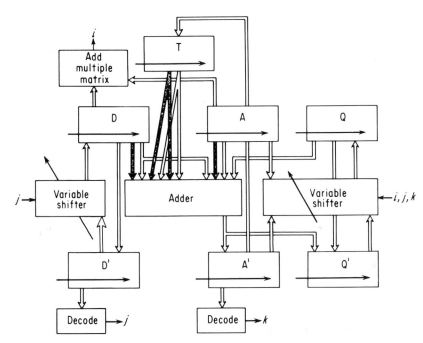

FIGURE 14.5   Hardware for division by shifting over 0's and 1's
using $\frac{3}{4}$, 1, $\frac{3}{2}$ multiples of the divisor.

D' register is required for normalizing the divisor. The T register is used for storing $\frac{3}{2}$ the divisor. Notice the variable shifters. This notation is used because of its simplicity in conveying the ability to shift left a variable number of places in transfers between the prime and the main register.

As previously, the arrow through the right-hand variable shifter in the case that this shifter moves information from the high-order position of the

Q′ register to the low-order position of the A register when called for. Notice also the decode boxes which are used to indicate the number of places of shift required during normalization and division.

Other aspects of the register configuration are self-explanatory, except perhaps the entering of information from the Q register through the adder. This is required for quotient correction because of the nature of 2's complement quotient.

Normalization of Divisor

The first phase of division requires the normalization of the divisor. This is performed by passing the divisor directly over to the D′ register. The decode network attached to the D register examines the left-hand end of the number to determine the number of shifts which are to be performed to normalize this quantity. If this number (indicated as j on the diagram) is less than or equal to the maximum K, it is applied to the variable shifter so that as the quantity is returned to the D register, it will enter there normalized.

If the quantity in the D register indicates that a shift greater than K, the maximum available in the variable shifter, is required, then the maximum shift is called for and another cycle of normalization is instituted after this one is complete.

At the same time divisor normalization is taking place, the dividend is shifted correspondingly. It is transferred directly from the A register to the A′ register. It is returned through its variable shifter to the A register. This variable shifter is actuated by the D′ decoder so that information passing from A′ to A is subjected to the same number of places of shifts as is the divisor.

Normalization of the Dividend and Preparation of $\frac{3}{2}$ Divisor

At the end of the last phase, the divisor was normalized and the dividend has been shifted correspondingly. We are now ready to prepare $\frac{3}{2}$ the divisor. This is done by entering the divisor into one adder input and half the divisor into the other input of the adder. The sum is passed from the adder into the A′ register. It is then transferred directly to the T register.

Entering the next phase of division, we have a normalized divisor and $\frac{3}{2}$ the divisor stored in corresponding registers. The dividend has not been completely normalized yet. It should be noted that, if during the normalizing process the dividend is found to be larger than the divisor, an alarm circuit interrupts division.

Now normalization of the dividend is to be completed. This is performed by passing the dividend into the A′ register where the decoder observes the number of places required to cause normalization. The right-hand variable shifter is actuated so as to produce this number of places of shift. At the same time that the dividend is passing through the adder into the A′ register, the contents of the quotient or Q register is also passed across to the Q′ register. The bits which are being shifted over in order to normalize the dividend must be observed in the A′ register and entered through the variable shifter and the bit reverser into the right-hand end of the Q register. Thus, if we are shifting over 0's to normalize the dividend, 0's are entered through the bit reverser into the Q register corresponding to the bits of the quotient now being developed. Similarly, if the dividend requires shifting over 1's to be normalized, 1's are thus entered through the bit reverser into the Q register. Of course, bit reversal is requested only when developing negative quotients and not for positive quotients.

If normalization is not complete in one cycle, several cycles are performed until the dividend is completely normalized. Each shift in this phase also enters 0's into the quotient register. The number of these is counted in the quotient bit counter.

Main Quotient Preparation Cycles

In the fourth phase of division, a cycle consists of arithmetic and shifting. To determine the multiple of the divisor which is to be used to reduce the partial remainder, the most significant end of both the D register and the A register must be examined. The add-multiple matrix does this job and makes one of seven choices. It can cause connection to one input of the adder of one of the following: the divisor, the divisor complement, $\frac{3}{2}$ the divisor, $\frac{3}{4}$ the divisor complemented; $\frac{3}{4}$ of divisor; $\frac{3}{4}$ of divisor complemented; no connection at all. The A register is connected to the other input of the adder. The sum is transferred to the A′ register. At the same time, the quotient is transferred directly to the Q′ register.

Now the control circuitry must consider these things: the request made by the add-multiple matrix; the affect of addition upon the sign of the remainder; the number of places of shift required to normalize the contents of the A′ register, as determined by the decoder examining the latter. The result of this examination determines the first two or three bits to be entered into the quotient register through the bit reverser. The other bits are the same as those of the remainder which are being shifted over to normalize it. The bit reverser is energized only for negative quotients. The number of places of leftward displacement which are called for is dictated by the A′ decoder and indicated in the figure by K.

Another way to go about actually entering the quotient bits requires three extra bits appended to the right of the Q′ register. As soon as the adder produces the new remainder, enter it into A′. Even before then, we know the three determiners of the first few bits: the old and new remainder sign and the divisor multiple. These are entered, complemented or true as required, into the extra bits of Q′. The number of 0's (1's) at the left of a positive (negative) remainder determines the setting of the variable shifter. The sign of the new remainder and the quotient determine what is to be entered into Q to the right of arithmetically derived bits of the quotient as it is passed from Q to Q′.

Notice that *both* the quotient bits derived from arithmetic and those from normalizing are developed in a *single* cycle. Up to K bits are thus developed.

If the new remainder requires a shift greater than the maximum in order to normalize it, then one or more non-add cycles follows *this* cycle. This is monitored by the add-multiple matrix.

Quotient Bit Count and Termination

During each cycle of both the dividend normalization phase and the division phase, a count is kept of quotient digits produced. This count is determined by the A′ register decoder—the quotient count is increased by the quantity k from the decoder as each cycle is performed. As the division process approaches an end, account must be taken of the number of quotient bits so far developed. Really, this is *always* taken account of but only has an effect as division nears an end.

Termination during the arithmetic half-cycle may change the multiple called for. The output of the add-multiple matrix must be tempered by considering the count stored in the quotient counter. When there are only one or two quotient bits which remain to be developed, then the choice of the divisor multiple to be used may be changed accordingly. As long as such is not the case, quotient-bit development continues as usual.

Termination may be indicated during the remainder-normalization portion of the division cycle. This will be true when the output of the remainder normalization decoder, k, is equal to or greater than the number of quotient bits which remain to be produced. In such cases, the number of shifts actually performed is equal to the number of quotient bits yet to be developed stored in the shift counter.

Correction

When the quotient counter indicates that the full quotient has been produced, a final correction cycle is necessary in the case of a negative quotient. This correction is performed by adding a 1 to the least significant bit of the quantity in the Q register. The Q register is connected to one input of the adder, while the second input of the adder is inhibited. The $^1C_0$ input of the adder is energized which automatically enters a carryin of 1. This result is passed into the Q' register. It is then returned to the Q register through the variable shifter without performing any shifts.

If the dividend and the remainder disagree in sign, a remainder-correction cycle is also necessary. This fact is ascertained by observing the present sign of the quotient remainder and divisor. It is effected by passing the complement of (A) through the adder, adding a single 1 to the least significant position, passing this to A' and finally over to A.

14.6 DISCUSSION OF METHODS FOR DIVISION

Introduction

As shown in an earlier section, the factors which influence the speed of arithmetic processing are circuit speed, adder type and logic. We try to make our discussion independent of the circuit speed. Again we choose the asynchronous adder because two methods (such as non-restoring versus non-performing) equivalent for the synchronous adder turn out to be of different speeds for the asynchronous. Otherwise the ordering of results is unchanged. The result is that our comparison contrasts the different logics which may be used for performing division. A typical shift register chain was presented in Figure 11.3. Such a chain is also typical in performing division.

Let us review the paths appearing in that figure which are of interest to us in analyzing division. First, there is the propagate path which occurs in our adder. This is unique to the asynchronous adder. The average time required for propagation we have indicated as π. If we omit the time required to propagate, then the path through the adder has been indicated as α. The path from the main register over to the prime register and back to the main register again, neglecting the path through the adder and the propagate chain, was indicated as ρ.

The more detailed analysis assumes values for these paths in terms of the time required for information to pass through a single stage of combined mixer and gate. The single state time was labeled σ. We use the following relationships:

$$\pi = 7\sigma$$

$$\alpha = \sigma$$

$$\rho = 8\sigma$$

Neglected Factors

In division, we encounter several subsidiary processes which are often performed in the course of division. Several of these have been neglected in order to simplify the analysis which does not introduce any considerable error. Let us now see what these factors are.

divisor normalization

Many of the methods require prenormalization of the divisor. The time required for this has been neglected. There are several ways to rationalize this. The first and most obvious is to regard the divisor as a random number. Then, half the time the sign bit and most significant bit agree and no normalization at all is required; one-quarter of the time only one place of normalization is required, etc. We will not investigate this assumption any further but will leave it to the reader as to whether he is willing to accept it.

More realistically, we might assume that the programmer would normalize his divisor in order to take advantage of the increase in speed by so doing. In addition, when we consider floating-point arithmetic in Chapter 15, we will find that numbers in floating-point form are almost always normalized. Then, when supplying a dvision method for floating-point arithmetic, we would wish to ignore the necessity of normalizing our divisor.

Another consideration is that all high-speed division methods require prenormalization. Since this is a common factor, it might be ignored in comparing these methods.

negative quotients

Negative quotients in 2's complement notation *always* require a correction. This correction is therefore common to every method that we analyze. Since it is a common factor we may neglect it in comparing these methods.

remainder correction

In all non-restoring division methods, the remainder sometimes ends up improperly recorded. An additional cycle is required to restore it. Again this may be considered a common factor to all non-restoring methods. We have noted that most computers supply the corrected remainder, even though a very small, even infinitesimal portion of the problems actually refer to the remainder. Therefore, it would seem that non-restoring division need not restore the remainder except when a special command was given to do so. In this case, the remainder correction cycle would be ignored in all cases and our comparison would be adequate.

14.7   TEMPORAL ANALYSIS OF DIVISION

We will now discuss each division method in turn and derive a formula which expresses the time required to perform division in terms of the propagate time, add time, and register time. The results of this analysis are presented in Table 14.7. The entries are labeled to correspond with the lettered topics below. Note that certain methods of division have variations within themselves. In such cases, entries on the table have a number following the letter to indicate the variation under consideration.

A. Restoring Division

When the partial remainder changes sign, this method provides another cycle for restoring the partial remainder. Our first approximation to the number of times that restoration is required would be that on the average when dealing with random numbers, we might expect it to take place half the time. Let N_R represent the number of restoring or direct-transfer cycles. We have,

$$N_R = \frac{N}{2} \qquad (14.7.A1)$$

In addition, there is one cycle required for each quotient bit generated. If N_A is the number of arithmetic cycles performed,

$$N_A = N \qquad (14.7.A2)$$

The time for an arithmetic cycle, t_A, is

$$t_A = \rho + \alpha + \pi \qquad (14.7.A3)$$

TABLE 14.7 Comparison of Division Time for Different Methods in Terms of Carry Propagation Time, π, Add Less Propagation Time, α, and Register Shift Less Add Time, ρ. These Are Translated in Single Stage Time, σ. Numerical Values are given for a Stage Time of 100 Nanoseconds. Normalizing Time Has Been Neglected and Is Required for Method D thru N. Also Time for Quotient Correct on (All) and Remainder Correction (B) (I thru N) Is Omitted

Entry	Description	Equation for T	$N = 48$ $\rho = 8\sigma$ $\alpha = \sigma$ $\pi = 7\sigma$ $\pi' = 2\sigma$	For $\sigma = 100$ Nano- seconds, Micro- seconds
A	Restoring	$\dfrac{3N}{2}(\rho + \alpha + \pi)$	1151σ	$115\ \mu s$
B	Non-restoring	$N(\rho + \alpha + \pi)$	768σ	77
C	Non-performing	$\dfrac{N}{2}(2\rho + 2\alpha + \pi + \pi')$	648σ	65
D	Shift over 0's, 5-bit divisor	$0.538N(\rho + \alpha + \pi)$	413σ	41
E	Shift over 0's, unlimited divisor	$0.575N(\rho + \alpha + \pi)$	442σ	44
F	Two-bit lookahead, one-bit compare	$(.615N + 1)(\rho + \alpha)$ $+ (.426N + 1)\pi$	425σ	43
G	Two-bit lookahead, two-bit compare	$(.552N + 1)(\rho + \alpha)$ $+ (.400N + 1)\pi$	389σ	39
H	Two-bit lookahead, four-bit compare	$(.512N + 1)(\rho + \alpha)$ $+ (.38N + 1)\pi$	365σ	37
I	Two-bit lookahead, non-restoring	$\left(\dfrac{N}{2} + 1\right)(\rho + \alpha) +$ $\left(\dfrac{3N}{8} + 1\right)\pi$	358σ	36
J1	0's and 1's, 5-bit divisor	$.392N(\rho + \alpha + \pi)$	301σ	30
J2	0's and 1's, unlimited divisor, 6-bit shift limit	$.392N(\rho + \alpha + \pi)$	301σ	30
J3	0's and 1's, unlimited divisor, no shift limit	$.376N(\rho + \alpha + \pi)$	289σ	29
K1	0's and 1's, $\frac{1}{2}$, 1, 2, two-bit decode, 5-bit divisor	$.365N(\rho + \alpha + \pi)$	280σ	28
K2	0's and 1's, $\frac{1}{2}$, 1, 2, two-bit decode, shift limit 6	$.365N(\rho + \alpha + \pi)$	276σ	28
K3	0's and 1's, $\frac{1}{2}$, 1, 2, two-bit decode, no shift limit	$.350N(\rho + \alpha + \pi)$	269σ	27

Table 14.7   (*Continued*)

Entry	Description	Equation for T	$N = 48$ $\sigma = 8\sigma$ $\alpha = \sigma$ $\pi = 7\sigma$ $\pi' = 2\sigma$	For $\sigma = 100$ Nano- seconds, Micro- seconds
L1	0's and 1's, $\frac{1}{2}$, 1, 2, optimum code or double adder, 5-bit divisor	$.355N(\rho + \alpha + \pi)$	273σ	27
L2	0's and 1's, $\frac{1}{2}$, 1, 2, optimum code or double adder, shift limit 6	$.350N(\rho + \alpha + \pi)$	267σ	27
L3	0's and 1's, $\frac{1}{2}$, 1, 2, opmum code or double adder, no shift limit	$.340N(\rho + \alpha + \pi)$	261σ	26
M1	0's and 1's, $\frac{3}{4}$, 1, $\frac{3}{2}$, two by three decode, 5-bit divisor	$(.284N + 1)(\rho + \alpha + \pi)$	234σ	23
M2	0's and 1's, $\frac{3}{4}$, 1, $\frac{3}{2}$, two by three decode, shift limit 6	$(.282N + 1)(\rho + \alpha + \pi)$	232σ	23
M3	0's and 1's, $\frac{3}{4}$, 1, $\frac{3}{2}$, two by three decode, shift unlimited	$(.265N + 1)(\rho + \alpha + \pi)$	219σ	22
N1	0's and 1's, $\frac{3}{4}$, 1, $\frac{3}{2}$, optimum decode, 5-bit divisor	$(.280N + 1)(\rho + \alpha + \pi)$	230σ	23
N2	0's and 1's, $\frac{3}{4}$, 1, $\frac{3}{2}$, optimum decode, shift limit 6	$(.278N + 1)(\rho + \alpha + \pi)$	228σ	23
N3	0's and 1's, $\frac{3}{4}$, 1, $\frac{3}{2}$, optimum decode, no shift limit	$(.262N + 1)(\rho + \alpha + \pi)$	217σ	22

that for a simple transfer, t_R, is,

$$t_R = \rho \tag{14.7.A4}$$

Therefore, the total time, T, is

$$T = N(\rho + \alpha + \pi) + \frac{N\rho}{2} \tag{14.7.A5}$$

B. Non-Restoring Division

The number of cycles performed for non-restoring division is the same as the number of quotient bits developed. Therefore, we can immediately write down the total amount of time required for this type of division as

$$T = N(\rho + \alpha + \pi) \qquad (14.7.\text{B1})$$

C. Non-Performing Division

We obtain an advantage by non-performing division only if the time to propagate sign information is less than the amount of time required for the full propagation associated with the addition. It has been assumed that such is the case, and now this will be verified by determining precisely what this time is.

Let us refer to the time required to propagate sign information as π'. To determine this time, we must assume that randomly distributed numbers are being added (or subtracted, as the case may be). We know that the probability that the final stage is a propagate or a generate stage is approximately equal. Let us call the probability that we generate the sign carry in one stage, P_1. We will label the expected number of stages arising from this situation, S_1. In general, the probability of generating the sign in i stages is P_i and the expected number of stages resulting from this situation is S_i. Then,

$$P_1 = \text{prob } \{1 \text{ stage}\} = \tfrac{1}{2} \qquad\qquad S_1 = 1 \cdot \tfrac{1}{2} = \tfrac{1}{2}$$

$$P_2 = \text{prob } \{2 \text{ stages}\} = \tfrac{1}{4} \qquad\qquad S_2 = 2 \cdot \tfrac{1}{4} = \tfrac{1}{2}$$

$$P_i = \text{prob } \{i \text{ stages}\} = (\tfrac{1}{2})^i \qquad S_i = i \cdot \left(\frac{1}{2}\right)^i = \frac{i}{2^i}$$

Then the average number of stages is called $\bar{S}$ and is

$$\bar{S} = \sum_{i=1}^{N} \frac{i}{2^i} \doteq \sum_{i=1}^{\infty} \frac{i}{2^i} = 2 \qquad (14.7.\text{C1})$$

Note that the summation in (14.7.C1) is the same as that which arose in connection with multiplication by shifting over 0's and 1's.

Our assumption for restoring division was that half the time restoration was required. If we maintain this here, we find that complete propagation occurs half the time so that,

$$N_{\text{p}} = \bar{N}_{\text{p}} = \frac{N}{2} \qquad (14.7.\text{C2})$$

The time for a cycle when propagation is completed is given as,

$$t_p = (\rho + \alpha + \pi) \qquad (14.7.C3)$$

When propagation occurs only to the point that the sign is finished,

$$t_p' = (\rho + \alpha + \pi') \qquad (14.7.C4)$$

Then the total time required for division by this method is

$$T = \frac{N}{2} (2\rho + 2\alpha + \pi + \pi') \qquad (14.7.C5)$$

D. Shifting Over 0's, Restoring Five-Bit Divisor

In this method, the divisor is either added to or subtracted from the partial remainder as it is shifted over to the prime register. On returning the remainder to the main register, it is shifted a number of times such that it is returned normalized to the main register. The time required for each cycle is, as before,

$$t = \rho + \alpha + \pi \qquad (14.7.D1)$$

The number of cycles is inversely proportioned to the number of shifts performed on each cycle, so that

$$N_C = \frac{N}{\bar{S}} \qquad (14.7.D2)$$

It now remains to determine the average number of shifts per cycle. To do this, we construct a table the same as Table 13.8.1, except that we enter a 1 wherever the result of subtraction produces a negative result. In other words, when arithmetic indicates a change in sign, the cycle consists of transferring the partial remainder from the main register to the prime register and then returning it from the prime register to the main register, shifted one place. The total number of shifts is determined by adding up all the entries on the table and is 477. This is a 16 × 16 table and therefore contains 256 entries. Therefore, the average entry is $477/256 = 1.86$, and this is the average number of shifts, so that

$$\bar{S} = 1.86 \qquad (14.7.D3)$$

The total time for this method is then

$$T = tN_C = \frac{N}{1.88} (\rho + \alpha + \pi) \qquad (14.7.D4)$$

E. Shifting Over 0's, Restoring Unlimited Divisor

The derivation for this method is the same as that of the previous one. The only difference is in the diagonal entries of the table which we prepare.

We now assume that the divisor and the dividend may have many more than five bits each. Table 13.8.1 was based on the fact that both divisor and dividend *consisted only of five bits after the binary point*. The diagonal entries represent the cases where the first five bits of the divisor and dividend are identical; previously the remaining bits were non-existent —now let us consider them as being unspecified. In this case, reduction of the remainder by the divisor will cause a sign change *half the time* for each diagonal entry. When the partial remainder does not change sign, a shift of five places is possible, as indicated by the previous diagonal entries all of which were five. When the remainder changes sign restoration or non-performance is called for followed by only a single shift. Since each of these events occurs in approximately equal frequency, we can say that the average diagonal entry is $\frac{5}{2} + \frac{1}{2} = 3$.

We form a new table identical to Table 13.8.1, replacing the diagonal entries by 3. When we total all the entries in the table we find that there are 445. The total number of cases examined, as previously, is 256. Therefore, the average shift length is

$$\bar{S} = 1.74 \qquad (14.7.\text{E1})$$

We then have for the total time for this method,

$$T = .575N(\rho + \alpha + \pi) \qquad (14.7.\text{E2})$$

F. Two-Bit Lookahead, One-Bit Compare

We found in Section 12.5 that three-eights of the time this method yielded a shift of one place and five-eighths of the time, a shift of two places. Therefore, our average shift length is

$$P_1 = \frac{3}{8} \qquad S_1 = 1 \cdot \frac{3}{8} = \frac{3}{8}$$

$$P_2 = \frac{5}{8} \qquad S_2 = 2 \cdot \frac{5}{8} = \frac{10}{8}$$

$$\bar{S} = \frac{13}{8}$$

We are also interested in the proportion of times where we encounter initial remainder bits 00, for then no arithmetic is called for and our time for a cycle is reduced. We find this proportion, P_{00}, is one-quarter, so that

$$P_{00} = \frac{1}{4} \qquad S_{00} = 2 \cdot \frac{1}{2} = \frac{1}{2}$$

Let us now call the proportion of the time when the proportion time must be considered P. Then this fraction is given as the ratio of the average shift length less the average number of shifts where a pair of 0's are encountered to the average shift length. Put into symbols, this is

$$P = \frac{\bar{S} - S_{00}}{S^-} \qquad (14.7.\text{F1})$$

In this case,

$$P = \frac{\frac{13}{8} - \frac{1}{2}}{\frac{13}{8}} = \frac{9}{13} \qquad (14.7.\text{F2})$$

We must also consider an extra addition cycle required for forming the divisor triple. Then the total time required for this process is

$$T = \frac{N}{S} (\alpha + \rho + P\pi) + (\alpha + \rho + \pi) \qquad (14.7.\text{F3})$$

When the values for the average shift length and propagate proportion are substituted into (14.7.F3),

$$T = \frac{8N}{13} \left(\rho + \alpha + \frac{9\pi}{13} \right) + (\rho + \alpha + \pi) \qquad (14.7.\text{F4})$$

This may be simplified to

$$T = (.615N + 1)(\rho + \alpha) + (.426N + 1)\pi \qquad (14.7.\text{F5})$$

G. Two-Bit Lookahead, Two-Bit Compare

The proportions of each shift length were discussed in Section 6.4. The calculation for determining the average shift length is

$$P_1 = \frac{3}{16} \qquad S_1 = 1 \cdot \frac{3}{16} = \frac{3}{16}$$

$$P_2 = \frac{13}{16} \qquad S_2 = 2 \cdot \frac{13}{16} = \frac{26}{16}$$

$$\bar{S} = \frac{29}{16}$$

We note the following rate of occurrence of the bit pair 00 and the consequent shifts caused by it.

$$P_{00} = \frac{1}{4} \qquad S_{00} = 2 \cdot \frac{1}{2} = \frac{1}{2} \qquad (14.7.\text{G}1)$$

This produces a propagate proportion

$$P = \frac{\frac{29}{16} - \frac{1}{2}}{\frac{29}{16}} = \frac{21}{29} \qquad (14.7.\text{G}2)$$

The total time for this process, again provided a single cycle for preparation of the divisor triple, is then

$$T = \frac{16N}{29}\left(\rho + \alpha + \frac{21\pi}{29}\right) + (\rho + \alpha + \pi) \qquad (14.7.\text{G}3)$$

This simplifies to

$$T = (.552N + 1)(\rho + \alpha) + (.400N + 1)\pi \qquad (14.7.\text{G}4)$$

H. Two-Bit Lookahead, Four-Bit Compare

The proportion of each shift length again is derived from the text so that the average shift length is calculated as

$$P_1 = \frac{3}{64} \qquad S_1 = 1 \cdot \frac{3}{64} = \frac{3}{64}$$

$$P_2 = \frac{61}{64} \qquad S_2 = 2 \cdot \frac{61}{64} = \frac{122}{64}$$

$$\bar{S} = \frac{125}{64}$$

The shift resulting from the bit pair 00 in the remainder is, as before,

$$P_{00} = \tfrac{1}{4} \qquad S_{00} = \tfrac{1}{4} \times 2 = \tfrac{1}{2} \qquad (14.7.\text{H}1)$$

The propagate proportion is then

$$P = \frac{\frac{125}{64} - \frac{1}{2}}{\frac{125}{64}} = \frac{93}{125} \qquad (14.7.\text{H}2)$$

The total time for the division, including a cycle for preparation of the divisor triple, is

$$T = \frac{64N}{125} \left(\rho + \alpha + \frac{93\pi}{125} \right) + (\rho + \alpha + \pi) \qquad (14.7.\text{H}3)$$

This simplifies to

$$T = (.512N + 1)(\rho + \alpha) + (.38N + 1)\pi \qquad (14.7.\text{H}4)$$

I. Two-Bit Lookahead, Non-Restoring

The average shift length in this case is always 2. We always can determine a pair of quotient bits after performing arithmetic. Again, the proportion of remainders which have initial bits 00 is assumed to be $\frac{1}{4}$, so that,

$$P_{00} = \tfrac{1}{4} \qquad S_{00} = \tfrac{1}{2} \qquad (14.7.\text{I}1)$$

The proportion of the time for which propagation logic is required is then, simply,

$$P = \frac{2 - \frac{1}{2}}{2} \qquad (14.7.\text{I}2)$$

The total time for this process, again allotting a single cycle for preparation of the divisor triple, is

$$T = \frac{N}{2} \left(\rho + \alpha + \frac{3\pi}{4} \right) + (\rho + \alpha + \pi) \qquad (14.7.\text{I}3)$$

This simplifies to

$$T = \left(\frac{N}{2} + 1 \right) (\rho + \alpha) + \left(\frac{3N}{8} + 1 \right) \pi \qquad (14.7.\text{I}4)$$

J1. Shifting Over 0's and 1's, Five-Bit Divisor

The average shift length now is simply found by totaling the *entries* in Table 6.7.1 and dividing by the total *number* of entries. Then,

$$S = \frac{651}{254} = 2.54 \qquad (14.7.\text{J}1.1)$$

The total length of time is therefore given by

$$T = \frac{N}{2.54}\,(\rho + \alpha + \pi) \qquad (14.7.\text{J}1.2)$$

This simplifies to

$$T = .392N(\rho + \alpha + \pi) \qquad (14.7.\text{J}1.3)$$

J2.* Shifting Over 0's and 1's, Unlimited Divisor, Shift Limit of 6

The average shift length for this case is found to be

$$\bar{S} = 2.54 \qquad (14.7.\text{J}2.1)$$

The total time is therefore given as

$$T = .392N(\rho + \alpha + \pi) \qquad (14.7.\text{J}2.2)$$

J3.* Shifting Over 0's and 1's, Unlimited Divisor, No Shift Limit

Calculations for this method reveal an average shift length

$$\bar{S} = 2.66 \qquad (14.7.\text{J}3.1)$$

Therefore, the total time for this method is,

$$T = .376N(\rho + \alpha + \pi) \qquad (14.7.\text{J}3.2)$$

K1. Shifting Over 0's and 1's Using Divisor Multiples $\frac{1}{2}$, 1, 2, Two-Bit Decode, Five-Bit Divisor

The average shift length is calculated here by referring to Table 13.8.3. We add up the numbers in all the entries and, where there are two num-

---

* The average shift lengths for the starred items are tabulated in O. L. MacSorely, "High-speed arithmetic in binary computers," *Proc. IRE*, V. 49, No. 1 (Jan. 1961), pp. 67–91. This tabulation is based on the statistical analysis performed by C. V. Freiman and presented in C. V. Freiman, "Statistical analysis of certain binary division algorithms," *Proc. IRE*, V. 49, No. 1 (Jan. 1961), pp. 91–103.

bers in a single box, we choose the dotted-line ones, since we are interested in a two-bit decode. Since the total number of shifts from this addition is 702, the average shift length is

$$\bar{S} = 2.74 \qquad (14.7.\text{K1.1})$$

The total time for division by this method is, therefore,

$$T = .365N(\rho + \alpha + \pi) \qquad (14.7.\text{K1.2})$$

K2.* Shifting Over 0's and 1's Using Divisor Multiples $\frac{1}{2}$, 1, 2, Unlimited Divisor, Shift Limit of 6

Calculations yield an average shift length

$$\bar{S} = 2.78 \qquad (14.7.\text{K2.1})$$

The total time for division by this method is, therefore,

$$T = .360N(\rho + \alpha + \pi) \qquad (14.7.\text{K2.2})$$

K3.* Shifting Over 0's and 1's Using Divisor Multiples $\frac{1}{2}$, 1, 2, Unlimited Divisor, No Shift Limit

The calculated average shift length is

$$\bar{S} = 2.86 \qquad (14.7.\text{K3.1})$$

The total time for division by this method is, therefore,

$$T = .350N(\rho + \alpha + \pi) \qquad (14.7.\text{K3.2})$$

L1. Shifting Over 0's and 1's Using Divisor Multiples $\frac{1}{2}$, 1, 2, Optimum Decoding or Double Adder, Five-Bit Divisor

Again we refer to Table 13.8.3. Since we have optimum decoding or its equivalent, two adders, we use the dashed portion of the table. In totaling the entries we use only the light-face numbers. Our total is 722. Therefore, the average shift length is

$$\bar{S} = 2.82 \qquad\qquad (14.7.\text{L1.1})$$

The total time then becomes

$$T = .355N(\rho + \alpha + \pi) \qquad\qquad (14.7.\text{L1.2})$$

L2.* Shifting Over 0's and 1's, Using Divisor Multiples $\frac{1}{2}$, 1, 2, Optimum Decoding, Unlimited Divisor, Shift Limit of 6

$$S = 2.86 \qquad\qquad (14.7.\text{L2.1})$$
$$T = .350N(\rho + \alpha + \pi) \qquad\qquad (14.7.\text{L2.2})$$

L3.* Shifting Over 0's and 1's Using Divisor Multiples $\frac{1}{2}$, 1, 2, Optimum Decoding, Unlimited Divisor, No Shift Limit

$$S = 2.94 \qquad\qquad (14.7.\text{L3.1})$$
$$T = .340N(\rho + \alpha + \pi) \qquad\qquad (14.7.\text{L3.2})$$

M1. Shifting Over 0's and 1's Using Divisor Multiples $\frac{3}{4}$, 1, $\frac{3}{2}$, Two-By-Three Decode, Five-Bit Divisor

This case is treated by examining Table 14.2.2. The entries are totalized by referring to the solid black line as described in Section 14.2. The total for this table is then 903. The average shift length is, therefore,

$$S = \frac{903}{256} = 3.52 \qquad\qquad (14.7.\text{M1.1})$$

In calculating the total time required for division by this method, an extra addition cycle must be allotted to preparation of the divisor triple. Therefore, we have, in general, for these divisor multiples, a time

$$T = \left(\frac{N}{S} + 1\right)(\rho + \alpha + \pi) \qquad (14.7.M1.2)$$

Substituting the value for shift length into the equation above, we have,

$$T = (.284N + 1)(\rho + \alpha + \pi) \qquad (14.7.M1.3)$$

M2.* Shifting Over 0's and 1's Using Divisor Multiples $\frac{3}{4}$, 1, $\frac{3}{2}$, Two-By-Three Decode, Unlimited Divisor, Shift Limit of 6

Calculations yield an average shift length

$$S = 3.55 \qquad (14.7.M2.1)$$

When this is substituted into (6.9.M1.2),

$$T = (.282N + 1)(\rho + \alpha + \pi) \qquad (14.7.M2.2)$$

M3.* Shifting Over 0's and 1's Using Divisor Multiples $\frac{3}{4}$, 1, $\frac{3}{2}$, Two-By-Three Decode, Unlimited Divisor, Shift Unlimited

$$S = 3.77 \qquad (14.7.M3.1)$$

$$T = (.265N + 1)(\rho + \alpha + \pi) \qquad (14.7.M3.2)$$

N1. Shifting Over 0's and 1's Using Divisor Multiples $\frac{3}{4}$, 1, $\frac{3}{2}$, Optimum Decode, Five-Bit Divisor

Again we refer to Table 14.2.2. We total the entries, this time referring to the jagged dashed line to determine the numeral to be used, as described in the text of Section 14.2. The total we get is 916; therefore, the average shift length is

$$S = \frac{916}{256} = 3.58 \qquad (14.7.\text{N}1.1)$$

Again we allot a cycle for preparation of the divisor triple. The total time for division by this method is, therefore,

$$T = (.280N + 1)(\rho + \alpha + \pi) \qquad (14.7.\text{N}1.2)$$

N2.* Shifting Over 0's and 1's Using Divisor Multiples $\frac{3}{4}$, 1, $\frac{3}{2}$, Optimum Decode, Unlimited Divisor, Shift Limit of 6

Calculations yield the following equations:

$$S = 3.60 \qquad (14.7.\text{N}2.1)$$

$$T = (.278N + 1)(\rho + \alpha + \pi) \qquad (14.7.\text{N}2.2)$$

N3.* Shifting Over 0's and 1's Using Divisor Multiples $\frac{3}{4}$, 1, $\frac{3}{2}$, Optimum Decode, Unlimited Divisor, No Shift Limit

$$S = 3.82 \qquad (14.7.\text{N}3.1)$$

$$T = (.262N + 1)(\rho + \alpha + \pi) \qquad (14.7.\text{N}3.2)$$

PROBLEMS

14.1 Find out by referring to Freiman's article how the optimum multiples were determined for lookahead associated with division by shifting over 0's and 1's.

14.2 Why does the $\frac{5}{4}$, 1, $\frac{3}{4}$ method require more hardware than the $\frac{3}{2}$, 1, $\frac{3}{4}$ method?

14.3 Make up a decision table for division by shifting over 0's and 1's using $3D/4$, 1, $5D/4$.

14.4 Do $(3456 \times 2^{-7}) \div (-21 \times 2^{-6})$ by
   a. Shifting over 0's and 1's using $D/2$, D, $2D$.
   b. Shifting over 0's and 1's using $3D/4$, D, $3D/2$.
   c. Shifting over 0's and 1's using $3D/4$, D, $5D/4$.

14.5 Make entries P1, P2, P3 for the method of Problem 14.3, using the table made for that problem for
   P1 optimum divide, 5-bit divisor.
   P2 optimum divide, shift limit of six.
   P3 optimum divide, no shift limit.

14.6 Why isn't a carry saver used to speed up division?

15

FLOATING-POINT NUMBERS,

ADDITION

AND

SUBTRACTION

15.1 FLOATING-POINT NUMBERS

In this chapter we are going to investigate floating-point numbers, arithmetic using these numbers, and how the computer performs these operations.

As a preview of what is to come, let us simply say that the floating-point notation describes a number in two ways. One portion of the floating-point number communicates the magnitude of the number; the other portion notes the exact size of the number within the range set off by the first portion. These two portions of the number are called, respectively, the exponent and mantissa. The terms arise from the similarity to their use with respect to logarithms. The exponent describes the order of magnitude —the power of the base; the mantissa describes the number within that range. Together for a given word size, these terms communicate as much or more in floating-point notation as compared with the normal fixed-point notation with which we are familiar.

Thus we might indicate the speed of light in scientific notation as 1.863×10^5 miles per second. The position of the decimal point is always after the left-most digit. The number of digits conveys the accuracy of measurement—in this case four figures. The fixed-point equivalent, 186, 300, is readily obtained.

Many of the large computers today, especially those for scientific applications, can perform floating-point arithmetic automatically. Almost any machine can be *programmed* to do floating-point arithmetic. The use of the floating-point notation extends the range of the numbers which can be handled by the machine with only a slight sacrifice, if any, in the total accuracy of the numbers manipulated. This notation is useful where it is anticipated that the range of numbers involved in a given problem is uncommonly great. It also finds use when the range of the numbers is unpredictable or where investigation of the range of the numbers encountered in the problem is almost as much trouble as doing the problem.

It might seem that the advantage gained in using the floating-point notation is counterbalanced by the extra time required for the computer to perform the calculations. This is not true. In fact, although floating-point addition and subtraction take longer than fixed-point, floating-point multiplication and division are as fast or faster than fixed-point. For instance, the IBM 7090 does floating multiply and divide in the same time as fixed-point; floating add/subtract can take as long as multiply which, of course, is longer than fixed-point add/subtract.

In the first section, of this chapter we talk about fixed-point notation, decimal floating-point notation, binary floating-point notation, binary floating-point arithmetic and, finally, the machine representation of binary floating-point numbers. The sections which follow are devoted to how a typical computer performs floating-point operations. Since addition and subtraction involve the most complications, three sections are devoted to them. The first of these sections is an analysis of what must be done to perform floating-point addition and subtraction. Next, we investigate the register configuration and the breakdown of each task for addition and subtraction. Finally, the machine implementation is investigated and the logical equations for each interconnection and timing for a typical layout are presented.

Properties of the Fixed-Point System

Fixed-point notation, with which we are most familiar, is the notation of commerce and business. In it, all numbers are represented on the same scale. The location of the decimal point indicates the size of the number. In business, the quantities we are dealing with are dollars and cents. We rarely encounter amounts measured in fractions of a penny. Therefore, we can depend on the fact that there are usually only two places to the right of the decimal point which will be used. To the left of the decimal point we will find varying numbers of digits. Again, the range of these figures can be estimated from the type of problems dealt with. A small business-man will never have to worry about six digits to the left of the decimal point, whether he is dealing with money or inventories.

In control problems, the quantities dealt with may be angular and would be measured then in degrees, minutes, and seconds. The range of such quantities is known so that fixed-point notation is easily adaptable to this kind of problem. Other quantities which might be used in control problems are speed, distance, force, pressure, and so forth. All these quantities have known or predictable ranges and can be tailored to fit into the fixed-point system.

Many scientific problems fall into this same category; that is, where the range of the numbers dealt with is predictable. Hence these problems face no hindrance when using fixed-point notation.

In the fixed-point system, difficulty arises in scientific problems such as those faced by astronomers, lens designers, and atomic physicists. The formulae they use often consider the difference of two large numbers. When these numbers are very close to each other, their difference will be a very small number. Thus, these problems deal at the same time with very large and very small numbers, and this is where the fixed-point notation fails. Floating-point notation, as discussed earlier, carries with it an indication of the size of the number. Usually this size coefficient can be made large enough to accommodate the wide range of numbers dealt with by most scientists, wider than required for other disciplines.

Another advantage which comes automatically when using floating-point notation is referred to by the programmer as scaling. In fixed-point problems, the numbers which are manipulated do not correspond exactly to the normal range of numbers manipulated by the computer. Thus, if the computer represents numbers as fractions less than unity, the number 538 must be scaled by a factor of one one-thousandth to bring it into the range of the numbers handled by the computer. To fit all the numbers that are the data of the problem and the numbers which will result, which are the answers, some thought must be given to the factors by which each datum must be multiplied. With floating-point numbers, scaling is automatic!

Decimal Floating-Point— Scientific Notation

Let us being our discussion of scientific notation by stating the procedure by which a number is converted from fixed-point notation to scientific notation. All numbers in scientific notation have a mantissa which lies between one and ten. The exponent, the portion of the number which indicates its size, may be any integer, any positive or negative whole number.

For any number which is larger than or equal to ten, we shift the number to the right, past the decimal point, until the number is in a desired range. We count the number of shifts that are performed. Of course, this is equivalent to moving a decimal point to the left and counting the number of places it is moved. This number of shifts is called the exponent. Thus,

$$338{,}230{,}000 = 3.3823 \times 10^8$$

That is, we represent "three-hundred-thirty-eight million, two-hundred-thirty-thousand" by shifting the decimal point eight places to the left and then writing it as "three-point-three-eight-two-three times ten to the eighth."

If the number we wish to represent is less than one, if it is a fraction in decimal form, we must shift the decimal point to the right until the number comes within the desired range. We count the number of shifts performed and attach a minus sign to it to indicate the direction in which we are shifting—to indicate that we are dealing with a less than one number. In other words, we are multiplying our original number by a negative power of ten. To recover our original number, we must divide by this power of ten. This accounts for the minus sign in the exponent. For example,

$$0.000033823 = 3.3823 \times 10^{-5}$$

We now introduce a notation which will be used throughout this and the next chapter. We indicate a floating-point number by bold type; the mantissa for the floating-point number is indicated by Roman type and the exponent by script type. Thus, we can say that any number is represented in scientific notation as

$$\mathbf{A} = A \times 10^{\alpha} \qquad (15.1.1)$$

where $10 > A \geq 1.0$. In theory, the exponent, α, has no limit; it may be as large or as small as we choose. To maintain equivalences with our previous notation, we use lower-case letters, Roman or script, to indicate the absolute value of a number. Thus,

$$a = |A| \qquad a = |\alpha| \qquad (15.1.2)$$

The Binary Point

Before discussing binary floating-point numbers we pause to investigate how binary fractions are represented in fixed-point binary notation.

As in decimal numbers, binary numbers can be considered to have two parts to them: the portion of the number to the left of the binary point indicates the whole number portion; the digits to the right of the decimal point indicate the fractional part of the number. In decimal numbers, as we proceed to the right of the decimal point, we get the higher negative powers of ten; proceeding to the right the digits represent tenths, hundredths, thousandths, etc. With binary numbers, as we proceed to the right of the binary point, we consider higher negative powers of two; proceeding to the right from the binary point, we have halves, quarters, eighths, etc.

For example,

$$101011.1101 = 43\tfrac{13}{16}$$

The non-fractional part of this number can be deduced directly by converting the natural binary number to the left of the point to decimal. Notice that the fractional part arises since the number is stated to contain one-half $(X.1X)$, one-quarter $(X.X1X)$, no eighths $(X.XX0X)$, and one-sixteenth $(X.XXX1)$. When we add these together, we get thirteen-sixteenths.

The mathematician would state more rigorously than a binary number represented as

$$B = b_n b_{n-1} \cdots b_2 b_1 b_0 . b_{-1} b_{-2} \cdots b_{-m+1} b_{-m} \qquad (15.1.3)$$

means

$$\sum_{i=-m}^{n} b_i 2^i \qquad (15.1.4)$$

Binary Floating-Point

The convention for binary floating-point notation is a little different than that for scientific notation; that is, all numbers are represented as fractions less than one (proper fractions) except for -1. This simplifies the description.

For numbers greater than one, we move the binary point to the left until the left-most 1 is to the right of the binary point. This amounts to multiplying the number by one-half repeatedly until it becomes a fraction. For numbers which are already fractions, we move the binary point to the right until we encounter the first 1. This procedure guarantees that all numbers are fractions greater than or equal to one-half but less than 1.

The observant reader will realize that the rules above apply to positive numbers only. Negative numbers written in 2's complement notation use a similar rule which the reader should derive.

Using the notation set forth previously in this section, we have, for normalized floating-point numbers,

$$\mathbf{A} = A \cdot 2^{\alpha} \qquad (15.1.5)$$

where $1 > A \geq \frac{1}{2}$ (positive number) or $1\frac{1}{2} > A \geq 1$ (negative numbers). Thus we have $\frac{3}{2} > A \geq \frac{1}{2}$ for all floating-point numbers.

Of course, any number which can be represented in fixed-point decimal notation or floating-point decimal notation can be represented in floating-point binary notation. The proof of this is a simple exercise.

15.2 BINARY FLOATING-POINT ARITHMETIC AND NOTATION

Arithmetic

It is very easy to multiply two floating-point numbers: we multiply the mantissas and add the exponents. In binary,

$$\mathbf{A} \times \mathbf{B} = (A \times B)2^{\alpha + \beta} \qquad (15.2.1)$$

Division, also, is very simple. We divide the mantissas and subtract the exponent of the divisor from that of the dividend. In binary,

$$\frac{\mathbf{B}}{\mathbf{A}} = \frac{B}{A} 2^{\beta - \alpha} \qquad (15.2.2)$$

Neither addition nor subtraction can be performed unless the numbers are properly aligned. This means that we must adjust one of the numbers so that its exponent corresponds to that of the other number. To do this, we must determine which of the numbers has the larger exponent. Then we align the mantissa of the smaller number and adjust the exponent correspondingly until the exponents of the two correspond. Suppose that we are going to add the two numbers $\mathbf{A}$ and $\mathbf{B}$ and that α is larger than β. Then,

$$\mathbf{A} + \mathbf{B} = (A + B \cdot 2^{-(\alpha - \beta)})2^{\alpha} \qquad \alpha > \beta \qquad (15.2.3)$$

that is, the number of shifts performed can be determined by subtracting the smaller exponent from the larger. Since $\mathbf{B}$ is the smaller number, B is shifted this number of times. The exponent of the result is that of the larger number. A little complication may arise which will be investigated later.

This occurs when the sum of the aligned mantissas exceeds 1 which requires another shift to be performed to bring the result into the proper range for binary floating-point numbers. Addition or subtraction of numbers where the exponent of B is the larger is described by

$$\mathbf{A} \pm \mathbf{B} = (A \cdot 2^{-(\mathfrak{B}-\mathfrak{a})} \pm B)2^{\mathfrak{B}} \qquad \mathfrak{B} \geq \mathfrak{a} \qquad (15.2.4)$$

Again, the same complication of mantissa overflow may arise.

Binary Floating-Point Machine Notation

As in fixed-point notation, the machine representation is limited by the size of the register which is built into the machine. Numbers are processed by manipulation in registers; therefore, the register size is a limiting factor. We postulate here a floating-point register which will be denoted by a bold-face letter such as $\mathbf{A}$.

Using the same symbols for a floating-point number and for the register containing it should present no problem. The distinction should be clear through context; otherwise ($\mathbf{A}$) may be used to specifically indicate the contents of $\mathbf{A}$. The register, $\mathbf{A}$, is partitioned artificially into two sections which represent, respectively, the mantissa and the exponent; these sections will be referred to as A and $\mathfrak{a}$. Then,

$$\mathbf{A} = A \cup \mathfrak{a} \qquad (15.2.5)$$

where $\cup$ is the set union symbol indicating that $\mathbf{A}$ is like a vector and has two components, A and $\mathfrak{a}$, each of which must be specified to specify $\mathbf{A}$. Similarly, $A \cup \mathfrak{a}$ represents a register $\mathbf{A}$ which has been partitioned to represent the two components. The reader is invited to peek ahead to page 363 where a floating-register configuration is presented in Figure 15.4; the partitioning of $\mathbf{A}$, $\mathbf{D}$, and $\mathbf{D}'$ is apparent there.

The mantissa or fraction portion of the register has a fixed size. At this point, we may wish to consider the fixed-point registers which we have been working with previously and either divide them into two sections or take the full register used for fixed-point arithmetic and append another section to it. In order to simplify our notation, it is the latter course of action which we shall follow. We then say that the mantissa register is comprised of N bits with an extra bit to designate the sign of the mantissa. Similarly, we will say that the exponent portion of our register is comprised of $\mathfrak{N}$ bits with one more bit reserved for the sign.

The largest positive mantissa which our register can store is denoted as W; it consists of N1's following the binary point; we have $W = 1 - e$. The largest exponent with which we can deal is called $\mathcal{W}$ and it has $\mathfrak{N}$1's in it. It is *not* a fraction. The largest number representable by $\mathfrak{N}$ bits is $2^{\mathfrak{N}} - 1$. Hence, $\mathcal{W} = 2^{\mathfrak{N}} - 1$.

In machines using 2's complement notation, the notation is extended to apply to both the mantissa and the exponent. For the mantissa where $A = -a$ we have A represented as $2 - a$. However, the exponent is not a fraction. To represent $\mathcal{a} = -a$, we use $2^{\mathfrak{N}}(2 - a)$, to be consistent with 2's complements.

We find that the *representation* of all numbers obeys the following relationship:

$$1 + W \geq A \geq 0 \tag{15.2.6}$$

To define upper and lower limits, we start with

$$W = 1 - e \tag{15.2.7}$$

$$\mathcal{W} = 2^{\mathfrak{N}} - 1 \tag{15.2.8}$$

Then,

$$W2^{\mathcal{W}} \geq \mathbf{A} \geq e2^{-\mathcal{W}} \qquad \mathbf{A} > 0 \tag{15.2.9}$$

The range of negative 2's complement numbers is

$$-2^{\mathcal{W}} \leq \mathbf{A} \leq -e2^{-\mathcal{W}} \qquad \mathbf{A} < 0 \tag{15.2.10}$$

The lower limit stems from the smallest fraction being -1 in 2's complement notation. In 1's complement or sign and magnitude notation, this limit becomes $-W2^{\mathcal{W}}$.

A Complication

A question arises as to how to represent 0. It is perfectly clear that the mantissa for 0 is 0. However, what should the exponent be? Really, 0 times any number gives the result 0. Therefore, we may say that regardless of the exponent, as long as the mantissa is 0, its representation is appropriate for the number 0. However, there is a preference in some circles to require that 0 be represented not only by a 0 mantissa but that it also should have the smallest conceivable exponent which the computer can store. Such 0's (with minimum allowable exponent) are called "clean 0's."

Establishing a convention requiring all zeros to be clean facilitates doing $\mathbf{A} + \mathbf{0}$. If it were possible that $\mathbf{0}$ had an exponent greater than $\mathcal{a}$ we might get into trouble by trying to align A; we might lose significant bits which would not occur if we could always be sure that the exponent of 0 is always less than α. We can be assured of this if **0** always has a minimum exponent. For 2's complement notation, this would require using the quantity $1.00\cdots0$. The hardware is supplemented with the capability that when a **0** result is encountered during arithmetic, the resulting exponent is replaced by $1.00\cdots0$. This will expedite future arithmetic using this result.

Numbers which have 0 mantissas but do not have the minimum exponent are referred to, in the trade, as "dirty 0's." Either hardware or programming can make clean 0's out of dirty 0's.

It must be said that converting dirty 0's prevents us from keeping track of the significance of a calculation. The argument is still open. One school of thought is that the appearance of **0** should automatically call for an error identification and correction subroutine. Ordinarily, **0** is never an expected intermediate result.

There are some machines in the field which use an adjusted exponent notation. Instead of allowing the exponent to range from $-\mathcal{W}$ to $+\mathcal{W}$ it is allowed to range from 0 to $2\mathcal{W} + 1$. In such computers, there are no negative exponents. This is, of course, a matter of semantics because the following mapping applies:

$$2^{\mathcal{X}} \longleftrightarrow 2^{\mathcal{X}+\mathcal{W}} \tag{15.2.11}$$

where $\mathcal{X}$ is an exponent in the proper range which we defined earlier. Thus negative exponents are represented as positive numbers whose range is from 0 to $\mathcal{W}$. This system has both advantages and disadvantages. The main advantage is that **0** is represented by a mantissa of 0 and an exponent of 0; it consists entirely of 0's! The disadvantage is the conversion required from negative to positive exponents. This system is used by the Univac 1105, among others.

15.3 ANALYSIS OF FLOATING-POINT ADDITION AND SUBTRACTION

The symbol we will use to indicate a command for floating-point addition is "Fa"; that for floating-point subtraction is "Fs." In this section, we will discuss three things: problems which are most closely associated with floating-point addition, an outline in flow-chart form of floating-point addition and subtraction, and the phases of operation into which floating-point addition may be analyzed.

Problems Associated with Floating-Point Addition and Subtraction

We are dealing with both a signed mantissa and a signed exponent. The digital computer places a physical constraint on the size of these numbers. This is due, of course, to the size of the registers (or semi-registers). Let us say that the maximum number of bits allowable in the mantissa is N. The word size of the exponent is designated as $\mathfrak{N}$. As mentioned in the last section, script letters are reserved for functions concerning the exponent and Roman letters with those concerned with the mantissa. In both cases, an extra bit is reserved for the sign—one for the exponent, one for the mantissa.

The fixed size of these portions of the floating-point number causes a problem to arise during addition and subtraction. The first problem is associated with the overflow of the mantissa. The second problem is associated with the overflow or underflow of the exponent. The former can occur when the mantissa overflows and an adjustment in the exponent is attempted. The latter can occur when normalizing a small result. Unlike the case in fixed-point addition, an overflow in the mantissa is not disabling; that is, such an overflow can be compensated for simply by shifting the mantissa and increasing the exponent.

Another problem connected with addition and subtraction is that of equalizing the exponents. Two numbers with dissimilar exponents cannot be added directly. First the exponent of the smaller number must be increased until it equals that of the larger number. For each increase of 1 in the exponent of the smaller number, the mantissa is shifted one place to the right. Only when exponent equality exists can we add or subtract the mantissas. Of course, so many shifts of the mantissa may be required that there is no mantissa left—it is completely pushed out of the register to the right. The exponent of the smaller number is so small compared to the exponent of the larger that the mantissa is recorded in the register after shifting as 0. In this case, there was no need to shift—we could have used the larger number, mantissa and exponent, as the result directly and saved ourselves some time.

The difference or sum of two mantissas may be a number which is not in normalized form. In order to maintain the consistency and uniqueness of floating-point numbers used throughout the problem, the result of arithmetic should be normalized before it is returned to memory.

Flow-Diagram Analysis of Floating-Point Addition and Subtraction

Figure 15.3.1 gives, in flow-chart form, the decisions and actions which take place in floating-point addition and subtraction. Here we wish to find **S** where $\mathbf{S} = \mathbf{A} \pm \mathbf{D}$.

compare exponents

The first thing that is done, box 1, is to compare the exponents α and $\mathfrak{D}$. Five possible results are indicated. The sign "$\gg$," pronounced "much greater than," indicates that α is larger than $\mathfrak{D}$ by at least N. In other words, α is so much larger than $\mathfrak{D}$ that it is not worth our trouble to shift D—the result of addition *is* the number **A**. Another way to put this is that $\alpha \gg \mathfrak{D}$ implies $\alpha > \mathfrak{D} + N$.

The second decision is that α is larger than $\mathfrak{D}$, indicated as "$>$." The single horizontal carat indicates that the difference between α and $\mathfrak{D}$ is less than N, and we wish to try to do addition. The third alternative is that the two exponents are equal; this should need no elaboration nor shifting. In the other direction again, two cases are distinguished where α is less than $\mathfrak{D}$ and where α is much less than $\mathfrak{D}$, indicated respectively as "$<$" and "$\ll$." Thus, $\alpha \ll \mathfrak{D}$ means $\alpha + N < \mathfrak{D}$. These five cases provide a finer division corresponding to when the difference of the exponents is less than N or greater than or equal to N.

α much greater than $\mathfrak{D}$

In this case, shifting of the mantissa of the smaller number will do us no good—the number will be shifted so much that it will disappear. Therefore, we can immediately use **A** as the result. This is shown in box 6 where **A** is used as the complete sum **S**.

α much less than $\mathfrak{D}$

Again, shifting of the mantissa or a smaller number will do us no good. Now we can enter the answer directly. Depending upon whether we are performing addition or subtraction, the result will be either $+\mathbf{D}$ or $-\mathbf{D}$, as shown in box 7.

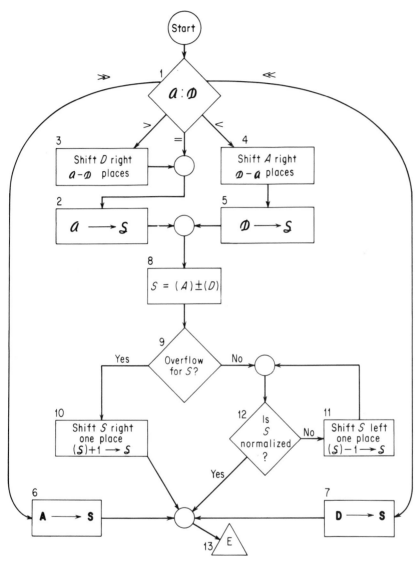

FIGURE 15.3.1 Flow chart of decisions required for floating-point addition and subtraction.

α equal to $\mathcal{D}$

When the two exponents are equal, box 2 makes the exponent of the sum the same as that of the augend. This will hold unless modified later.

Ⅽ greater than Ⅾ

Before addition can be performed, we must shift the smaller mantissa D to the right. The number of places we must shift is Ⅽ − Ⅾ, box 3. We can then enter as the exponent of the sum that of the augend, Ⅽ.

Ⅽ less than Ⅾ

In this case, we must shift the mantissa of the smaller number to the right until proper alignment is produced. The number of shifts we perform is Ⅾ − Ⅽ, box 4. When this is done, we can enter as the exponent for the sum that of the addend, Ⅾ.

adding the mantissas

Now that the numbers have been aligned by shifting the one with the smaller exponent and reducing the exponent until the exponents of the two numbers are equal, we can perform addition of the mantissas, box 8.

mantissa overflow

In box 9, we examine the result of addition to determine if the condition defined in fixed-point addition as an arithmetic fault has occurred. If it has, our procedure is simple. We know that the mantissa result is spread out over the register and encroaches into the sign position. In fixed-point addition, we would have to stop our computation. Now, however, there it a simple remedy. We shift the result one place to the right. Not only does this correct our result, it also leaves us with a properly normalized number. We simply add 1 to the exponent of the result and we are finished. The one exception is when our exponent was so high that adding 1 to it causes the exponent to overflow; then we must stop because of an exponent fault.

normalization

If mantissa addition has not resulted in an arithmetic fault, box 9, we must proceed to normalize the sum. A positive result should be a number greater than $\frac{1}{2}$. A negative result should be represented by a quantity greater than 1 and less than $1\frac{1}{2}$. If the mantissa are not in this form, they are shifted one place at a time to the left until they do take this form. Each left shift requires that the exponent of the sum be reduced by 1. When normalizing is complete, our floating-point process is finished.

The Processing Phases of Floating-Point Addition and Subtraction

The discussion in the next sections will view floating-point addition and subtraction in five phases. These are also indicated by a timing number, to simplify the implementation and hardware. We have the following phases.

T1. Check exponents.

T2. Align mantissas.

T3. Add mantissas and enter exponents.

T4. Check result and shift mantissas.

T5. Adjust exponent.

Examples

To see how floating-point addition (and subtraction) works, we go over a few examples appearing in Figure 15.3.2. They use decimal numbers so that they can be followed easier, but the principles apply to floating-point binary as well. We use a five digit mantissa ($N = 5$) with a one digit

1	2	3	4	5	6		
31200/3 22400/3	49000/5 88000/5	49000/8 88000/6	49000/9 88000/1	49000/9 88000/9	00490/3 00088/4	T1	Check exponent
		49000/8 00880/8			00049/4 00088/4	T2	Al'gn mantissas
53600/3	137000/5	49880/8		137000/9	00137/4	T3	Add mantissas
						T4	Shift mantissas
53600/3	13700/6	49880/8	49000/9	X_f	13700/2	T5	Adjust exponent

FIGURE 15.3.2 Example of floating-point addition using decimal numbers, 5-digit mantissa and one-digit exponent (to the right of the slash). Phases numbered as in text

exponent ($\mathfrak{N} = 1$) following the slash and on its right. The cycles used are as enumerated above.

For (1), the exponents are the same, so we go directly to T3 and add the mantissas. There is no overflow and the mantissas are normalized so that the sum is correct.

For (2), the exponents again are the same, so we add the mantissas. There is mantissa overflow, so in T4, 5 we shift the mantissa right and add 1 to the exponent. It is below 10, so the result is OK.

For (3), the addend exponent is smaller. We shift the addend mantissa two places in T2 and enter the larger exponent, 8. Addition finds the sum normalized with no overflow so the result is correct.

For (4), the augend exponent is *much larger* than that of the addend. It exceeds it by 8, whereas there are only 5 mantissa positions ($N = 5$). Therefore, the augend *is* the result.

For (5), no mantissa shift is required. However, an overflow occurs during addition. When we try to correct the exponent by adding 1, it, too, overflows. We can do naught but record an exponent fault, Xf.

In (6), we have unnormalized numbers of different exponents. We align the mantissas in T2 by shifting the mantissa of the number with smaller exponent, the augend, one place to the right. The sum does not produce an overflow. On the contrary, it is too small and must be normalized by shifting the mantissa left two places. As this is done, the exponent is reduced by two.

15.4 REGISTER CONFIGURATION AND TASK ANALYSIS, FLOATING-POINT ADDITION AND SUBTRACTION

In Figure 15.4, we see how the registers can be partitioned for use in floating-point arithmetic. We will now consider an **A** register consisting of an A register with N bits for the mantissa plus one sign bit, and an $\mathfrak{a}$ register consisting of $\mathfrak{N}$ bits for the exponent plus one bit for the exponent sign. The **D** register is similarly partitioned. As previously, quantities are shifted between the main registers and the prime registers. Therefore, **A′** and **D′** are partitioned in a similar fashion.

Again, notice that the **adder** is partitioned into two sections. One will be used to process the mantissa and is called the "adder"; the other is used for processing the exponent and is called the "adder." For fixed-point arithmetic, these two sections of the **adder** must be connected together. To do this, $^0\mathcal{C}_s$ is connected to $^0C_0$ and $^1\mathcal{C}_s$ is connected to $^1C_0$. The carry-complete for the adder is CC; the carry-complete for the adder is $\mathcal{C}\mathcal{C}$. The

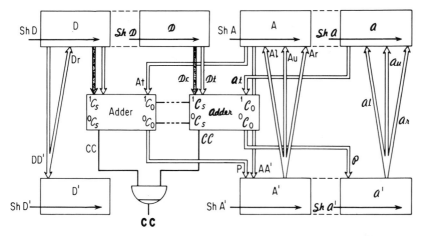

FIGURE 15.4   Connection of the adder and registers for floating-point arithmetic.

carry-complete for the entire **adder** is **CC**. The input to the adder (the adder) is either $^0\mathcal{C}_0$ ($^0C_0$) for addition or $^1\mathcal{C}_0$ ($^1C_0$) for subtraction, respectively. When we wish to use the adder separately, it is disconnected from the adder and the entries of $^0C_0$ for addition and $^1C_0$ for subtraction must be made separately.

The true or complement of the D register can be entered into the adder via the line Dt or Dc; the true output of the A register can be entered into the other input of the adder via the line At. Similarly, the adder may have a complement or true input from the $\mathcal{D}$ register indicated by $\mathcal{D}$c and $\mathcal{D}$t, the other input is entered from the $\mathcal{C}$ register as indicated by $\mathcal{C}$t.

During shifting, information is returned from the prime registers to the main registers offset one bit position to the right or to the left. The notation used is Au, Ar, or Al, for an unshifted, a right-shifted, or a left-shifted return transmission from A' to the A register, respectively; similarly, $\mathcal{C}$u, $\mathcal{C}$r, and $\mathcal{C}$l are used to indicate an unshifted, right-shifted, and left-shifted from $\mathcal{C}$' to the $\mathcal{C}$ register, respectively. Entry from the adder to the A' register is indicated by P; entry from the adder to the $\mathcal{C}$' register is indicated by $\mathcal{P}$.

The entry of information into any given register is indicated by the shift entry pulse. A separate line is used for each register, since the registers need not be coordinated as to the time of entry. Thus, to enter information into $\mathcal{C}$', use a pulse on the line labeled $\mathcal{S}h\mathcal{C}$'.

In later sections when we examine how the registers function for floating-point arithmetic, we will separate the A register from the $\mathcal{C}$ register and so forth, both verbally and on the figures, to expedite our discussion. Even though these registers are physically contiguous, we will discuss them as though they were separate entities.

Exponent Comparison, T1

In this phase of addition we are going to compare the exponents to determine which is larger and by how much. Since shifting a mantissa register more than N places to the right will cause the mantissa to disappear (it is shifted out completely), we wish to detect these cases immediately.

We need a criterion to determine whether shifting is to be done and, if so, by how much. A natural choice is to take the difference of the exponents. Let us find,

$$\varepsilon = \mathfrak{a} - \mathfrak{D} \tag{15.4.1}$$

If this number, ε, is positive, it will always indicate that $\mathfrak{a}$ is greater than $\mathfrak{D}$; if it is negative, it will always indicate that $\mathfrak{D}$ is larger than $\mathfrak{a}$. There is only one catch; we are dealing with numbers in registers where addition of two large numbers may produce a false result, one that exceeds the size of the register. Thus, if we are adding two large positive numbers, a carry may be produced from the most significant place. Normally it will be recorded in the sign bit of the sum and, hence, will erroneously indicate a negative sum. We must beware of this contingency.

Notice that since we are performing subtraction, if the exponents we are processing are of the same sign, subtracting them will require addition of oppositely signed numbers. Such an addition cannot exceed the word size of the register so we need take no precautions in that case. If the exponents are oppositely signed, then we change our sign and add, we may produce an overflow condition. This is detected in the same way we detect an arithmetic fault in signed fixed-point addition, by referring to the carry from the most significant.numerical bit.

To begin to examine the conditions which define the exponent inequalities which we desire, we make the following definitions:

$\mathfrak{a}_s$ is the sign bit of $\mathfrak{a}$.

$\mathfrak{D}_s$ is the sign bit of $\mathfrak{D}$.

ε_s is the sign bit of the difference between $\mathfrak{a}$ and $\mathfrak{D}$.

$^1\mathfrak{C}\mathfrak{R}$ is a carry of 1 from the most significant bit when we subtract $\mathfrak{D}$ from $\mathfrak{a}$.

$^0\mathfrak{C}\mathfrak{R}$ is a carry of 0 from the most significant bit when we subtract $\mathfrak{D}$ from $\mathfrak{a}$.

($<N$) indicates that the difference of the exponents is less than the number of numerical bits in the mantissa.

($\geq N$) indicates that the difference of the exponents is greater than or equal to the number of numerical bits in the mantissa register.

Now, to derive the conditions for each inequality, we take α to be much greater than $\mathfrak{D}$ for the following condition:

$$\alpha \gg \mathfrak{D} \equiv (\alpha_s \mathfrak{D}_s + \overline{\alpha_s} \overline{\mathfrak{D}_s}) \overline{\mathcal{E}}_s (\geq N) \qquad (15.4.2)$$

$$+ \overline{\alpha_s} \mathfrak{D}_s {}^0 \mathcal{C} \mathcal{R} (\geq N)$$

$$+ \overline{\alpha_s} \mathfrak{D}_s {}^1 \mathcal{C} \mathcal{R}$$

The first line of (15.4.2) represents the conditions that the exponents have the same sign, their difference is positive, and it exceeds N; the second line

TABLE 15.4 Examples for Logical Equations (15.4.2) through (15.4.5)

Example	A	D	E	Condition
15.4.2.1a	$+101$	$+25$	$+76$	
15.4.2.1b	-25	-80	$+55$	
15.4.2.2	$+12$	-41	$+53$	$\alpha \gg \mathfrak{D}$
15.4.2.3	$+2000$	-1000	A_f	
15.4.3.1a	$+25$	$+101$	-76	
15.4.3.1b	-80	-25	-55	
15.4.3.2	-41	$+12$	-53	$\mathfrak{D} \gg \alpha$
15.4.3.3	-1000	-2000	A_f	
15.4.4.1a	$+80$	$+70$	$+10$	
15.4.4.1b	$+63$	$+63$	$+0$	$\alpha \geq \mathfrak{D}$
15.4.4.1c	-8	-16	$+8$	$\overline{\& \; \alpha \gg \mathfrak{D}}$
15.4.4.2	$+8$	-16	$+24$	
15.4.5.1a	$+70$	$+80$	-10	
15.4.5.1b	-16	-8	-8	$\mathfrak{D} > \alpha$
15.4.5.2	-16	$+8$	-24	$\overline{\& \; \mathfrak{D} \gg \alpha}$

indicates that α is positive, $\mathfrak{D}$ is negative, there is no arithmetic fault, and the difference exceeds N; the third condition applies for an arithmetic fault with α positive and $\mathfrak{D}$ negative. To see this more clearly, examine Table 15.4 where numbers are substituted into the equations.

In a very similar manner, we can define the conditions for $\mathfrak{D}$ much greater than $\mathfrak{a}$ as

$$\mathfrak{D} \gg \mathfrak{a} \equiv (\mathfrak{a}_s\mathfrak{D}_s + \overline{\mathfrak{a}_s\mathfrak{D}_s})\mathcal{E}_s(\geq N) \qquad (15.4.3)$$

$$+ \mathfrak{a}_s\overline{\mathfrak{D}_s}{}^1\mathfrak{C}\mathfrak{N}(\geq N)$$

$$+ \mathfrak{a}_s\mathfrak{D}_s{}^0\mathfrak{C}\mathfrak{N}$$

When $\mathfrak{a}$ is greater than $\mathfrak{D}$, which includes equality ($\mathfrak{a} = \mathfrak{D}$),

$$\mathfrak{a} \geq \mathfrak{D} \equiv (\mathfrak{a}_s\mathfrak{D}_s + \overline{\mathfrak{a}_s\mathfrak{D}_s})\, (<N)\overline{\mathcal{E}}_s \qquad (15.4.4)$$

$$+ \overline{\mathfrak{a}}_s\mathfrak{D}_s\, {}^0\mathfrak{C}\mathfrak{N}(<N)$$

The first line applies for exponents with the same sign for which the difference is positive and does not exceed N. The second line indicates the case of a positive $\mathfrak{a}$, a negative $\mathfrak{D}$, no arithmetic fault, and a difference less than N. In a similar fashion, we can define the conditions for $\mathfrak{D}$ greater than $\mathfrak{a}$ as,

$$\mathfrak{D} > \mathfrak{a} \equiv (\mathfrak{a}_s\mathfrak{D}_s + \overline{\mathfrak{a}_s\mathfrak{D}_s})\mathcal{E}_s(<N) \qquad (15.4.5)$$

$$+ \mathfrak{a}_s\overline{\mathfrak{D}_s}\, {}^1\mathfrak{C}\mathfrak{N}(<N)$$

Although we are delineating four cases, we need not have four conditions to define these cases. Alluding to the binary system, we recall that two each of a bit storage device can define four possibilities: two choices each for each of their two states. In the present situation, we can define the four conditions by indicating whether or not each of two conditions is present. For this we will define two conditions and store them on appropriate bit storage devices as follows:

$\mathfrak{M}\mathcal{G}$: either $\mathfrak{a}$ is much greater than $\mathfrak{D}$ or $\mathfrak{D}$ is much greater than $\mathfrak{a}$. In other words, it indicates a "much greater" condition.

$\mathfrak{a}\mathcal{G}$: either $\mathfrak{a}$ is greater than $\mathfrak{D}$ or $\mathfrak{a}$ is much greater than $\mathfrak{D}$. In other words, this is an "$\mathfrak{a}$ greater" condition and includes the condition $\mathfrak{a} = \mathfrak{D}$.

The four combinations of the two states of each of these two bit storages corresponds to the four conditions of interest to us.

The reason for the seemingly circuitous manipulations is to provide us with briefer conditions; this in turn saves us precious logic. Let us now combine (15.4.2) and (15.4.4) to form the single condition for $\mathcal{Q}$ greater or much greater than $\mathcal{D}$.

$$\mathcal{Q}\mathcal{G} = (\geq N)(\mathcal{Q}_s\mathcal{D}_s + \overline{\mathcal{Q}}_s\overline{\mathcal{D}}_s)\overline{\mathcal{E}}_s \tag{15.4.6}$$

$$+ (<N)(\mathcal{Q}_s\mathcal{D}_s + \overline{\mathcal{Q}}_s\overline{\mathcal{D}}_s)\overline{\mathcal{E}}_s$$

$$+ (\geq N)\overline{\mathcal{Q}}_s\mathcal{D}_s \, {}^0\mathcal{C}\mathfrak{R}$$

$$+ (<N)\overline{\mathcal{Q}}_s\mathcal{D} \, {}^0\mathcal{C}\mathfrak{R}$$

$$+ \overline{\mathcal{Q}}_s\mathcal{D}_s \, {}^1\mathcal{C}\mathfrak{R}$$

To combine the terms of (15.4.6), we note that the first two lines are the same except for the size condition $(\geq N)$ or $(<N)$, which can then be dropped. Similarly, on the next two lines, the size condition can be combined. The last line is combined with the previous two when we note that the carries can be ignored. Thus, combining the terms reduces (15.4.6) to

$$\mathcal{Q}\mathcal{G} = (\mathcal{Q}_s\mathcal{D}_s + \overline{\mathcal{Q}}_s\overline{\mathcal{D}}_s)\overline{\mathcal{E}}_s + \overline{\mathcal{Q}}_s\mathcal{D}_s \tag{15.4.7}$$

In a similar fashion, we can combine the terms for the condition "much greater than." However, if we compare this with the condition for "not much greater," we find the latter easier to derive. It is formed by combining (15.4.4) and (15.4.5) to yield,

$$\overline{\mathfrak{M}\mathcal{G}} = (\mathcal{Q}_s\mathcal{D}_s + \overline{\mathcal{Q}}_s\overline{\mathcal{D}}_s)\overline{\mathcal{E}}_s(<N) \tag{15.4.8}$$

$$+ (\mathcal{Q}_s\mathcal{D}_s + \overline{\mathcal{Q}}_s\overline{\mathcal{D}}_s)\mathcal{E}_s(<N)$$

$$+ \overline{\mathcal{Q}}_s\mathcal{D}_s \, {}^0\mathcal{C}\mathfrak{R}(<N)$$

$$+ \mathcal{Q}_s\overline{\mathcal{D}}_s \, {}^1\mathcal{C}\mathfrak{R}(<N)$$

When combining terms, this reduces to,

$$\overline{\mathfrak{M}\mathcal{G}} = (<N)(\mathcal{Q}_s\mathcal{D}_s + \overline{\mathcal{Q}}_s\overline{\mathcal{D}}_s + \overline{\mathcal{Q}}_s\mathcal{D}_s \, {}^0\mathcal{C}\mathfrak{R} + \mathcal{Q}_s\overline{\mathcal{D}}_s \, {}^1\mathcal{C}\mathfrak{R}) \tag{15.4.9}$$

The function of this phrase is to determine which phase is to be performed next and what is to be done when we get to the next phase. The result of the exponent subtraction may be in true form or complement form. This can be determined by examining the state of $\mathcal{Q}\mathcal{G}$. As long as $\mathcal{Q}$ is greater than or equal to $\mathcal{D}$, the result is positive and is in true form. Otherwise, it is negative and is in complement form. If we are going to shift a mantissa, the amount by which it is shifted is determined by the difference between $\mathcal{Q}$ and $\mathcal{D}$. If this number is in complement form, it has to be converted to true form before it can be used as a proper indication of the number of shifts to be performed. The means for doing this is to examine $\alpha\mathcal{G}$; if it is not set, we must complement the sum presented at the output of the adder. To do this, the 1's complement of the sum is transferred to a counter. This counter is then tallied up—1 is added to it. The result is the 2's complement of the difference of α and $\mathfrak{D}$ which is the true number of shifts of the mantissa which must be performed.

The decision on where to go in leaving this phase of operation is based on the setting of $\mathfrak{MG}$. For a "much greater" condition, no mantissa arithmetic is performed and we can go to T3. If a "much greater" condition is absent, we go to T2 to align the mantissas.

The "not much greater" condition can be simplified by the use of (7.4.15). In that case, it becomes

$$\overline{\mathfrak{MG}} = (<N)\,(^0\mathfrak{C}_s\,{}^0\mathfrak{C}_\mathfrak{N} + {}^1\mathfrak{C}_s\,{}^1\mathfrak{C}_\mathfrak{N}) \qquad (15.4.10)$$

To keep the condition $\alpha\mathcal{G}$ in consistent notation, we convert (15.4.7) into

$$\alpha\mathcal{G} = (^0\mathfrak{C}_s\,{}^0\mathfrak{C}_\mathfrak{N} + {}^1\mathfrak{C}_s\,{}^1\mathfrak{C}_\mathfrak{N})\bar{\mathcal{E}}_s + {}^0\mathfrak{C}_s\,{}^1\mathfrak{C}_\mathfrak{N} \qquad (15.4.11)$$

T2 Aligning the Mantissas

In this phase we are going to shift the smaller number to the right a number of times such that the exponents of the two numbers will be the same. This will be necessary only when we have the condition $\overline{\mathfrak{MG}}$, for only in that case will addition be performed. The number of places by which shifting is to be performed is indicated by the number contained in the counter. The number that is to be shifted is determined by the setting of $\alpha\mathcal{G}$. Thus, if α is greater than or equal to $\mathfrak{D}$, we are going to shift D; otherwise, we have $\mathfrak{D} > \alpha$ and we shift A.

A typical cycle of this phase would be as follows: Suppose we are shifting D. We transfer the contents of D to D'. In returning the contents of D' to D, we shift it one position to the right. As we perform this shift, we deduct 1 from the shift counter. Before we perform another cycle, we compare the number in the counter with 0. If we have reduced the count in the counter to 0, we have completed our shift operation; otherwise, we perform another cycle. Of course, if our arithmetic unit contains variable or multiple shifters, we use them to expedite this phase.

Obviously we will not perform as many as N cycles of shifting, for if the number in the counter were N or greater, we would have detected a "much greater than" condition.

Add Mantissas and Enter Exponents

When addition is to take place, the numbers have been properly aligned in the previous phase. To check whether addition is to be performed in this phase, we examine the storage element $\overline{\mathfrak{M}\mathcal{G}}$ and perform addition if it contains a 0.

Whether or not addition is performed, we will set the exponent in this phase; the exponent of the sum is that of the larger number. Therefore, we examine $\mathcal{C}\mathcal{G}$ to determine which number is larger. A 1 in this device indicates that the exponent of the sum is that of $\mathcal{C}$. Since our sum is eventually to be contained in the **A** register, the $\mathcal{C}$ register now contains the proper exponent quantity and no exponent addition or transfer is required. When $\mathfrak{D}$ is the proper exponent, indicated by $\overline{\mathcal{C}\mathcal{G}}$, we transfer the contents of $\mathfrak{D}$ into $\mathcal{C}$. This is done by passing it through the adder into $\mathcal{C}'$ and then returning it, unshifted, into $\mathcal{C}$.

Adding the mantissas and setting the exponent into $\mathcal{C}$ is performed at the same time in this phase. The mantissa addition may cause an arithmetic fault which should be detected and recorded in this phase. This is indicated by setting a bit storage device which we shall call Af.

Normalize the Mantissas

During this phase we wish to arrange the sum so that it is normalized. This means that for positive numbers the first position to the right of the binary point contains a 1; for negative numbers written in 2's complement notation, a 0 should appear in the first position to the right of the binary point. These two conditions can be summed up by saying that the sign bit and the most significant bit are opposite. $(0.1 \lor 1.0.)$

A normalization phase is necessary if the result is to be in normal form. In adding two numbers which are very nearly the same in size and opposite in sign, the result is a small number, most of whose significance lies in the right side of the register. To normalize it, we must shift it to the left of the register. A particular problem arises when the result of the addition is zero.

test

To test whether a number is normalized, we apply the criterion of the first paragraph; the number is normalized when the sign bit and the most significant bit are not the same; as long as they are the same, a cycle of normalization must be performed.

shift cycle

The non-normalized mantissa is shifted one position to the left to effect normalization. After each shift, 1 is subtracted from the number in the shift counter. As we shall see later, the shift counter was returned to 0 before we entered this phase. We are now tallying down from 0 so that, in effect, we have a negative number in the counter. When this is added to the exponent in a later phase, the result will be the proper exponent of the normalized number. When multiple shifts are performed, the multiple, not 1, is subtracted from the counter. We alternate shift cycles and test cycles until the number is normalized. Before shift cycles start, the mantissa of the sum must be tested and if it is zero normalization is inhibited; otherwise, these cycles could continue indefinitely.

**normalization after a mantissa
arithmetic fault**

Adding two numbers whose sum exceeds the size of the register is not a problem in floating-point. This condition is detected as a mantissa arithmetic fault, Af, which conveys that the most significant bit of our answer has been placed in the sign position of the number. Since this is an overflow on positive addition, it is recorded there as a 1. On the contrary, when adding two negative numbers, a lack of overflow is recorded as an arithmetic fault and a 0 exists in the sign position of the result. In both cases, a single, right shift of the result will yield a properly normalized number. This requires that the sign bit of the result be corrected. Thus, during the normalization phase for a mantissa arithmetic fault, we

1. Shift the mantissa one position to the right.
2. Adjust the sign bit.
3. *Add 1* into the shift counter.

The last step assures that the exponent of the result will be corrected during phase 5.

If we are sure that all numbers are normalized before use, this phase need not be performed for the case we call 𝔐G; here the sum *is* the larger number if all floating-point numbers are not entered into the computer in normalized form, then it is desirable to perform phase T4 in all cases. This guarantees that all results, including those arising from the case 𝔐G, are in normal form regardless of the state of the original numbers to be summed.

T5 Exponent Adjustment

The number of shifts performed during normalization is recorded in the shift counter, $\mathcal{C}$. It may contain $+1$, 0, or a negative number greater than $-N$ in 1's complement form. The unadjusted exponent for the result is contained in $\mathcal{C}$. This phase adds these two numbers to obtain the adjusted exponent $\mathcal{S} = (\mathcal{C}) + (\mathcal{C})$. We must monitor this addition to be sure that exponent overflow or underflow does not occur; that is, if the resulting exponent is larger than the register size, there is nothing that we can do to accommodate this result. This is true when we try to produce $\mathcal{S} > \mathcal{W}$ or $\mathcal{S} < -\mathcal{W}$. On these occasions we must indicate to the operator that a fault has occurred in floating-point arithmetic. In the more modern computers with auto-control units or other types of executive routines built into them, the exponent fault will call forth an appropriate routine to handle this matter.

Notice that underflow ($\mathcal{S} < -\mathcal{W}$) is much more likely than overflow. The latter is possible only when one of the numbers has the maximum exponent and the mantissa addition produces an overflow. One way to "correct" an underflow is to *unnormalize*! We shift the mantissa right and increase the exponent until it is within bounds. This sacrifices the significance of the sum but at least produces a result of sorts.

The completion of phase 5 ends floating-point addition and subtraction.

15.5 IMPLEMENTATION OF FLOATING-POINT ADDITION AND SUBTRACTION

Configuration

We have discussed most of the register requirements in Section 15.3. The full hardware requirements, except for control, are illustrated in Figure 15.5.1. We have added a shift counter, $\mathcal{C}$, into which we may enter the contents of $\mathcal{C}'$, either in true of complement form. The shift counter may be tallied up by a pulse at cu. It may be tallied down by entering a pulse at cd. The counter is constantly monitored by the decoder, $d(\mathcal{C})$, which reports the size of the number contained in the counter.

For addition and subtraction, only the true output of $\mathcal{C}$ need be supplied to the adder. The other input to the adder may be one of three quantities: we require *the complement of* $\mathcal{D}$ for subtracting the exponents on the initial

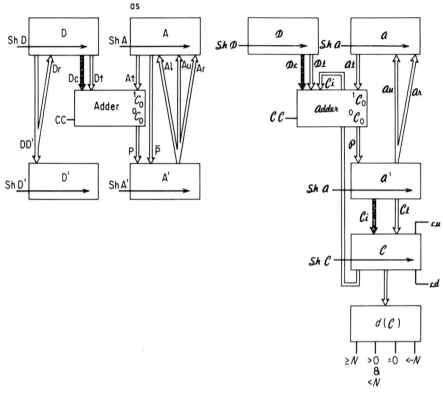

FIGURE 15.5.1 A configuration for floating-point addition and subtraction.

exponent test phase; we require *the true quantity* $\mathfrak{D}$ when we have found that $\mathfrak{D}$ is larger than $\mathfrak{a}$, hence, $\mathfrak{D}$ is the exponent for the result; after normalization, the unadjusted exponent of the result is contained in $\mathfrak{a}$—it is modified by adding *the contents of the shift counter* to it via $\mathfrak{C}i$.

Processing Flow

Figure 15.5.2 illustrates how information flows through the registers and other hardware associated with floating-point addition and subtraction. In box 1 the difference of the exponents is found and entered into $\mathfrak{a}'$. We can determine during this subtraction whether or not $\mathfrak{a}$ is greater than $\mathfrak{D}$; which allows us to set the bit storage device $\mathfrak{a}\mathfrak{G}$, box 2. The setting of $\mathfrak{a}\mathfrak{G}$ determines, box 3, whether we enter the result of subtraction into the shift counter directly, box 4, or whether we complement it before entering

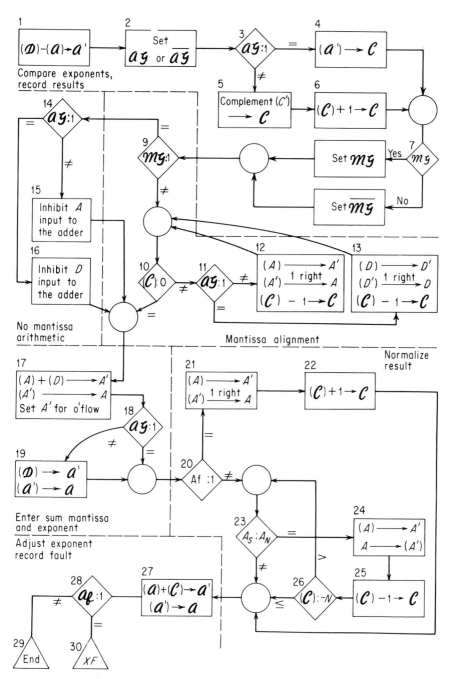

FIGURE 15.5.2 Flow diagram for implementation of floating-point addition and subtraction with the configuration of Figure 15.5.1

it into the shift counter, box 5. Although we fill the shift counter, we do not return the contents of α' to α; we preserve the contents of $\mathfrak{D}$ and α since one of them will be called for as the unadjusted exponent of the result. Notice that if the complement of α' is entered into the shift counter, it is done in 1's complement form; we are interested in the 2's complement of the result and must therefore enter an additional count of 1 into the shift counter to obtain the correct 2's complement of the exponent difference, box 6. We now have enough information to know whether one exponent is much greater than the other. This will usually call for a comparison of the absolute value of the contents of the shift counter with the maximum number of numerical bits which the mantissa register may contain, box 7. This, combined with the other criteria, determines whether we reset $\mathfrak{MG}$, box 8 which ends the first phase.

We examine $\mathfrak{MS}$ to determine if mantissa addition is to be performed, box 9. If so, the mantissa of the smaller number must be shifted to the right until proper alignment is achieved. The criterion for this is the contents of the shift counter as examined in box 10. If it is not 0, we look at $\alpha\mathfrak{G}$ to determine whether we are shifting A or D, box 11. Then we perform one or more shifts of the appropriate register to the right, box 12 or 13, during which time we also reduce the count in the shift counter by 1. We return to box 10 to test the shift counter after each alignment cycle.

When mantissa addition is not performed, we enter phase 3 out of the "equal" side of box 9. Box 14 examines $\alpha\mathfrak{G}$ to determine which number is much greater. When α is much greater than $\mathfrak{D}$, both the mantissa and the exponent are correctly contained in the **A** register and addition can be inhibited during phase 3. When $\mathfrak{D}$ is much greater than α, we wish to transfer D into A and $\mathfrak{D}$ into α. This requires that the A input to the adder is inhibited, as well as the α input to the adder, box 15.

When mantissa addition is called for, we add the contents of the D and A register together and enter it into A', box 17. This result is returned unshifted to the A register. The exponent transfer is tested for, box 18. If α is not greater than nor equal to $\mathfrak{D}$, we transfer the contents of $\mathfrak{D}$ through the adder into α', box 19. Then it is returned unshifted from α' to α which ends phase 3.

In the beginning of phase 4, we check to see if an arithmetic fault has occurred during mantissa addition, box 20. If it has, we transfer the contents of A to A' and return it from A' to A, shifting one place to the right. At the same time, 1 is added into the shift counter, box 22. This completes normalization when an arithmetic fault has taken place.

If a mantissa arithmetic fault has not taken place, box 20, we check to see if the result is normalized. If not, we transfer the contents of the A register to A′ and, when returning it to the A register, we shift it one position to the left, box 24. After this, the shift counter is reduced by 1, box 25. Since several shifts of the mantissa may be required, we check to see if we have finished by returning to box 23. If the sign bit and the most significant bit of the mantissa are different, normalization is complete. When the mantissa result is 0, no number of shifts can produce normalization. After N shifts, the test in box 26 reveals a 0 mantissa was produced and the arithmetic is aborted.

Exponent adjustment is done in box 27. The contents of the α register and the shift counter $\mathcal{C}$ are added and entered into the α' register. Then, it is transferred, unshifted, to α. If no arithmetic fault occurs in exponent addition, box 28, we have completed floating-point addition and subtraction, box 29. Should an arithmetic fault occur during exponent addition, this must be reported to the operator or to the program as an exponent overflow or underflow, box 30.

At this point, we can develop the equations which apply to each phase of the floating-point process and use the configuration of Figure 7.5.1.

Exponent Test

Phase 1 begins with the start pulse,

$$T1 = St \tag{15.5.1}$$

To perform the subtraction, $\alpha - \mathcal{D}$, we must make connections to and from the adder,

$$\mathcal{D}e = 1 \tag{15.5.2}$$

$$\alpha f = 1 \tag{15.5.3}$$

$${}^1\mathcal{C}_0 = 1 \tag{15.5.4}$$

$$\mathcal{P} = 1 \tag{15.5.5}$$

The result is entered into α' when the adder indicates completion by issuing a carry-complete pulse,

$$Sh\alpha' = \mathcal{C}\mathcal{C} \tag{15.5.6}$$

During addition, we determine whether α is greater than $\mathcal{D}$, using the condition of (15.4.11) restated here as,

$$\alpha\mathcal{G} = ({}^0\mathcal{C}_s\,{}^0\mathcal{C}_\mathcal{R} + {}^1\mathcal{C}_s\,{}^1\mathcal{C}_\mathcal{R})\bar{\mathcal{E}}_s + {}^0\mathcal{C}_s\,{}^1\mathcal{C}_\mathcal{R} \tag{15.5.7}$$

We refer to this condition to determine whether the shift counter is filled directly or in complement form. Thus,

$$\mathcal{C}\mathfrak{e} = \overline{\mathfrak{a}\mathcal{g}} \qquad (15.5.8)$$

$$\mathcal{C}\mathfrak{f} = \mathfrak{a}\mathcal{g} \qquad (15.5.9)$$

We enter this information shortly after $\mathfrak{a}'$ has been filled,

$$\mathfrak{Sh}\mathcal{C} = \Delta \cdot \mathfrak{Sh}\mathfrak{a}' \qquad (15.5.10)$$

When we are entering the complement of $\mathfrak{a}'$, we must tally up the counter,

$$\mathcal{C}\mathfrak{u} = \mathfrak{Sh}\mathcal{C}\overline{\mathfrak{a}\mathcal{g}} \qquad (15.5.11)$$

Now we are ready to check for a "much greater" condition using the criterion of (15.4.10), which we now record as

$$\overline{\mathfrak{m}\mathcal{g}} = d(<N)\,({}^{0}\mathcal{C}_{s}\,{}^{0}\mathcal{C}_{N} + {}^{1}\mathcal{C}_{s}\,{}^{1}\mathcal{C}_{N}) \qquad (15.5.12)$$

If mantissa addition is to be performed, we will start phase 2.

$$\mathrm{St}2 = \mathrm{T}2 = \Delta \cdot \mathfrak{Sh}\mathcal{C}\overline{\mathfrak{m}\mathcal{g}} \qquad (15.5.13)$$

Otherwise, we start phase 3.

$$\mathrm{St}3 = \mathrm{T}3 = \Delta \cdot \mathfrak{Sh}\mathcal{C}\mathfrak{m}\mathcal{g} \qquad (15.5.14)$$

Mantissa Alignment

We are now going to connect one of the main registers directly to its corresponding prime and then connect the prime register back to the main, performing a shift of one place to the right as we do so. The criterion for this connection is the presence of the signal $\mathfrak{a}\mathcal{g}$. Thus,

$$\mathrm{AA}' = \mathrm{Ar} = \mathfrak{a}\mathcal{g} \qquad (15.5.15)$$

$$\mathrm{DD}' = \mathrm{Dr} = \overline{\mathfrak{a}\mathcal{g}} \qquad (15.5.16)$$

We enter into the prime register at the start of this phase or whenever a test (Te) of the shift counter reveals that we are to perform another alignment cycle.

$$\mathrm{ShD}' = (\mathrm{St}2 + \mathrm{Te})\overline{\mathfrak{a}\mathcal{g}} \qquad (15.5.17)$$

$$\mathrm{ShA}' = (\mathrm{St}2 + \mathrm{Te})\mathfrak{a}\mathcal{g} \qquad (15.5.18)$$

We return to the main register shortly after the prime register has been entered,

$$\text{ShD} = \Delta \cdot \text{ShD}' \qquad (15.5.19)$$

$$\text{ShA} = \Delta \cdot \text{ShA}' \qquad (15.5.20)$$

The shift counter is counted down after each entry into the prime register, so that

$$\text{cd} = \text{ShA}' + \text{ShD}' \qquad (15.5.21)$$

We use this tally-down pulse, delayed a smidgin, to test the contents of the shift counter by examining the decoder. As long as the decoder registers a number larger than 0, we will issue a pulse for a new cycle designated as Te.

$$\text{Te} = \Delta \cdot \text{cd}d(>0) \qquad (15.5.22)$$

If the decoder indicates that the shift counter now contains 0, we start a new phase, knowing that the mantissas are now properly aligned.

$$\text{St3} = \text{T3} = \Delta \cdot \text{cd}d(0) \qquad (15.5.23)$$

Add the Mantissas and Set the Exponents

We are going to connect the D register directly to the adder if the proper conditions prevail. The only case we wish to *exclude* is where α is much larger than $\mathfrak{D}$. The case to be excluded arises only when we find 1 in both $\mathfrak{M}g$ and αg. Connect D directly when at least one of these is 0; thus,

$$\text{Dt} = \text{Fa}(\overline{\mathfrak{M}g} + \overline{\alpha g}) \qquad (15.5.24)$$

The complement connection occurs on floating-point subtraction in the same instance as indicated above,

$$\text{Dc} = \text{Fs}(\overline{\mathfrak{M}g} + \overline{\alpha g}) \qquad (15.5.25)$$

We enter the true contents of the A register for all floating-point add or subtract with one exception; we exclude the case where D is transferred directly through the adder to A', $\mathfrak{M}g$.

$$\text{At} = \overline{\mathfrak{M}g} \qquad (15.5.26)$$

The adder is connected directly to A' when addition, subtraction, or transfer is called for. That is, for all except α *much greater than* $\mathfrak{D}$,

$$\text{P} = \overline{\mathfrak{M}g} + \alpha g \qquad (15.5.27)$$

Quantities are entered into A′ when the carry-complete pulse from the adder is sensed,

$$ShA' = CC(\overline{\mathfrak{M}\mathfrak{g}} + \overline{\alpha\mathfrak{g}}) \tag{15.5.28}$$

Notice that the adder is not used for the condition $\alpha\mathfrak{g}\mathfrak{M}\mathfrak{g}$ since then **A** is correct. Transfer after processing is performed directly from A′ to A,

$$Au = \overline{\mathfrak{M}\mathfrak{g}} + \overline{\alpha\mathfrak{g}} \tag{15.5.29}$$

Entry is done a little after the information was set into A′.

$$ShA = \Delta \cdot ShA' \tag{15.5.30}$$

Meanwhile, exponent transfer is performed whenever the exponent of the result is to be recorded as what is now contained in $\mathfrak{D}$. In this case, we set up a transfer of $\mathfrak{D}$.

$$\mathfrak{D}\mathfrak{t} = \overline{\alpha\mathfrak{g}} \tag{15.5.31}$$

and at the same time we set up the adder for an addition,

$$^0\mathfrak{C}_0 = 1 \tag{15.5.32}$$

Transfer into the prime register is accomplished when a carry-complete signal is issued by the adder.

$$sh\alpha' = \mathfrak{C}\mathfrak{C}\overline{\alpha\mathfrak{g}} \tag{15.5.33}$$

It is returned directly to the main register.

$$\alpha u = \overline{\alpha\mathfrak{g}} \tag{15.5.34}$$

It is entered there by the delayed entry for the prime register.

$$sh\alpha = \Delta \cdot sh\alpha' \tag{15.5.35}$$

We will go on the next phase when one of two conditions has been met: we have α much greater than $\mathfrak{D}$ when we start phase 3; the proper mantissa is stored in A and the proper exponent is stored in α. That is,

$$St4 = T4 = St3\mathfrak{M}\mathfrak{g}\alpha\mathfrak{g} + ShAsh\alpha \tag{15.5.36}$$

Before leaving, let us note that an arithmetic fault for mantissa addition is recorded during this phase under the following circumstance,

$$Af = {}^0\mathfrak{C}_s\,{}^1\mathfrak{C}_{\mathfrak{N}} + {}^1\mathfrak{C}_s\,{}^0\mathfrak{C}_{\mathfrak{N}} \tag{15.5.37}$$

Align Mantissas

The equation for entering a quantity into the A′ register is

$$ShA' = (A_sA_N + \bar{A}_s\bar{A}_N)(St4 + ShA)\overline{Af} + St4Af \tag{15.5.38}$$

If an arithmetic fault has occurred, a shift of one and only one place right is always made, as is indicated by the last term of (15.5.38). The result of phase 3 may not require any normalization—it may already be in normalized form. Therefore, before each cycle we must make a test to see if the present result need be normalized further. This test is done at the time either of the pulses appear: the start-of-phase pulse, St4; the entry-to-the-main-register pulse, ShA. A test is made only when no mantissa arithmetic fault, Af, has been recorded. It calls for another cycle of shifting when the sign bit and the most significant bit are the same. The last term in (15.5.38) dictates that *exactly one* right shift is done when a mantissa fault arises.

The connection from the adder to A′ is maintained during the normalizing phase,

$$P = T4 \qquad (15.5.39)$$

The return pulse to the main register is the entry pulse to the prime register slightly delayed.

$$ShA = \Delta \cdot ShA' \qquad (15.5.40)$$

We are going to shift to the left when an arithmetic fault has not occurred.

$$Al = \overline{Af} \qquad (15.5.41)$$

We will shift to the right when an arithmetic fault has occurred.

$$Ar = Af \qquad (15.5.42)$$

We must tally the shift counter up or down according to whether a mantissa arithmetic fault was recorded or not,

$$cu = AfShA' \qquad (15.5.43)$$

$$cd = \overline{AfShA'} \qquad (15.5.44)$$

The sign of the mantissa portion of the result must be set in if a mantissa arithmetic fault was reported earlier.

$$as = AfShAA_N \qquad (15.5.45)$$

The occurrence of a zero mantissa complicates matters slightly, requiring repeated reference to the shift counter to be sure it does not contain $-N$. For d $(\leq -N)$ we will stop. This changes (15.5.38) to

$$ShA' = (A_sA_N + \bar{A}_s\bar{A}_N)d(> -N)(St4 + ShA)\overline{Af} + St4Af \quad (15.5.46)$$

The condition for completion of phase 4 is given as

$$St5 = T5 = AfShA + \overline{Af}ShAd(\leq -N) \qquad (15.5.47)$$
$$+\bar{A}_sA_N + A_s\bar{A}_N$$

Adjust Exponent

In order to adjust the exponent, the following connections must be made to the adder

$$ei = 1 \qquad\qquad (15.5.48)$$

$$\alpha f = 1 \qquad\qquad (15.5.49)$$

$${}^0c_0 = 1 \qquad\qquad (15.5.50)$$

$$\wp = 1 \qquad\qquad (15.5.51)$$

$$\alpha u = 1 \qquad\qquad (15.5.52)$$

The result of adding the shift counter to the unadjusted exponent of the result is recorded in α' when the adder indicates that it is complete,

$$sh\alpha' = cc \qquad\qquad (15.5.53)$$

This result is returned a little later to

$$sh\alpha = \Delta \cdot sh\alpha' \qquad\qquad (15.5.54)$$

When this is done, we are finished with adjusting the exponents, and floating-point addition and subtraction has been completed.

$$E = sh\alpha Te5 \qquad\qquad (15.5.55)$$

Notice that a floating-point result of zero is stored as a zero mantissa while the exponent may be anything which is allowable to the computer. Some computers elaborate this by recording a clean 0, a zero mantissa with an exponent which $1.00\cdots00$—the smallest possible negative number in 2's complement notation.

PROBLEMS

15.1 The exponent portion of the floating-point word can be placed on the left or right. Also the mantissa and exponent sign bit could be on the right or left. Give pros and cons for these four combinations.

15.2 For addition in adjusting the exponent, why not shift the larger number instead of the smaller?

15.3 Some authors have justified maintaining a nonminimum exponent with **0** to indicate the significant figures contained therein. Can you elaborate this explanation (see Section 15.2—*A Complication*)?

15.4 For a five-digit mantissa and one-digit exponent, do the following additions:

a. $+0.53217/8$
   $+0.61176/2$

b. $+0.53217/9$
   $+0.61176/9$

c. $+0.53217/6$
   $+0.61176/4$

d. $+0.53212/-3$
   $+0.61176/-3$

e. $+0.53212/-3$
   $+0.61176/+2$

f. $+0.53212/-9$
   $+0.61176/-9$

g. $-0.53212/-9$
   $-0.61176/-9$

h. $+0.53212/-3$
   $-0.61176/-2$

i. $+0.53217/+7$
   $-0.61176/+7$

15.5 Using the number pairs above, do subtraction.

15.6 For the flow chart, Figure 15.3.1, carry through a description of the events required to do Problem 15.4a, b, and f and 15.5a, b, and f.

16

FLOATING-POINT

MULTIPLICATION

AND

DIVISION

16.1 INTRODUCTION

The rules for multiplying and dividing floating-point numbers was discussed in Section 15.1. For multiplication, we simply add the exponents and multiply the mantissas. For division, we subtract the exponent of the divisor from that of the dividend and perform the indicated mantissa division. In this chapter, we develop the hardware for performing floating-point multiplication and division under the simplest conditions:

1. We assume that the numbers we are dealing with have all been normalized.
2. We omit means for post-normalizing the numbers.
3. We ignore all the exceptions, of which there are many, and leave these for later discussion.

Register Configuration

In Figure 16 we find a configuration of registers which performs floating-point multiplication and division in the simplest cases in a manner similar to the technique discussed for fixed-point arithmetic in Chapter 7. Notice that the configuration is considered as two separate ensembles, one for the exponents and the other for the mantissas. Although the mantissa register

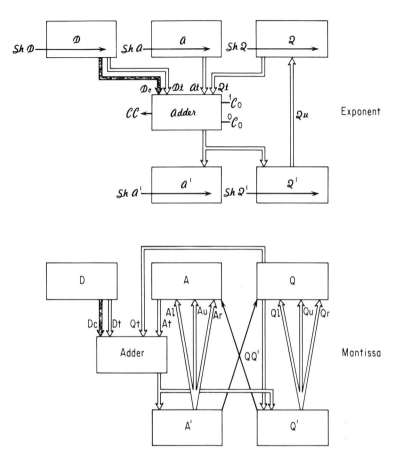

FIGURE 16   Hardware for floating-point multiplication and
division using the simple mantissa multiply and divide methods.

and the exponent register may be physically contiguous, it is easier to
visualize them in this fashion. The arithmetic control unit sees to it that
the operation of the two units are properly dovetailed.

Notice that the exponent section only performs addition and subtraction. We will never need to do multiplication or division with the exponents
to perform floating-point arithmetic.

The mantissa section in Figure 16 is identical with that described in
Chapter 7. Hence, it performs mantissa multiplication and division by the
simplest and slowest parallel means. It could be replaced by any of the
high-speed or compound units formed by combining methods described in
the foregoing chapters on high-speed multiplication and division.

The equations for the control of mantissa multiplication and division by the simple method are those listed in Table 7.7. The mantissa portion of the control unit is, for the most part, the same as described in Chapter 7.

Exponent Arithmetic

The symbol for floating-point multiply is Fm and for floating-point divide is Fd. For multiplication, we are going to take the contents of the $\mathcal{Q}$ register, add the contents of the $\mathcal{D}$ register, and enter the result in the $\mathcal{Q}'$ register. The result is then returned unshifted to the $\mathcal{Q}$ register. For division, the contents of the $\mathcal{Q}$ register are entered into the adder directly. The contents of the $\mathcal{D}$ register are to be subtracted from this so that its input to the adder is the complement input. The result is to be stored in the $\mathcal{Q}$ register so that the output of the adder is entered directly into the $\mathcal{Q}'$ register. It is returned unshifted to the $\mathcal{Q}$ register.

The contents of $\mathcal{Q}$ are always one of the operands,

$$\mathcal{Q}f = Fd + Fm \tag{16.1.1}$$

The contents of $\mathcal{Q}$ are added for multiplication,

$$\mathcal{Q}f = Fm \tag{16.1.2}$$

The contents of $\mathcal{D}$ are subtracted during division,

$$\mathcal{D}e = Fd \tag{16.1.3}$$

Carry inputs must be provided for; these are

$$^0\mathcal{C}_0 = Fm \qquad ^1\mathcal{C}_0 = Fd \tag{16.1.4}$$

Timing signals are also furnished,

$$Sh\mathcal{Q}' = \mathcal{C}\mathcal{C}Fd \tag{16.1.5}$$

$$Sh\mathcal{Q} = \Delta \cdot Sh\mathcal{Q}'\overline{\mathcal{Q}f} \tag{16.1.6}$$

Also,

$$Sh\mathcal{Q}' = \mathcal{C}\mathcal{C}Fm \tag{16.5.7}$$

$$Sh\mathcal{Q} = \Delta \cdot Sh\mathcal{Q}'\overline{\mathcal{Q}f} \tag{16.5.8}$$

where $\mathcal{Q}f$ indicates an arithmetic fault during exponent addition or subtraction. This is one of the special cases we mentioned earlier and is discussed in the following sections.

16.2 NORMALIZED NUMBERS FOR MULTIPLICATION

One thing that the designer must decide at the outset is whether un-normalized numbers will be permitted within the machine. If they are not permitted, then it can be assumed that numbers encountered at the beginning of floating-point arithmetic will all be normalized. This places a definite responsibility on the designer to make sure that the numbers he returns to memory upon the completion of arithmetic are normalized.

An alternative is to assume that no number is normalized. Then, if normalization is required for the arithmetic process, it must be done when the process is started. It is also possible that no normalization is required if a non-normalized result is satisfactory. Therefore, we may assume that no number is normalized at the beginning of arithmetic, nor is it returned to the memory in normalized form.

A third alternative assumes that no number is normalized but requires that the result be in normalized form. In implementing this design, the engineer must be careful to optimize for already normalized numbers. Since he can now assume that, in most cases, the numbers coming into an arithmetic process will be normalized, if a benefit accrues, he may design his arithmetic so that it is shortened when the numbers are already normalized and takes longer when normalization is required.

We shall look at the worst case where numbers enter unnormalized and leave normalized. We have the choice whether to perform arithmetic before normalization or to normalize first, perform arithmetic, and then perform another stage of normalization if it is required.

Prenormalization

For multiplication, both numbers enter into the processing and, therefore, one, both, or neither may be normalized. With normalized numbers, our product may still require an extra step of normalization, as will be demonstrated later on in this section. However, only one post-normalization shift will be required. In contrast, with unnormalized numbers the product may be so small as to require more than one word-length worth of shifts. That is, with a two-word result the significant bits of the product may lie in the less significant word. In that case, it must be shifted out of the less significant word register into the more significant word register. This is a double-length shift across two registers which is eliminated by *prenormalizing*. The exponent of the product is obtained with prenormalized numbers to within one unit of its final result. This is still not quite good enough to predict whether exponent overflow can be compensated for. This is discussed in the section entitled "Problem Exponents."

No Prenormalization

An alternative is to perform all normalization after multiplication—to rely wholly on post-normalization. This completely eliminates the cycles required for prenormalization. It requires that multiplication be performed regardless of exponent overflow or underflow. In this case, overflow and underflow distinguish the cases where the desired sum of the exponents exceeds the word size of the register and is a positive number in the case of overflow and a negative number in the case of underflow. Thus, we can predict that mantissa multiplication is performed in all cases when pre-normalization is absent. As mentioned above, if prenormalization is absent, post-normalization may take place over a double register; therefore, it may require as many as $2N - 1$ shifts.

Problem Mantissas

Three kinds of problems can arise in the mantissas used for multiplication: 0 multiplier, 0 multiplicand, and 1.0×1.0 (minus $1 \times$ minus 1).

zero mantissa: multiplier or multiplicand

The cases of a multiplier or multiplicand with zero mantissa are handled in the same manner. These cases can be detected by using a decoder on the appropriate registers. Such a decoder is handy to have for division also. As soon as a 0 multiplier or multiplicand is detected, multiplication can be stopped, thus eliminating many needless cycles of shifting. Special logic is then required to place 0's in the mantissa product and to indicate $-W$ as the exponent if dirty 0's are disallowed.

An alternative is to allow multiplication to proceed to completion. If dirty 0's are permitted, the result is now correct and nothing further need be done. If dirty 0's are disallowed, it is necessary to check to see if the product, either single- or double-length, has a 0 mantissa. If it does, $1.00\cdots000$ must replace the present product exponent.

multiply -1 times -1

-1 is represented by $1.00\cdots00$. On fixed-point arithmetic, this problem cannot be solved; when -1 is included in the field of operands, that field is not closed with respect to multiplication. That is, $+1 = -1 \times -1$ is not representable in fixed-point form.

For floating-point numbers, $+1$ may be properly represented by $+\frac{1}{2}$ by shifting the mantissa one place and adding one to the exponent. The problem is to determine that this special case exists and to correct for it. One way is to detect that both operands are -1. If we already monitor the operands for 0 in the numerical portion of the mantissa, this only means an additional check for the mantissa sign bit.

Another way suggests that we go ahead with multiplication as usual, first recording the sign of the product; in this case it is $+$. Now we find on completion that the mantissa product produces an overflow from the *sign* position. No other case arises for a positive product where a sign overflow occurs. Our cure is a single shift of the mantissa to the right combined with an exponent tally of $+1$.

16.3 PROBLEM EXPONENTS IN MULTIPLICATION

Exponents are a problem only when addition or subtraction causes an underflow or an overflow.

Underflow

In all cases of underflow, whether prenormalization is performed, whether unnormalized numbers are used, or whether no normalization takes place, we can make a general statement: normalization of mantissas only reduces the size of the exponent. Therefore, if underflow occurs when manipulating exponents which are too large, certainly it would have occurred if the exponents were the right size (that is, if they were smaller yet). Hence, once we discover an exponent underflow, we know that the result is too small for the capacity of the machine to represent it. We may inhibit all mantissa multiplication and make the mantissa of the product 0. If dirty 0's are permissible, no manipulation of the exponent is required. Otherwise, we must substitute $-w$ for the exponent of the product.

Overflow

Exponent overflow indicates that the sum or difference of the exponents as originally stated exceeds the capacity of the machine. However, post-normalization may reduce the size of the exponent and, in so doing, may bring it into the proper range whereby overflow is not indicated. When the numbers we are dealing with are prenormalized, one cycle of post-normalization, at most, is performed.

To illustrate this, we note that the smallest normalized mantissa is $\frac{1}{2}$ which is $0.10\cdots0$. Subtracting e, we have $0.011\cdots11$ which is unnormalized. When we perform $\frac{1}{2} \times \frac{1}{2}$, the result is $\frac{1}{4}$. This is the smallest possible product when multiplying prenormalized numbers. Thus, one shift left normalizes $\frac{1}{4}$ to $\frac{1}{2}$, causing a reduction in the exponent of the product by 1. Larger products are already normalized, and there are no smaller products for prenormalized numbers. Hence, we normalize one place or not all.

Now, if we provide circuitry to determine when an overflow condition could not be reduced to non-overflow if 1 were subtracted from the overflow exponent, then we would eliminate a lot of multiplication cycles for prenormalized numbers. All exponent sums or differences that exceed the register size by more than 1 result in an alarm condition, an exponent fault. If these are detected before mantissa multiplication takes place, mantissa multiplication would be eliminated for *all* these alarm conditions.

However, in most computers which provide floating-point arithmetic, an exponent overflow condition allows multiplication to continue to completion and is detected only after post-normalization. Usually, this is done as follows. A record is kept of the fact that an overflow has taken place and the overflow quantity is stored in the form of a negative 2's complement number. At the end of mantissa multiplication, the product is normalized and the number of shifts required to normalize the number is counted in a shift counter. When this count is added to the number stored in the exponent register, the removal of the exponent fault can be detected by monitoring the carry of this addition. If the overflow condition is not removed, an exponent fault is recorded which automatically takes care of unnormalized operands.

Often an exponent fault will cause the computer to stop. If the computer is equipped with some kind of automatic control device or if it is so programmed, an executive routine will be called forth to handle the situation.

16.4 AUXILIARY MULTIPLICATION MANIPULATION

Prenormalization

There are several ways to normalize the mantissas before multiplication is performed when this is the plan. If it is desired to normalize both numbers at once, a means for saving time, two counters are used to tally the number of shifts. Let us call the counters corresponding to the D and Q registers $\mathcal{C}\mathcal{D}$ and $\mathcal{C}\mathcal{Q}$ respectively. Then for each shift of D we count down $\mathcal{C}\mathcal{D}$ and for each shift of Q we count down $\mathcal{C}\mathcal{Q}$. When either one of the mantissas is normalized, we continue normalizing the other until it is properly oriented, and, naturally, we continue to count down only the corresponding counter. A problem may arise at this point if the normalization of either number causes an exponent underflow. This really is not much of a problem if we establish the convention that a number whose exponent has underflowed becomes 0. This simplifies both the representation and the multiplication. We now make this substitution and carry along the multiplication, either detecting the 0 immediately and acting at once to identify the product as 0 or detecting a 0 product during product normalization. If this solution is not satisfactory, a more elaborate one can be devised.

Instead of using counters to keep track of the shifts performed in normalization, the exponent registers may be tallied down directly. Again we have the problem of exponent underflow which may be solved as above.

We have described simultaneous normalization of both numbers. Of course, this may be done serially. We may normalize first one number using only one counter and then adjust the exponent accordingly. We continue with the second mantissa after the first normalization is completed using the same counter.

Post-Normalization

We have two cases to contend with, one following the multiplication of prenormalized numbers, and the other following the multiplication of unnormalized numbers. Certainly the former is the easier. In that case, as explained earlier, no more than one left shift of the mantissa is ever required. Then we only need to provide a means for checking whether such a shift is required. If not, the result is correct. If so, we perform one left shift (or right for $(-1) \times (-1)$) and do not have to check further. The exponent must either be left the same, reduced by 1, or increased by 1.

When no prenormalization has taken place, we may require the maximum of $2N - 1$ shifts. If means were provided to detect all 0's in the more significant word of the product, we could perform a full-word shift in one step by passing the less significant word through the adder into the more significant word prime register. This would require that the exponent be decreased by N at the same time or that N be added to the shift counter. If such a 0 detection device were not available, then normalizing shifts are performed one or several bits (K) at a time. For each shift, 1 to K is added to the shift counter and a check is made to see whether the number is in normalized form $(A_s \neq A_N)$. When the product is finally normalized, the contents of the shift counter is subtracted from the product exponent.

The criterion for normalization for 2's complement numbers is that the number is normalized when the sign bit and the most significant bit of the number are opposite, 1 and 0 or 0 and 1.

At the start of post-normalization the product exponent may be a very small negative number. This means that normalization may cause an underflow in this exponent. If this happens, the product should be recorded as 0 and if dirty 0's are disallowed, $-w$ is substituted for the product exponent.

Two-Word Product

As described in Section 16.1, multiplication produces a two-word product and we lose the multiplier. Since we have two words in the product, there is an exponent associated with each word. What is the exponent of each word to be? We have indicated how the exponent for the more significant words is acquired. In most cases, it is not necessary to use the less significant exponent. Therefore, some machines let it be whatever it turns out to be. An alternative is to duplicate the exponents so that they are the same for the less and more significant portion of the word. Another alternative is to have these exponents differ by N, since then they could be used separately in a double-length problem.

In the case of single-length multiplication, it can be performed as described and the less significant portion of the word thrown away. Rounding of the mantissa may take place as requested. Another alternative is to perform single-length multiplication, preserving the multiplier. This requires a slight modification in the control logic, but is not difficult to realize.

16.5 FLOATING-POINT DIVISION CONTINGENCIES

Normalization

The alternatives as well as the advantages and disadvantages, for normalization during division are the same as for multiplication. Some additional items apply to division because of the nature of the process. These are revealed under the topics of prenormalization and post-normalization which appear later in the section.

Problem Mantissas

0 operands

A 0 divisor or dividend may be detected in the same fashion that a 0 multiplier or multiplicand were detected. 0 dividend detection may save a lot of time in the division process by eliminating all the mantissa manipulation cycles. 0 divisor detection will save the normalization phase which, naturally, will take the maximum time since 0 is being normalized. However, an alternative is to detect the 0 divisor by the fact that it cannot be normalized.

$(-1) \div (-1)$

This problem does fulfill the requirement that the dividend be smaller than or equal to the divisor. In fixed-point arithmetic, the insurmountable obstacle is that the answer is $+1$, which is not representable. However, this is not so in floating-point, for we may shift the mantissa right one place, adding one to the exponent. This also provides the answer in normal form. The procedure for detecting the problem and correcting the answer may involve additional hardware. But this is usually provided when we relax the relative size requirements for the operand below.

relative operand size

In fixed-point division we have a problem when the dividend exceeds the divisor. In dealing with normalized floating-point numbers, this problem is eliminated, since we are sure that the quotient is normalized, even if the divisor is less than the dividend, a single right shift of the dividend remedies this, and assume that the quotient is normalized. If we are dealing with unnormalized numbers, the result can be corrected by post-normalization; no more than the usual number of division cycles will be performed whether the number is normalized or not.

even division

As in fixed-point division, we may find that at some point along the line a 0 remainder is produced. This effect is caused by "even" division; that is, the result is integral. If the logic provides a means for detecting a 0 remainder at any time during division, time will be saved for "even" division, at least for a single-word dividend. When a 0 remainder is detected, division cycling can be halted. Following this, adjustment of the quotient mantissa and the quotient exponent must be made so that they are in the proper form. A further cycle of quotient normalization is also required.

Of course, such a speedup is not required and "even" division may be left to complete itself. In some high-speed division techniques, a 0 remainder may call for an extra correction cycle.

Problem Exponents

As in multiplication, exponent arithmetic for division may result in underflow or overflow. All cases of underflow result in a 0 quotient so that division need not be performed if quotient exponent underflow is detected. Again, dirty 0's must be eliminated if this is required by the machine setup.

When exponent overflow occurs, mantissa division is performed to determine if this overflow may be compensated for during quotient mantissa normalization. This is necessary whether prenormalized numbers or unnormalized numbers are used for division. In the post-normalization period, the number of shifts performed on the quotient may compensate for the amount by which the exponent has overflowed. The number of post-normalization shifts is kept track of in a counter. When these are added to the overflow exponent, a proper exponent is noted by monitoring the carryout for the exponent adder.

Overflow of the exponent cannot occur during normalization because this process always reduces the exponent. The one exception is that $(-1) \div (-1)$ may produce $+1$ requiring an increase of 1 in the exponent which may cause an overflow for an already maximum-quotient exponent.

Prenormalization

When prenormalization is required in division, it is performed in exactly the same fashion as for multiplication. The reader is referred to Section 16.4 for this explanation.

Post-Normalization of the Quotient

If prenormalized numbers are used, then post-normalization cannot exceed one cycle. If the divisor is larger than the dividend and both are normalized, then the result, too, is normalized and the exponent needs no correction; if the dividend is larger than the divisor, the exponent of the quotient may need to be increased by 1. The counter requirement can be obviated if the quotient register can be tallied up and down.

With unnormalized numbers, post-normalization may require shifting over the full length of the quotient register. This is performed in a routine normalization mode. Some machines maintain greater accuracy in spite of post-normalization by performing a subtract-and-shift cycle (divided cycle) for each position of shift required. This reduces division speed but increases accuracy (and hardware).

When the dividend is larger than the divisor, the situation must be remedied because the quotient cannot exceed $+1$. It is remedied by a rule preventing it or by relative shifts of the divisor or dividend. These must be counted and subtracted from the exponent which may cause underflow. This is the only way underflow can arise, since, mantissa division should not start until the participants are in the proper relation. A positive quotient is then at least as great as $\frac{1}{2}$.

The Remainder

Although some fixed-point routines make use of the remainder, most programs do not refer to the remainder left after *floating-point* division but, rather, use the quotient directly. The question arises whether to make a hardware investment in producing a fully useable remainder. The question is answered affirmatively when computer checking is an important function. Division can be checked in a complementary fashion by multiplying the divisor and the quotient together and adding the remainder to this product; the result should be the dividend. To do this correctly, in floating-point, requires that both the mantissa and exponent of the remainder be correct.

The mantissa is usually correct after division, provided the proper division rules are observed. The exponent is not usually correct but can be found by reducing the exponent of the quotient by N.

The form of the remainder may be made more acceptable if we are willing to go through up to N normalizing cycles for it. This requires hardware for normalizing the remainder without corrupting the quotient, a counter for keeping track of the number of shifts, and a means for altering the remainder exponent. In addition, underflow of the remainder exponent may occur. This means additional logic for setting the remainder mantissa to 0 and the remainder exponent to $-\mathcal{W}$.

Double-Length Division

To do double-length division, only the dividend is a double-length word. Normal left-to-right, floating-point division is pictured in Figure 16. We do single-length division by attempting to subtract the contents of the D register from that of the A register. If this subtraction is "successful," this result is presented in the A′ register. In returning this number to the main register, it is shifted one position to the left. At the same time, a 0 is entered from the Q′ register into the least significant bit of the A register. 0's have been stored in the Q register at the beginning of division so that as the left shift from Q′ to A occurs, 0's are furnished into the least significant portion of the A register.

To perform double-length division, the less significant word is placed in the Q register. Then, as bits are shifted from Q′ to A, they are the bits of the less significant word. Note that the shift from Q′ to A is from the most significant numerical portion of Q′ across the sign bit of the lesser word to the least significant bit portion of A.

16.6   AN INTEGER FLOATING-POINT
NOTATION

Need for a Combined
Notation

Data in the computer memory for processing may be organized in many different ways. This is especially true of commercial applications where the memory word may be divided into fields, differently according to which portion of the record the word came from.

In scientific applications, it is customary to provide a separate word for each number appearing in the problem and its solution. This still leaves two kinds of data to be distinguished: fixed and floating-point. The commands for handling each are different. Two floating-point numbers operated upon by a floating-point multiply command produce a floating-point product. The same two floating-point numbers operated on by a fixed-point multiply command produce something, the meaning of which we might fathom, but it is certainly not a useful answer.

Why does one choose either fixed or floating-point numbers when both kinds of commands are available? Fixed-point offers greater precision and floating-point offers automatic scaling. Assume, for the moment, that the available precision of floating-point will suffice. Then the only other need filled by fixed-point is its convenience for counting. In this use, numbers are manipulated as integers and the need is for a compatible integer and floating-point notation. Is this attainable?

A method has been described[*] for doing just this. It has been adopted for the Burroughs B5000. Such a scheme may be installed in any binary computer regardless of the representation to be used.

A System—Integral Floating-Point

Let us examine a possible system, a variation of the one suggested by Grau, and its ramifications. Since the most benefits accrue in the sign and magnitude representation, let us examine such a design. A floating-point number $\mathbf{A}$ consists of two parts, with the exponent at the left,

$$\mathbf{A} = \alpha \cup A \qquad (16.6.1)$$

where α consists of $\mathfrak{N}$ bits and a sign bit, and A consists of N bits and a sign bit.

All words have the size $N + \mathfrak{N} + 2$. Looking at the bits from left to right in a register which we call $\mathbf{A}$, we have

$$\alpha \doteq \alpha_s \alpha_{\mathfrak{N}} \alpha_{\mathfrak{N}-1} \cdots \alpha_2 \alpha_1; \qquad A = A_s A_N A_{N-1} \cdots A_2 A_1 \qquad (16.6.2)$$

where α_s and A_s are the exponent and mantissa sign bits, respectively, $\alpha_{\mathfrak{N}}$ and A_N are the most significant numerical bits of the exponent and mantissa, and α_1 and A_1 are the least significant bits of the mantissa.

In the proposed system, all integers from $-2^{N-1} + 1$ to $+2^{N-1} - 1$ can be uniquely represented and identified as integers. The range of floating-point numbers is almost the same as for the corresponding fractional system described elsewhere. Further, except for a small set, they are immediately recognizable as floating-point numbers.

The simple device for setting up the system is to define $\mathbf{A}$ as an integer whenever α is identically 0—all bits of α are 0—and when the most significant bit of the numerical portion of A is 0—A_N is 0. Thus,

$$+27 \simeq \alpha \equiv 0 \qquad A = 0.00\cdots011011 \qquad (16.6.3)$$

$$-115 \simeq \alpha \equiv 0 \qquad A = 1.00\cdots0111011 \qquad (16.6.4)$$

and

$$0 \simeq \alpha \equiv 0 \qquad A \equiv 0 \qquad (16.6.5)$$

[*] A. A. Grau, "In a floating-Point number representation for use with algorithmic languages," *Comm. ACM*, V. 5, No. 3 (March, 1962), p. 160–161.

Obviously, here the point separates the sign from the numerical bits; it is not a binary point.

Floating-point numbers are identifiable for $\alpha \neq 0$ and almost always left-normalized to the binary point (for the exception, read on). Thus, these are readily noted as floating-point numbers:

$$+27.0 \simeq \alpha = -N + 5 \qquad A = 0.110110\cdots0 \qquad (16.6.6)$$

$$-115.0 \simeq \alpha = -N + 6 \qquad A = 1.1110110\cdots0 \qquad (16.6.7)$$

$$0.0 \simeq \alpha \equiv 0 \qquad A \equiv 0 \qquad (16.6.8)$$

$$2^{N+1} \simeq \alpha = +2 \qquad A = 0.10\cdots0 \qquad (16.6.9)$$

Again the point serves only to demarcate the sign bit.

There is a set of representations for which it is not clear whether the number concerned is an integer or a floating-point number. The value of the number, however, is unequivocally defined. These cases arise when $\alpha \equiv 0$ and when the most significant numerical bit of A is 1. Thus,

$$2^{N-1} + 3 \simeq \alpha \equiv 0 \qquad A = 0.100\cdots011 \qquad (16.6.10)$$

and this may be either a floating number or an integer.

TABLE 16.6 Showing the Range and Granularity of the Floating Integer Binary Number System

	Given α				
Exponent, α	Maximum mantissa	Maximum number	Maximum positive mantissa	Minimum positive number	Increment
$0.11\cdots1$ $= 2^{\mathfrak{N}} - 1$	$0.11\cdots1$ $= 2^N - 1$	$2^{(2^{\mathfrak{N}}-1)}(2^N - 1)$	$0.10\cdots0$ $= 2^{N-1}$	$2^{(2^{\mathfrak{N}}-1)}(2^{N-1})$	$2^{2^{\mathfrak{N}}-1}$
$0.00\cdots0$ $= 0$	$0.11\cdots1$ $= 2^N - 1$	$2^N - 1$	$0.10\cdots0$ $= 2^{N-1}$	2^{N-1}	1
$1.11\cdots1$ $= -2^{\mathfrak{N}} + 1$	$0.11\cdots1$ $= 2^N - 1$	$2^{-2^{\mathfrak{N}}+1}(2^N - 1)$	$0.00\cdots01$ $= 1$	$2^{-2^{\mathfrak{N}}+1}$	$2^{-2^{\mathfrak{N}}+1}$

Finally, to improve the granularity of the system in the neighborhood of 0, it is permissible to leave a number with a minimum exponent in unnormalized form when an attempt to normalize results in underflow.

To get a picture of the system, examine Table 16.6. When $\mathcal{C}$ is 0, numbers from 2^{N-1} to $2^N - 1$ may be represented in floating-point form. The representation of integers of the same size is the same. The very largest floating-point numbers have the exponent $2^{(2^{\mathfrak{N}}-1)}$ and range from 2^{N-1} times this to $2^N - 1$ times this. The smallest floating-point numbers have the exponent $2^{-(2^{\mathfrak{N}}-1)}$. Because of the low range convention, numbers range from $2^{-(2^{\mathfrak{N}}-1)}$ to $2^N - 1$ times this.

Naturally, negative numbers are identical, except the sign bit, A_s, of A, is 1.

There is only one representation for 0! It requires that both $\mathcal{C}$ and A contain all 0's. Whenever A is 0 is the result of calculation, $\mathcal{C}$ is also set to 0 so that 0 is always clean.

Finally, note the consistency between $\mathcal{C}$ and A in this system. Now both are in integral form. In a fractional floating-point system, $\mathcal{C}$ is an integral binary number and A is a signed binary fraction.

Arithmetic

How do we define arithmetic for this system? First let us re-examine the representation. Call the set of definitely floating-point numbers, $\mathfrak{F}$; the set of unequivocal integers is called $\mathfrak{I}$; the questionable numbers call $\mathfrak{Q}$. Then, since this is sign and magnitude notation,

$$\mathbf{A} \, \epsilon \, \mathfrak{F} \leftrightarrow \mathcal{C} \not\equiv 0 \qquad\qquad (16.6.11)$$

$$\mathbf{A} \, \epsilon \, \mathfrak{I} \leftrightarrow \mathcal{C} \equiv 0 \quad \text{and} \quad A_N = 0 \qquad\qquad (16.6.12)$$

$$\mathbf{A} \, \epsilon \, \mathfrak{Q} \leftrightarrow \mathcal{C} \equiv 0 \quad \text{and} \quad A_N = 1 \qquad\qquad (16.6.13)$$

When arithmetic is done with two numbers from $\mathfrak{F}$, the result should be a floating-point number. Usually, the result will be in the form of $\mathfrak{F}$. As part of the arithmetic, left normalization is done. Thus, the result, 27.0, will not appear as in (16.6.3) but, rather, as in (16.6.6), the correct form for $\mathfrak{F}$. The only other problem arises when the result is of the form of $\mathfrak{Q}$. It then appears ambiguous.

In the hardware, a bit storage device may be supplied to indicate the proper form of a number in one of the registers when the form is known but is not immediately apparent. Thus, a result appearing as $\mathfrak{Q}$ but resulting from floating operations can be identified as belonging to $\mathfrak{F}$.

Overflow and underflow can take place as for arithmetic in other floating-point representations and should be noted on bit storages labeled OF and UF.

When arithmetic is requested and one number is in $\mathfrak{F}$ and the other is in $\mathfrak{I}$, the result is defined to be in $\mathfrak{F}$. As above, an intermediate result found in form $\mathfrak{I}$ is normalized left to be in form $\mathfrak{F}$. For a result in $\mathfrak{Q}$, bit storage is set to F (floating) to identify the result.

Arithmetic for two integers should result in an integer. Integral division (/) is defined differently from floating division ($\div$) so that the quotient is always integral. For addition or subtraction, an overflow of one bit may occur. A bit storage can store the integer overflow (IO) event. Additionally, note should be made that an integral result is present (I).

When a sequence of arithmetic operations is done in the processor, intermediate results, although they appear to belong to $\mathfrak{Q}$, are now tagged either F or I so that operations that follow are fully determined. For example, let it be required to calculate $(A \times B)/C$. The result should be integral. Suppose $A \times B$ is large. It is carried as a floating number ($\mathfrak{a} > 0$) and I and IO are both set. If integral division produces a result in $\mathfrak{I}$, IO is reset. If A/C is found first, the answer is in question. Integral division truncates the fractional part. Hence, $5/3$ is recorded as 1. Thus $(5/3) \cdot 3$ is found to be 3 whereas $(5 \cdot 3)/3$ is 5.

In a similar way, an intermediate floating result in $\mathfrak{Q}$ is manipulated to produce a floating-point answer. It is when the final answer is ready to be stored in memory but is in $\mathfrak{Q}$ that difficulty arises. Before storage, the program may consult one or more of OF, UF, IO, I, and F. If the final result is to be read out, there is less reason for concern (see Input and Output Operations).

One device for distinguishing floating-point numbers of $\mathfrak{Q}$ is to purposely *unnormalize* them one position before storing them in memory. This sacrifices one bit of precision in these isolated cases but may be well worth it. Thus, instead of storing $2^{N-1} + 3.0$ as in (10), we have

$$2^{N-1} + 3.0 \simeq \mathfrak{a} = +1 \qquad A = 0.01\cdots01 \qquad (16.6.14)$$

The lost bit makes the number look like $2^{N-1} + 2.0$, but this is only a slight penalty.

Now let us examine arithmetic with numbers in $\mathfrak{Q}$. If the numbers are tagged by reference to F and I, it is clear that they are referred to as members of $\mathfrak{F}$ or $\mathfrak{I}$, respectively. Further, if one number is untagged and in $\mathfrak{Q}$ and the other is in $\mathfrak{F}$, clearly the result is in $\mathfrak{F}$. There remain two cases: both in $\mathfrak{Q}$ untagged; one in $\mathfrak{Q}$ untagged, and the other in $\mathfrak{I}$. There is latitude in setting rules for those cases.

One approach is to permit the result to take any form and not to set either F, I, or IO. The absence of an I or F setting indicates the equivocality of the answer. Of course, OF and UF must be set for floating overflow or underflow, since these are problem situations, more so for integers than for floating-point numbers. If untagged numbers from Ω are to be stored, they may either be used again or be sent to output. For the former, the hope is that the other participants in arithmetic will indicate either $\mathfrak{F}$ or $\mathfrak{J}$ to be the proper type for the result.

If there is any danger in mistaking floating numbers for integers, or vice versa, precautions must be built into the program so that results are examined before they are stored in memory. Otherwise there is the risk of *drifting*. Results from floating operations may produce numbers in Ω. When these are operated on, a result in $\mathfrak{J}$ may be stored. Hopefully, this will not affect decisions or cause other difficulties. Drift from $\mathfrak{J}$ to $\mathfrak{F}$ is also possible. If this drift could not cause misinterpretation, then *no* check before storage is necessary.

Other Representations for A and $\mathfrak{a}$

It is a simple matter to extend this notation to 1's complement or 2's complement representations for A and $\mathfrak{a}$. For instance, for the 2's complement integers $\mathfrak{a} \equiv 0$ and negative numbers are complemented with respect to 2^N. In mathematical form,

$$\begin{aligned} \mathbf{A} &= A & \text{for} \quad \mathfrak{a} &\equiv 0 & 0 \leq A &< 2^{N-1} \\ &= -2^N + A & \text{for} \quad \mathfrak{a} &= 0 & 2^{N-1} \leq A &< 2^N \end{aligned} \qquad (16.6.15)$$

The integer floating-point numbers in 1's complement form are similarly defined.

Output

To format information for output only requires examination of the exponent $\mathfrak{a}$. When it is 0, the output is integral; only A is converted from binary to decimal and the output is produced as an integer without a decimal point. Notice that numbers in Ω are outputted as integers too; this should prove acceptable.

Floating-point numbers may be printed in one of several ways. Frequently, conversion from floating binary to fixed binary is done first. Then fixed binary to fixed decimal follows. The decimal point is monitored and appears in the proper position in the printout. This would require a lot of paper for exponents of very large magnitude.

Often the binary exponent must be converted to a corresponding exponent for ten. This produces a factor (which varies with the decimal exponent) by which the mantissa must be multiplied. Then both the tens exponent and the mantissa must be converted from binary to decimal. Finally, both numbers are printed with the decimal point in the mantissa indicating the floating-point number and that the number is in two parts, exponent and mantissa.

Input

Integers within the range of the word size, such as 155, are less, in magnitude, than $2^N - 1$. These are converted from decimal to binary and $\mathfrak{N} + 1$ 0's are prefixed to this.

Floating-point numbers in single form are often used to input information to the computer. Usually the decimal point alerts the program that a floating number is to be converted. A floating-point number, such as 10,240.0 or 0.00387, totally in the integer or fractional range, is converted directly from decimal to binary. It is then normalized and the exponent generated by counting the shifts. Since this is an integral binary floating-point notation, N must be subtracted from the exponent $(\mathfrak{a})$ that would result from conversion to a fractional binary floating-point notation.

Information in double form, such as $10^8 \times 3.27$, must be handled in several stages. The exponent of ten is converted to an exponent of two *and* a binary factor. The mantissa is converted to binary; it is then multiplied by the factor. The product may require normalization, in which case the exponent is altered correspondingly. Finally, the exponent is reduced by N to compensate for the integral system.

There are several ways to cope with numbers having both a fractional and integral part but no associated exponent, such as 27.38. It is simplest to program a conversion to one of the forms above, at which point subsequent conversion to the binary integral floating-point representation is possible.

Compatibility

This system is *not at all* compatible in data format with either fractional floating-point or fixed-point systems. Thus if this system were designed into a new machine, that machine *could not do* problems where the data was *not specifically formated for integral floating-point*.

If it is necessary to design a machine to run problems in the old format, either new commands or a switch could be provided. Thus, the computer could have fixed, floating-fractional, and floating-integral commands.

Summary

An integer floating-point system is described which provides a consistent notation for both exponent and mantissa. The system allows integers and floating-point numbers to be represented with *one single notation*. Further, only *one set of arithmetic commands* is required to do all the arithmetic processes, as long as integral and floating-point divide are distinguished. In addition, except for a small set, *integers and floating-point numbers can always be distinguished from context*. No reduction in range or granularity from the fractional floating-point system is observed.

PROBLEMS

16.1 At least one computer has the exponent apply to the base 8 instead of two, so that
$$A = A \cdot 8^a$$
This requires three normalized forms:
$$0.1X \qquad 0.01X \qquad 0.001X$$
What are the benefits and disadvantages of this scheme?

16.2 Generalize the above to a computer for which
$$A = A \cdot (2^p)^a$$

16.3 Do these multiplications (with rounding) for a five-digit mantissa and one-digit exponent.

a. $+0.50500/0$
   $+0.30300/0$
   _____

b. $+0.50500/+2$
   $-0.50300/-1$
   _____

c. $-0.50300/-4$
   $-0.30500/-5$
   _____

d. $-0.40400/+5$
   $+0.40600/+6$
   _____

e. $+0.40400/-7$
   $+0.40600/-8$
   _____

16.4 Do these divisions as above.

a. $+0.10240/+5$
   $-0.40000/-3$
   _____

b. $-0.20480/+3$
   $-0.25600/+3$
   _____

c. $-0.4096/+8$
   $-0.32000/-4$
   _____

d. $+0.512/-8$
   $-0.20000/+4$
   _____

16.5 The system of Section 16.6 does not require that operands are normalized.
   a. What are the complete rules for addition and subtraction of integer float-ing-point (IFP) numbers?
   b. Draw a flow chart as in Figure 15.5.2 for IFP addition and subtraction.

16.6 Discuss completely the procedure for IFP multiplication and division, with flow charts where necessary.

16.7 Write a set of logical equations for an IFP arithmetic unit.

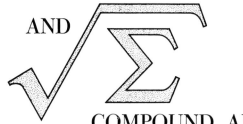

17

SPECIAL ARITHMETIC
AND
COMPOUND ARITHMETIC

17.1 INTRODUCTION

Scope

It is the aim of this chapter to investigate what complex or compound tasks can be assigned to the arithmetic unit in the areas of arithmetic or mathematical functions. These are discussed in principle in the Introduction. The specific hardware to do two specific tasks is investigated in the sections that follow.

It is difficult to find basic, integral, numerical processes other than the simple ones of arithmetic. It is possible to define an iterative multiplication process of a number upon itself. This is one way to define the power of a number. Of course, this definition applies to integral powers. Then we define the process by which we determine the number which, when raised to a given power, yields the number on hand and call this the root. Thus the nth power and the nth root are inverse operations.

Both the power and the root may be implemented with hardware without much difficulty. In fact, several sections will be devoted to hardware for extracting the square root.

403

Compound Processing

One more way to define basic arithmetic packages is to combine several arithmetic operations. Thus, accumulative multiplication adds the product of two specified numbers to another number stored in a register within the arithmetic unit. Subtractive multiplication is similarly defined. Other combinations are left to the ingenuity of the reader.

Transcendental Functions

Many functions which are trigonometric or transcendental in nature can be made amenable to computer processing by incorporating a complete table of these functions for all required arguments. In other words, we can resort to table lookup-function generation. At first glance it may seem that in order to incorporate a table of sufficient depth to include all desired values would require an immense list of arguments. However, both the computer and the programmer have at their disposal interpolative methods for deriving intermediate values from a much coarser table of functions. Beyond simple linear interpolation there are even more sophisticated methods of guaranteeing high accuracy during table lookup.

Usually interpolation is implemented by the programmer with a subroutine. However, a computer which approaches many problems with a table lookup activity might very well incorporate hardware which would expedite this activity at a slight additional cost. Methods for performing automatic interpolation have been investigated, and are discussed in the literature. As indicated later, specific processing hardware is illustrated by a polynomial evaluater rather than a table lookup device. Two such examples would be somewhat redundant. The polynomial evaluator is chosen because of its application to such a large variety of mathematical problems. The Univac 1103 or 1105 has a command somewhat of this nature.

Calculus

Differential and integral calculus are performed in the computer using iterative techniques. It is possible to build a computer which accumulates small digital intervals uniformly presented at uniform, small intervals of time. Such devices have found moderate applications to military and, especially, navigational problems. They are referred to as incremental computers or digital differential analyzers (familiarly, DDA's). Much has been written about these devices and much effort has been devoted to trying to determine whether there is an inherent superiority for certain applications of the DDA over the so-called general-purpose computer. The reader interested in this topic might begin his search in the American Institute of Electrical Engineers compilation.*

The Square Root

The first process to be treated extensively is the square root. This is a frequently encountered function which may be performed much more efficiently if hardware is incorporated within the computer. Not much attention has been given in the literature to explain how hardware is constructed to perform this process. Yet, as the reader will find out, it is not difficult to comprehend. It is useful for the design engineer to understand square-root hardware, for then he can evaluate whether it will be of value for the particular design effort in which he is engaged.

Polynomial Evaluator

The polynomial evaluator is used to evaluate a function which is described in the equation below:

$$F(X) = \sum_{i=0}^{n} A_i X^i \qquad (17.1.1)$$

It cannot be said in all confidence that this is frequently used, but, if available, it would be frequently used. Most trigonometric and transcendental functions can be expressed in a rapidly converging series. The adjective "rapidly converging" indicates that only a few terms of the series need be summed in order to obtain a result which is accurate to a large number of decimal places. Series evaluations are usually, by necessity, performed by programming the computer. The method proposed and discussed in Sections 17.5 and 17.6 requires a limited amount of extra hardware plus a few extra registers. To compensate for this, the resulting hardware is capable of evaluating a series several times faster than the same computer would operate if doing this job by an internally stored program.

17.2 DECIMAL SQUARE ROOTS

We are going to investigate hardware for performing square roots. We are primarily interested in fast arithmetic units and, hence, should confine ourselves to straight binary notation. However, before we can tackle the

---

* American Institute of Electrical Engineers, *Computers in Control* (New York: AIEE Publication S-132), September, 1961, $5.00.

hardware we must completely understand the methodology. To bring this home, we will first investigate taking a square root with decimal numbers. This section then is devoted to describing the manual method by which square roots are taken and then to defining the rationale for the method.

The Paper and Pencil Method

Figure 17.2 shows a gentleman doing a square root problem with paper and pencil. Let us try to follow his procedure, referring to the ex-

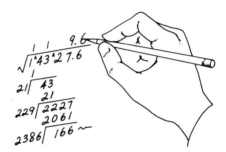

FIGURE 17.2   Pencil and paper decimal square root

ample that is illustrated. The first thing the gentleman has done is to mark off pairs of operand digits. He has done this starting at the decimal point and proceeding to the left. He has indicated the beginning of each pair by placing a carat sign before the digit pair.

He starts with the left-most pair; in the example this is 01. He now finds the largest square contained in this pair; in the example his answer is 1. 1 is the first digit of his answer. He also subtracts 1^2 ($= 1$) from the first digit pair. In performing a subtraction, he brings down the next digit pair, in this case 43.

Now he takes the answer so far, doubles it, and places it at the left of the remainder. In the example, he doubles 1 to get 2. To find the next digit, he will do a little experimentation. His guess at the next digit will be put in two places: to the right of the doubled result so far; as the next digit of the square root being developed if it is correct. In the example the gentleman has tried a 1. He finds that 1×21 can be subtracted from 43 and still yield a positive difference. Note that, if he used 2, 2×22 is 44 and when we subtract 44 from 43 the result is negative.

Having found the correct difference, he brings down the next digit pair. We find in the next line the difference, 22, and the next digit pair, 27, which, when placed together, become the new partial remainder, 2227.

He proceeds as above. He doubles the result so far; twice 11 is 22. The next digit he determines by experimentation. Apparently 9 works so that it is put in two places, after the 22 and after the 11. The product of 9 and 229 is found to be 2061, which the gentleman has just subtracted from 2227, and he still has a positive number, 16, as the difference.

Notice that to get the next result he doubles 119 to get 238. His next trial digit is 6. If you want to find out how he makes out, you have to try this for yourself.

In general, to determine the next digit we double the result-so-far and place it on the left of the present remainder. The trial-new-digit is placed tentatively as the next new result digit and to the right of the doubled result-so-far. If the product of the new digit and this total quantity is subtracted from the partial remainder and the difference is still positive, this new digit is acceptable provided that no larger digit would do the same. Processing continues until sufficient result digits have been obtained.

Rationale

Let us put the number for which the square root is desired in the following form:

$$N = A_n 10^{2n} + A_{n-1} 10^{2(n-1)} + \cdots + A_1 \qquad (17.2.1)$$

where n is the number of digit pairs. The A's are the digit pairs and may vary between 00 and 99, except for the nth digit pair which, in order to be of some significance, must vary between 01 and 99. Hence, the number of significant digits in our original number is $2n$ or $2n - 1$.

As can be seen above, our discussion is limited to positive integral numbers, but this is for simplicity only, since the extension is simple. Note in passing, that the number of digits in the square root we are developing is n and corresponds to the number of digit pairs in the original number.

Now let us develop the nth digit of the result. Recall that to do this we find the largest digit which when squared is contained in the nth digit pair of the original number. Define the remainder after performing the sub-traction as R_n. It is defined by the following two inequalities:

$$R_n = N - D_n^2 10^{2n} \geq 0 \qquad (17.2.2)$$

$$N - (D_n + 1)^2 10^{2n} < 0 \qquad (17.2.3)$$

We are interested in determining the next remainder, R_{n-1}. It is formed by subtracting something from this remainder, R_n. The quantity that is subtracted is shifted $n - 1$ pairs to the left. This is equivalent to multiplying that quantity by $10^{2(n-1)}$. What we subtract is found by doubling our first digit and then adding to it the next digit developed and multiplying all this by the new digit we are developing.

In algebraic form,

$$R_{n-1} = R_n - D_{n-1}(20D_n + D_{n-1}) 10^{2(n-1)} \qquad (17.2.4)$$

Another condition, an inequality, should be stated along with this equation. This inequality would state that if D_{n-1} used in (17.2.4) were increased by 1 and this same equation were written, the resulting remainder would be negative.

The next thing to do is to restate our current remainder in terms of our original number and the digits developed so far. This is done by substituting (17.2.4) into (17.2.2). The result is

$$R_{n-1} = N - D_n{}^2 10^{2n} - 2D_n D_{n-1} 10^{2n-1} - D_{n-1}{}^2 10^{2n-2} \qquad (17.2.5)$$

Collecting terms,

$$R_{n-1} = N - (D_n 10^n + D_{n-1} 10^{n-1})^2 \qquad (17.2.6)$$

Thus, the remainder R_{n-1} is the result of subtracting the square of the digits developed times a power of ten. The first two digits of the root we are developing are the best that we can obtain. If we try to make either digit larger, the remainder would go negative.

Next, suppose that we have developed not only the nth (or left-hand) digit, but other digits up to the ith digit, and that a relation similar to (17.2.6) holds when we express the current remainder R_i in terms of our original number, N, and the digits of the root that we have developed so far, D_n through D_i. This is expressed as

$$R_i = N - (D_n 10^n + D_{n-1} 10^{n-1} + \cdots + D_i 10^i)^2 \qquad (17.2.7)$$

To get the next digit, D_{i-1}, we are going to double the root so far and add the trial digit to it. Multiply this by that digit, shift it appropriately, and subtract it from the present remainder. All this in algebraic form appears as

$$R_{i-1} = R_i - D_{i-1}[2(D_n 10^{n-i+1} + D_{n-1} 10^{n-i} + \cdots + D_i 10)$$

$$+ D_{i-1}] 10^{2(i-1)} \qquad (17.2.8)$$

Again, it is understood that if D_{i-1} were increased by 1 in (17.2.8), the remainder, R_{i-1}, would now be a negative instead of a positive number.

Next, to show that the remainder truly results from subtracting the square of the number developed so far times a power of ten, let us state our present remainder in terms of the original number and the digits developed so far. To do this, we substitute (17.2.6) into (17.2.7). The result is

$$R_{i-1} = N - (D_n 10^n + \cdots + D_i 10^i)^2 - (D_n D_{i-1} 10^{n+i-1}$$

$$+ D_{n-1} D_{i-1} 10^{n+i-2} + \cdots + D_i D_{i-1} 10^{2i-1}) - D_{i-1}^2 10^{2i-2} \quad (17.2.9)$$

Now, if we gather the terms together, we find that the remainder is the difference between our original number and a perfect square and is given as

$$R_{i-1} = N - (\sum_{i-1}^{n} D_\alpha 10^\alpha)^2 \qquad (17.2.10)$$

We recall from above that if the last digit developed had been any larger, upon squaring the result it would exceed our original number and therefore would be too large. Therefore, we have the best fit for the number of digits we have developed so far. The procedure we are using guarantees us that we will get the best fit for the number of digits that we have developed, and this is sufficient demonstration of the validity of our procedure.

17.3 BINARY SQUARE
ROOTS–RESTORING METHOD

The title of this section indicates that there is more than one way to do binary square roots. Because of the yes/no nature of binary digits, it is possible to work the square root process as we did division; that is, if a subtraction causes the remainder to go negative, we can make up for this in succeeding processing. But first things first—we should understand how to do restoring square roots before we venture into a more advanced method.

Procedure

An example, a square root problem, is illustrated in Figure 17.3. The reader should follow the explanation of the procedure in specific terms by referring to the example. Since the procedure is much the same as in the decimal case, the explanation will be done in general terms.

First, partition the operand into digit pairs (in this case bit pairs) going in both directions from the binary point. We consider the problem of integral numbers in this discussion because the extension to fractions is obvious and the explanation is simpler here.

$$
\begin{array}{l}
\phantom{\sqrt{0}}\;\; 1 \quad 0 \quad 0 \quad 1. \;\; 1 \\
\hline
\sqrt{0} \;\; 1\mathord{\wedge}0 \;\; 1\mathord{\wedge}1 \;\; 1\mathord{\wedge}1 \;\; 1\mathord{\wedge}0 \;\; 0 \\
\;\; -\;1 \\
\hline
0 \;\; 0 \; 0 \; 1 \\
-\; 1 \; 0 \; 1 \\
\hline
1\,.\,1 \; 0 \; 0 \\
+\; 1 \; 0 \; 1 \\
\hline
0 \;\; 0 \; 0 \; 1 \; 1 \; 1 \\
-1 \; 0 \; 0 \; 1 \\
\hline
1\,.\;1 \; 1 \; 1 \; 1 \; 0 \\
+1 \; 0 \; 0 \; 1 \\
\hline
0 \; 1 \; 1 \; 1 \; 1 \; 1 \\
-1 \; 0 \; 0 \; 0 \; 1 \\
\hline
0 \; 1 \; 1 \; 1 \; 0 \; 0 \; 0 \\
-1 \; 0 \; 0 \; 1 \; 0 \; 1 \\
\hline
0 \; 0 \; 1 \; 0 \; 0 \; 1 \; 1
\end{array}
$$

FIGURE 17.3   Restoring binary root

The fourth bit pair is non-0. Therefore, the first bit developed, D_4, must be 1. Substraction yields the new remainder. Below this we place the doubled answer-so-far. The easiest choice for the next bit is a 1. If we are doing this manually, we might be able to make a better guess (this is obvious in the example). Next we subtract this from the remainder. If the new remainder is negative, our choice was incorrect. Since only two choices for D_3 are possible and 1 is incorrect, we make $D_3 = 0$.

When a trial subtraction yields a negative remainder, we restore status quo by adding the quantity that we have subtracted; thus the label *restoring square rooting*.

In general, the procedure consists of taking the square root developed so far, appending 01 to it and subtracting it, properly shifted, from the current remainder. The 0 in 01 corresponds to multiplying by 2; the 1 is the new trial bit. If the resulting remainder is positive, the new root bit developed is truly 1; if the new remainder is negative, the new bit developed is 0 and the remainder must be restored by adding the quantity just subtracted.

Rationale

To justify the processing, let us first express the number to be rooted in terms of the bit pairs,

$$N = A_n 2^{2n} + A_{n-1} 2^{2(n-1)} + \cdots + A_1 \qquad (17.3.1)$$

where the A's are binary numbers between 00 and 11 with exception of A_n which must be 01 or larger—otherwise, it is not the highest order non-zero bit pair. As before, we are developing n digits of our root. The nth remainder is

$$R_n = N - 2^{2n} \qquad (17.3.2)$$

The next remainder, R_{n-1}, is

$$R_{n-1} = R_n - D_{n-1}(2^2 D_n + D_{n-1}) 2^{2(n-1)} \qquad (17.3.3)$$

where D_{n-1} is the next root bit developed and is either a 0 or a 1. If it is a 0, the remainder is restored so that R_{n-1} is the same as R_n. This can be verified by substituting 0 for D_{n-1} in (17.3.3).

Now let us substitute (17.3.2) into (17.3.3); the result is

$$R_{n-1} = N - D_n^2 2^{2n} - D_{n-1}(2^2 D_n + D_{n-1}) 2^{2(n-1)}$$

$$= N - D_n^2 2^{2n} - 2 D_n D_{n-1} 2^{2n-1} - D_{n-1}^2 2^{2n-2} \qquad (17.3.4)$$

By gathering terms, we obtain, as expected,

$$R_{n-1} = N - (D_n 2^n + D_{n-1} 2^{n-1})^2 \qquad (17.3.5)$$

The subtrahend is a perfect square and the largest of just two bits.

The proof continues, as in the decimal case. We suppose that we have developed the ith digits and, consequently, have the ith remainder. It has been placed in the form below:

$$R_i = N - (D_n 2^n + \cdots + D_i 2^i)^2 \qquad (17.3.6)$$

Next we determine the new root digit by subtracting the root so far with 01 appended to it, this being shifted properly to the left before subtraction. The result is maintained if the remainder is positive; the remainder of the previous step is restored and D_{i-1} is set to 0 if the new remainder is negative. This is expressed as

$$R_{i-1} = R_i - D_{i-1}[2(D_n 2^{n-i+1} + D_{n-1} 2^{n-i} + \cdots + D_i 2) + D_{i-1}] 2^{2(i-1)}$$

$$(17.3.7)$$

Substituting (17.3.7) into (17.3.6),

$$R_{i-1} = N - (D_n2^n + \cdots + D_i2^i)^2 - (D_nD_{i-1}2^{n+i-1} + D_{n-1}D_{i-1}2^{n+i-2}$$
$$+ \cdots + D_{i-1}D_i2^{2i-1}) - D_{i-1}{}^22^{2i-2} \quad (17.3.8)$$

Gathering terms, we find

$$R_{i-1} = N - (D_n2^n + \cdots + D_i2^i + D_{i-1}2^{i-1})^2 \quad (17.3.9)$$

We now have the best binary root made up of $n - i + 1$ bits. This is attested to by the fact that if we increase this number by the least possible quantum, when it is squared it will yield a negative remainder.

17.4   NON-RESTORING BINARY ROOTS

In this section, we first discuss the means of finding a root by the non-restoring method. Next, we see why this procedure is successful. Finally, since we have a good algorithm for performing square roots, we can discuss hardware for implementing this algorithm.

Method

The reader may follow the discussion using the example illustrated in Figure 17.4.1. As previously, we partition the number to be rooted into pairs of bits starting at the binary point. We label these pairs, starting at the highest order, A_n, A_{n-1}, $\cdots$, A_1. The first bit of the root, D_n, of necessity, as discussed in the last section, is a 1 because we have assumed that A_n is non-void. Of course, this requires that the remainder, R_n, be equal to or greater than 0.

As long as the remainder for a given cycle is non-negative, we proceed as in the previous section; we enter a 1 in the corresponding root bit being developed; we append 01 to this number; we shift it the correct number of times and *subtract* it from the present remainder.

When the remainder goes negative, we do not restore as in the previous section. First we enter a 0 as the next root bit developed. To this we append 11. This result is shifted left the proper number of times and *added* to the present remainder.

When a cycle is completed, the next thing that we do is determined completely by the sign of the remainder. It is unimportant whether addition or subtraction was performed in this cycle. When the remainder is positive, a root bit of 1 is always developed, 01 is appended, and subtraction is performed on the next cycle; when the remainder is negative, the

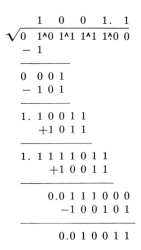

FIGURE 17.4.1   Non-restoring binary root

root bit is always a 0, 11 is appended, and addition is performed on the next cycle.

The accumulation of root bits may be discontinued as soon as sufficient bits are developed *or* when the remainder for any given cycle is exactly 0. Since hardware for detecting a 0-remainder may be expensive in comparison with allowing the process to continue to normal completion, the latter is often the accepted course of action.

Rationale

When the remainder is positive, the procedure and rationale are exactly as before. Formerly, when the remainder is negative, we would restore the remainder by adding the number we have just subtracted and then on the succeeding cycle subtract a new number. These two things can be incorporated into one operation: instead of adding the number we have subtracted, we add the number that we subtracted less the new number to be subtracted.

It is obvious that when the remainder is positive the root bit developed is a 1. When the remainder goes negative or remains negative from one cycle to the next, we develop a 0 root bit. It remains to be shown that the proper number was appended to the root before it was shifted and added back to the negative remainder.

For the demonstration, assume that the remainder, R_{i+1}, is greater than or equal to 0 and that the next remainder developed R_i is less than 0. Using the notation of the previous section, we define this remainder, R_i, as

$$R_i = R_{i+1} - 2^{-n+i}[D_n D_{n-1} \cdots D_{i+2} 101] \qquad (17.4.1)$$

Recalling our procedure, we get the next remainder, R_{i-1}, by *adding* to this remainder. The result is

$$R_{i-1} = R_i + 2^{-n+i-1}[D_n D_{n-1} \cdots D_{i+2} 1\ 0\ 1\ 1] \qquad (17.4.2)$$

Notice within the bracket that following D_{i+2} we have the $(i + 1)$th bit developed which is a 1 because R_{i+1} is non-negative. The next bit is a 0 because R_i is negative. The two 1's that follow are appended to fill out the addend. The number of places to be shifted is the coefficient to the left of the brackets.

It remains to show that the remainder, R_{i-1}, is the same for this non-restoring operation as it would be for the restoring operation. To see this, we write R_{i-1} in terms of R_{i+1} and the two numbers that we have subtracted from it.

$$R_{i-1} = R_{i+1} - 2^{-n+i}[D_n D_{n-1} \cdots D_{i+3} 1 \quad 0\ 1\ 0\ 0]$$

$$+ 2^{-n+1}[0 \ D_n \ \cdots D_{i+3} D_{i+2} 1\ 0\ 1\ 1] \qquad (17.4.3)$$

In the expression above, notice that we have shifted the addend within its brackets so that it is properly aligned beneath the subtrahend which produces the remainder, 2_i. Aligning the numbers in this fashion enables us to see at a glance what happens to most of the bits of the numbers we are manipulating. This alignment indicates that we are adding, for instance, $D_n/2$ to $-D_n$. This produces the single term $-D_n/2$. Similarly, we are subtracting D_{n-1} and adding $D_{n-1}/2$. This is simplified to read $-D_{n-1}/2$, and so on down the line.

We can then represent the remainder, R_{i-1}, simply as

$$R_{i-1} = R_{i+1} - 2^{-n+1}[0 \ \underbrace{D_n \cdots D_{i+3} D_{i+2} 1}_{\{\text{Partial Root}\}_i}\ 0\ 0\ 1] \qquad (17.4.4)$$

Examining the expression above, it is obvious that the number indicated by the horizontal brace is the root that we have developed so far. The two bits which follow, 01, are the properly appended bits when subtraction takes place. Notice further that we are *subtracting* and that the subtraction is performed upon R_{i+1}—this is what we would be doing if we had restored R_{i+1} and then gone through another cycle.

Example

Assuming that the result-so-far is stored in the D register and the remainder in the A register, as in Figure 17.4.3, an example would be per-

Register	Circuits	Notes
A	0.0 1 0 1 1 1 1 1 0 0	Operand
D	0.0 *1* 0 0 0 0 0 0 0 0	First bit
A	0.0 0 0 1 1 1 1 1 0 0	Subtract; (A) > 0
A	0.0 0 1 1 1 1 1 0 0 0	Shift A
D	0.*1 0 1* 0 0 0 0 0 0 0	Enter 101 into D
A	1.1 0 0 1 1 1 1 0 0 0	Subtract; (A) < 0
A	1.0 0 1 1 1 1 0 0 0 0	Shift A
D	0.1 *0 1 1* 0 0 0 0 0 0	Enter 011 into D
A	1.1 1 1 0 1 1 0 0 0 0	Add; (A) < 0
A	1.1 1 0 1 1 0 0 0 0 0	Shift A
D	0.1 0 *0 1 1* 0 0 0 0 0	Enter 011 with D
A	0.0 1 1 1 0 0 0 0 0 0	Add; (A) > 0
A	0.1 1 1 0 0 0 0 0 0 0	Shift A
D	0.1 0 0 *1 0 1* 0 0 0 0	Enter 101 into D
A	0.0 1 0 0 1 1 0 0 0 0	Subtract; (A) > 0
A	0.1 0 0 1 1 0 0 0 0 0	Shift
D	0.1 0 0 1 *1 0 1* 0 0 0	Enter 101 into D

root-so-far

FIGURE 17.4.2 Register contents when performing the non-restoring root-process

formed as in Figure 17.4.2. Initially, a 1 is entered into D as shown on the second line. New bit triples are jamset into D (bold italics) according to the result of arithmetic. Whether addition or subtraction is performed is also determined by this result—specifically its sign.

Hardware

This subsection outlines the operational hardware for performing the square-root algorithm, while omitting the control equations which must be specified for the proper supervision of the algorithm. By using the register configuration of Figure 17.4.3, we may store the operand in the A register and place the result, the square root, in the D register. The hardware is

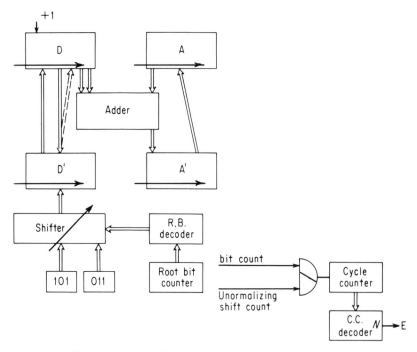

FIGURE 17.4.3   A logic for non-restoring binary rooting

for finding roots of integers to fit the explanation. The extension to fractions is left to the reader.

The first step is to normalize the operand, unless it is already normalized. We must observe the operand in the A register to determine if the first bit pair is 00. If it is, normalization takes place. The operand is shifted from A through the adder to A'. It is then returned from A' to A, shifted two places to the left. As it passes through the adder, the second input to the adder is inhibited, so that normalizing simply consists of shifting the operand to the left, two places at a time. As each shift is performed, it is tallied in the counter. This counter is used to determine how many bits of the result have been determined. The operand is normalized when either of its first two bits are non-0.

The normalized operand, of course, must be positive, for it is impossible for us to take the square root of a negative number. Logic may be necessary to insure a positive operand. This being the case, we are ready to perform the first subtraction. A 1 must be set into the D register corresponding to the right-hand bit of the first bit pair. This is done as D is cleared at the start of the square-root process.

Now the contents of the D register is subtracted, using the adder, from the contents of the A register, the result being placed in A'. The sign of this remainder is observed by the control unit. A count of 1 is added to the answer-bit counter *and* the bit-pair counter. The purpose of the answer-bit counter is to record how many answer bits are prepared so that the answer can be adjusted when termination is indicated.

According to the sign of the remainder, either 101 or 011 is entered into the answer-so-far which is stored in D'. The position in the D register into which these bits are entered is determined by the answer-bit counter. Its contents are applied to the right shifter so that they will be properly positioned.

Next, the answer is returned from D' to D. At the same time, the partial remainder is passed from A' to A, undergoing a single shift to the left. We are now ready to perform another cycle of processing.

The sign of the partial remainder determines whether we add or subtract the answer-so-far which was developed in D'. In either case, the arithmetic is performed and the answer is passed over to A'. The answer-so-far is entered directly into D'.

Processing continues in this fashion, observing the total cycle counter before each new cycle is attempted. When the total cycle counter indicates that the end bit pairs of the operand have been operated with, we know that sufficient bits of the square root have been developed. The operand may have been processed by normalizing or by doing arithmetic.

Whether normalization cycles have preceded arithmetic or not, the answer now sitting in the D register is normalized. It must be denormalized if normalization was done so as to be properly oriented with respect to the original operand. The number of denormalization cycles required is the difference between the answer-bit counter and the cycle counter. We now denormalize the answer by passing it over to D' and then back from D' to D, shifting it right as we do so. Single- or multiple-bit right shifts are performed according to the shift ability built into the computer. Multiple shifts require a decoding network to determine what multiples need be performed. As each denormalizing shift is performed, the answer-bit counter is tallied. When it contains the same number as the cycle counter, the answer is properly denormalized and the square-root operation is complete.

This is only one method and one configuration by which the square-root process can be performed; others might be equally appealing or even more appealing than this one.

17.5 THE POLYNOMIAL EVALUATOR

One of the most frequent tasks of the scientific computer is to determine the value of a function, given the value of a variable. The functions which must be evaluated might include trigonometric functions, exponential functions, transcendental functions, and so forth. All of the above-mentioned functions can be approximated by polynomials; that is, they can be written in the following form:

$$S_K = \sum_{j=0}^{K} A_j X^j \qquad (17.5.1)$$

When such problems arise in the normal, general-purpose computer, it is programmed to do the series evaluation, or else another method is found which may be faster than the *programmed* series evaluator.

This section seeks to examine the effectiveness with which a series evaluation might be performed and implemented in hardware in a general-purpose computer. If a polynomial evaluator were available in hardware, much more use would be made of series expansion because of the speed with which it might be executed.

As will be seen later in this section, most of the hardware required for the polynomial evaluator takes the form of extra registers to store intermediate results. However, it is this ability to store intermediate results that allows the evaluation to take place at a much faster rate than if it were programmed. Instead of registers, a small amount of very high speed memory could be substituted. This section shows the design and implementation of equipment which would be of specific benefit to the general-purpose computer, shows how the design of special-purpose equipment is approached, and shows how special equipment is integrated with a currently operating system.

The Problem

It is required to evaluate a series as stated in (17.5.1). Data available to the hardware is the value of the independent variable X, the value of the coefficient A_j, and the stopping point. There are two ways to terminate the series expansion: we may expand to a fixed number of terms, k or we may expand until the difference between successive sums is less than a fixed value ϵ—$A_j X^j$ less than ϵ for some value of j less than k. It may also be required to include some other parameters of the series when that series is restated as discussed below.

At this point, it pays us to examine expansions for a few common functions. Four common series expansions are

$$\sin x = x - \frac{x^3}{3:} + \frac{x^5}{5:} - \frac{x^7}{7:} + \cdots \qquad (17.5.2)$$

$$e^{-x^2} = 1 - x^2 + \frac{x^4}{2:} - \frac{x^6}{3:} + \cdots \qquad (17.5.3)$$

$$\tan^{-1} x = x - \frac{x^3}{3} + \frac{x^5}{5} - \frac{x^7}{7} + \cdots \qquad (17.5.4)$$

$$\cosh x = 1 + \frac{x^2}{2:} + \frac{x^4}{4:} + \frac{x^6}{6:} + \cdots \qquad (17.5.5)$$

As noted earlier, almost all transcendental functions can be put into the form of one or more series expansions. Many books are devoted solely to the topic of finding series expansions which converge rapidly and, therefore, are most suitable for numerical evaluations.

The Chebyshev expansion is a case in point. When the minimum number of terms of a series to be used for evaluation is known ahead of time, the series can be replaced by a Chebyshev polynomial. The latter consists of a finite and fixed number of terms and looks like the original series except for the coefficients. These coefficients are determined by a separate iterative process. As the number of terms increases, the calculations required to find the optimum coefficients become very long. It has become the practice to calculate near-optimum coefficients. These provide a great improvement over the truncated series and require much fewer calculations than the optimum coefficients.

In any case, the task of the polynomial evaluator begins *after* the coefficients have been calculated *and* inserted into memory in their proper position. Thus, the new polynomial will appear as

$$S_K' = \sum_{j=0}^{K} A_j' X^j \qquad (17.5.6)$$

where 0 coefficients for (17.5.6) and (17.5.1) are identical and non-zero coefficients have the same sign.

Because of this similarity between the two polynomials, we continue the discussion referring to the truncated series representations, it being understood that the coefficients from any improved expansion could be substituted for the original coefficients.

The series of (17.5.2) through (17.5.5) are typical of those encountered in numerical analysis; therefore, some of the generalizations we can make about the corresponding polynomials will be valid. For instance, note that certain powers of the independent variable are missing in all the series above. Also note that the series may begin with the constant or with the first power of the variable. Some series even begin with the second power of the variable. It is possible for the computer to consider every term in the polynomial if it is supplied with a coefficient for each term. In evaluating a polynomial in this effective manner, powers of the variable which do not appear in the polynomial would have 0 coefficients. Thus, in the expansion for sin x of (17.5.2), the coefficients A_0, A_2, A_4, etc., are all 0. The hardware for evaluating a series with missing powers would certainly operate more efficiently if there were some way to predict these powers.

A simple way to predict missing powers is to make a restatement of the series.

$$S_K = \sum_0^K A_i X^{a+ib} \qquad (17.5.7)$$

The restatement contains the following explicit or implied information:

X is the independent variable.

A_i is the ith constant.

K is one less than the number of constants available (there are K constants plus the 0th constant).

a is the starting power of the variable in the series; a may be 0 when the series starts with a constant.

b is the increment power—this allows us to skip intervening powers with 0 coefficients.

ϵ is the difference tolerance—when a new term is less than ϵ we are permitted to terminate our expansion.

The restatement (17.5.7) allows us to evaluate the series by accumulating only non-0 terms and, thus, considerably reducing the number of steps required.

Method

To make the evaluator pay, we must have immediate access to all the registers in the arithmetic unit and several additional registers. We have the arithmetic registers A, D, and Q, and we now postulate three additional registers, R_a, R_b, R_o.

The control required for a series evaluation includes supervision of arithmetic. Addition, subtraction, and multiplication are all required during the evaluation process. We might say that the series evaluator has a super-algorithm control unit which directs memory and register access and also delegates arithmetic processing to the arithmetic algorithm control units. Thus, when the program control unit—the main control unit—encounters a command indicating series evaluation, it turns control over to the series evaluation super-algorithm control. This, in turn, delegates arithmetic processing to the algorithm control units which then become autonomous. After an algorithm control unit has completed its task, it reports to the super-algorithm control that it has finished and surrenders autonomy to it. This delegation and return of authority continues until the super-algorithm control determines that its task is finished. Then it reports to program control which takes over to conclude the program.

To facilitate the control of series evaluation, a fourth register, R_c, is postulated which holds various constants appropriate to the evaluation

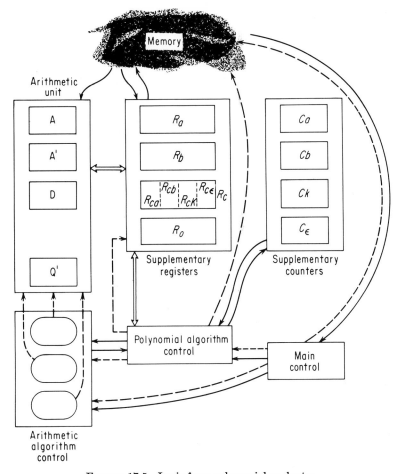

FIGURE 17.5 Logic for a polynomial evaluator

process. This register consists of several subregisters, each of which is countable.

The plan for operation of the series evaluation is illustrated in Figure 17.5. Data is supplied to the arithmetic unit and the supplementary registers from the memory unit. The polynomial evaluation command is passed over to the polynomial algorithm control from the main control unit. It also passes over a start command. At this point, the polynomial algorithm control takes over and supervises the processing. It controls the starting and stopping of the arithmetic algorithm control units and it controls information passing among the arithmetic registers, the supplementary registers, and memory. It uses the count register, R_c, to keep track of the processing as it is going on. When it is finished and the polynomial is evaluated, the polynomial algorithm control unit returns control to the main control unit.

17.6 POLYNOMIAL EVALUATION COMMAND STRUCTURE AND HARDWARE

Polynomial Specification

To perform an expansion, a polynomial evaluation command is submitted to the main control unit. This command has the mnemonic POL. The operand address, MMM, is really the starting address of the set of data applying to the evaluation command; that is, starting at location M, we will find a series of data all of which are required for the expansion.

To do the job right, let us specify that the independent variable, X, is stored at M. The four constants, a, b, K, and ϵ, are compressed and stored in the next word, $M + 1$. $M + 2$ and the locations which follow contain successive constants A_0, A_1, etc., up to A_k.

For an example, let us set up a truncated series expansion for sin x. The pertinent information is as follows:

$$(I) = \text{POL } 00M$$
$$(M) = X$$
$$(M + 1) = 001 \quad 002 \quad 006 \quad 000$$
$$(M + 2) = 1$$
$$(M + 3) = \tfrac{1}{3}!$$
$$(M + 4) = \tfrac{1}{5}!$$
$$\cdots$$
$$(M + 7) = \tfrac{1}{11}!$$

This provides an expansion of six terms. The expansion will always provide six terms because ϵ has been indicated as 000. Thus, unless a term is contained in the register as all 0's, it will be added to the expansion and the expansion will continue until we reach the sixth term.

Hardware Configuration

The general hardware configuration for the polynomial evaluation was illustrated in Figure 17.5. Notice that there is a main information bus. This shows diagramatically that the main registers of the arithmetic unit and the supplementary polynomial evaluater registers can be interconnected if controlled by the polynomial algorithm control (henceforth familiarly referred to as PAC). Another supplementary register, R_c, is divided into four parts, R_{ca}, R_{cb}, R_{cK}, $R_{c\epsilon}$. One word from memory is plunked into these four portions of the register. Also, supplementary counters and decoders are required to provide effective control information to PAC.

Flow Diagram

A flow diagram for the processor has been constructed, Figure 17.6. First we procure X and then the set of series constants which is dumped into R_a. In box 3 we calculate the initial power of X, X^a. Following this, we calculate the incremental power of X, X^b.

Our procedure is slightly different according to whether the initial power, a, is 0 or not. When a is equal to 0, as tested in box 5, the first constant, A_0 is entered into the accumulator directly, as indicated in box 6. When a is non-0, the initial coefficient is multiplied by the initial power of X and this is entered into the accumulator, as indicated in box 7. We now perform the loop, indicated by boxes 0 through 14, wherein the next term of the polynomial is calculated and added into an accumulator (indicated by Σ) for which R_0 is used. As we start, we indicate that a new term is being calculated by increasing our index i by 1. Next, we find the new power of X to be used and place it into the R_a register, box 9. Since the R_a register contained the previous power of X that was used, the new power is determined by simply multiplying the contents of R_a by X^b contained in R_b.

The coefficient corresponding to *this* term is stored in memory; it must be brought in from memory. Then it is used as a factor for the power of X now in R_a. This product, which is formed in the A register, as shown in box 11, is added to the sum which is being accumulated, box 12. The size of the last term accumulated is now compared with our difference tolerance,

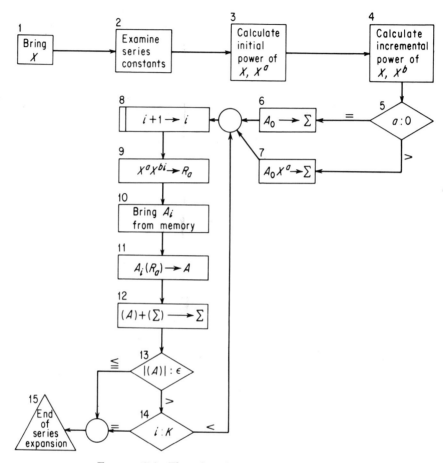

FIGURE 17.6 Flow chart for polynomial evaluator

ϵ. If it is less than or equal to this tolerance, our series evaluation is complete.

Another way to end the polynomial evaluation is to run out of coefficients. We check to see if we have used the last coefficient in box 14; if so, we terminate the evaluation. Otherwise we go on and pass through another loop again, boxes 6 through 14.

Details of Operation

Without developing the full equations for PAC, let us investigate some of the details of its operation. The first step is for the program control to recognize a POL command. In so doing, it relinquishes control to PAC, it clears all registers which will be used for the processing, and it fetches the independent variable, X, entering it in both the A and D registers.

Next, PAC increments the operand address, M, starts a new fetch cycle, and guides the transfer of $(M + 1)$ into R_c. Then PAC prepares X^a. It does so by requesting a multiplication of the arithmetic unit whereby X is multiplied by X. This product is tallied in a counter, C_a. The counter is compared with the a portion of the register, R_{ca}. If they are not identical, another multiplication is requested until X^a is prepared. At that time (R_{ca}) and (C_a) will be identical. Upon completion, X^a is passed over to R_a.

Next, PAC supervises the preparation of X^b which is done in exactly the same manner as described for X^a. We use C_b, a counter which keeps track of the multiplications performed to prepare X^b. In practice, we may be able to get away with just one counter to perform both functions.

While these calculations are going on, we can procure the initial co-efficient, A_0. To do this, we must increment the operand address and request a fetch cycle. Since the coefficient is placed directly into R_0, it will in no way interfere with the multiplications which are going on. When both powers of X are available and the initial coefficient is contained in R_0, we are ready to form the initial term. To do this, we check R_{ca}. If it is 0, we do nothing, for we are going to place our accumulated terms in R_0. When a is non-0, we transfer the first coefficient, A_0, to 0 and perform a multiplication using (R_a) as the multiplier. The result is the initial term and it is entered into R_0 after it is formed.

To construct the new power of X, we multiply (R_a) and (R_b), maintaining this quantity in D and also duplicating it in R_a. As we do this, we also request that the new coefficient, A_i, be fetched. When it has appeared, it is used as a factor for the power of X contained in D. The result is the new term which is added to the sum-so-far now contained in R_0 and the result is returned to R_0.

Now we perform tests for termination. We check the size of D against ϵ. ϵ is merely a shift coefficient causing us to shift out information from the D register, shifting 0's into the left-hand side. If the term contained in D is small enough, then if we shift it a number of places corresponding to ϵ, we enter enough 0's into D to make it equal to 0. The test for completion then is simply a comparison of (D) with 0. In the meantime, we are decrementing R_{cK}. If the first test is unsuccessful, we compare (R_{cK}) with 0. If successful, this test causes termination.

If both tests are unsuccessful, we continue by preparing the next power of X, getting the appropriate factor, calculating the term, and so forth.

PROBLEMS

17.1 Assume the same times for arithmetic and transfer as used on the analysis of multiplication of Section 11.4.

$$\rho = 8 \text{ nanoseconds}$$
$$\pi = 7 \text{ nanoseconds}$$
$$\alpha = 1 \text{ nanoseconds}$$
$$\sigma = 100 \text{ nanoseconds}$$
$$\text{Add time} = 1.6 \text{ microseconds}$$
$$\text{Multiply time} = 40 \text{ microseconds}$$

Estimate the time required to take the square root of a 48-bit number using the hardware proposed here.

17.2 Using typical instructions and supposing that memory time is the same as addition—1.6 microseconds—and multiply takes 40 microseconds,
a. Construct a square-root program.
b. Estimate the time for the program.
c. Compare with Problem 17.1.

17.3 Let us use a polynomial (untruncated) to evaluate sin x with the expression (17.5.2). For the parameter of Problems 17.1 and 17.2, how long does this take for
a. Four terms.
b. Six terms.

17.4 As in Problem 17.3, write a program for the determination of sin x by (17.5.2) for
a. Four terms.
b. Six terms.
c. n terms.
d. What time is required for each run?

17.5 Determine the equations for simple linear interpolation. It is desired to look up a function $f(x)$ in a table with equal intervals for the independent variable, x.
a. Design a program as in Problem 17.2 to do this.
b. What hardware could be devised to do this?
c. Contrast the performance of the two approaches.

18

MODULUS

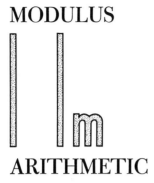

ARITHMETIC

18.1 INTRODUCTION

One of the projects currently under research is the investigation of radix notation for use in computers ("radix," "residue," and "modulus" are words which are used interchangeably to describe this particular kind of notation). The notation under investigation has been known in principle for many years. It offers an especial advantage for it provides the capability to perform addition, subtraction, and multiplication without considering the carries which take place from one digit to the next. Parallel operations on words occur in a single bit time!

This chapter is devoted to a study of radix notation and its application to special and general-purpose computers. This first section reviews the single-base notation familiar to the reader and introduces multiple-base notation. Section 18.2 is devoted to congruences, the basis for radix notation. In Section 18.3, the radix notation is introduced. Its interpretation for computers as binary-coded radix notation is also presented there. Sections 18.4 and 18.5 are devoted to a discussion of addition, subtraction, and multiplication using radix notation. The special functions encountered in evaluating radix numbers, $A(x)$, $B(x)$, and $D(x)$ are covered in Section 18.6. Translation from and to the radix system is the subject of Section 18.7. The very important topics of sign and overflow get attention in Section 18.8. Other considerations in applying radix arithmetic to systems design are discussed in Section 18.9. Finally, the future for radix notation is commented upon in Section 18.10.

Single-Base Notation

A number is represented, using single-base notation, as

$$N \simeq d_n d_{n-1} \cdots d_1 d_0 \qquad (18.1.1)$$

Using the summation notation, we find that the number is equal to the sum of multiples of powers of a base, so that

$$N = \sum_0^n d_i b^i \qquad (18.1.2)$$

where the multiples, d_i, are integers which are greater than or equal to 0 but less than the integral base, b. Historically, the first use of 0 is associated with the single-base notation. Thus, in representing a number where one power of the base was absent, the multiple corresponding to that power of the base was entered either as a 0 or as a large dot. The arithmeticians and philosophers later broadened the concept to encompass the void or *null* class.

The method for translating from one number system to another— from a representation using one base to that using a different base— allows us a little more insight into the single-base number representation. Thus, we can represent the number N as

$$N = \dot{d}_0 b + d_0 \qquad (18.1.3)$$

where $\dot{d}_0$ represents the number of times the number is divisible by the base. In other words, if we subtract the units multiple from the number, division by the base should be exact and should yield the quantity $\dot{d}_0$; thus,

$$\dot{d}_0 = \frac{(N - d_0)}{b} \qquad (18.1.4)$$

In a similar way, we define $\dot{d}_1$ as the number of times the second power of the base is contained in the original number. This is implicit in the following equation.

$$\dot{d}_0 = \dot{d}_1 b + d_1 \qquad (18.1.5)$$

Similarly,

$$\dot{d}_1 = \dot{d}_2 b + d_2 \qquad (18.1.6)$$

and, in general,

$$\dot{d}_i = \dot{d}_{i+1} b + d_{i+1} \qquad (18.1.7)$$

Then $\dot{d}_n$ represents the number of multiples of the nth power of the base which is contained in the original number and, hence, should be exactly equal to d_n, as is conveyed by

$$\dot{d}_n = 0 \cdot b + d_n \qquad (18.1.8)$$

Mixed-Base Notation

In the description above, we use one base and its powers. We are going to generalize and permit a different base corresponding to each digit. Proceeding from right to left, we shall use the different bases, distinguished as $b_1, b_2, \cdots, b_n$. Let us again consider the number represented as below.

$$N \simeq d_n d_{n-1} \cdots d_1 d_0 \qquad (18.1.9)$$

We find that n is given by

$$N = d_0 + d_1 b_1 + d_2 b_1 b_2 + d_3 b_1 b_2 b_3 + \cdots + d_n b_1 b_2 \cdots b_n \qquad (18.1.10)$$

Thus, each digit moving to the right is represented by a product of one more of the bases. We can put (18.1.10) in product notation as

$$N = d_n \prod_0^n b_j + d_{n-1} \prod_0^{n-1} b_j + \cdots + d_i \prod_0^1 b_j + d_0 \prod b_0 \qquad (18.1.11)$$

where $b_0 = 1$ or

$$= \sum_{i=0}^n d_i \prod_0^i b_j \qquad (18.1.12)$$

with $b_0 = 1$. This is really a generalization of the single-base notation and when we make all of the bases, b_j, identical and call them b, (18.1.12) degenerates to (18.1.3).

Is the mixed-base system just another mathematical toy—would anyone use a multiple-base notation in practice? An example of it graces many buildings and monuments. It is traditional to indicate the year when construction was started on a public edifice in Roman numerals. The notation indicates both the base (alternating between 2 and 5) and its power. For Roman notation, b_1, b_3, and all odd-numbered bases are 5; b_2, b_4, and even-numbered bases are 2. The coefficient of a base *is* the number of identical base symbols in the representation.

examples

To convert from Roman notation, first convert to modified Roman, where the number of symbols for a base is replaced by an Arabic numeral.

Consider Roman numeral LXXXVII. This becomes, in modified Roman, 1312. Thus, we have the general form given by

$$\text{LXXXVII} = 2 + b_1 + 3b_2b_1 + b_3b_2b_1 \qquad (18.1.13)$$

Recalling the rule for odd and even bases, this reduces to

$$\text{LXXXVII} = 2 + 1 \cdot 5 + 3(2 \cdot 5) + 1(5 \cdot 2 \cdot 5) = 87 \qquad (18.1.14)$$

The only remaining consideration is the prefix convention. Thus the Romans, instead of writing XXXX for 40, indicates it simply as XL, so that a multiple of 4 is indicated as one of the symbol for that base, followed by one of the symbol of the next higher base.

As an example of this, the following Roman number is converted into modified Roman as

$$\text{CCXLIV} = 20404 \qquad (18.1.15)$$

which, when expanded, is obviously 244.

18.2 CONGRUENCES

Radix notation uses multiple bases, but instead of referring for each digit to the product of the succeeding bases, a digit is examined in terms of congruences. For this reason, we address ourselves to an explanation of the subject of congruences.

Concept

The concept of congruences depends on a reference number which is referred to as the modulus which plays a role similar to the base in the single- or multiple-base systems. The congruence concept is best explained with reference to division. Numbers are equivalent with respect to a given modulus if division by this modulus produces the same remainder. This equivalence is referred to as congruence. It is impossible to enumerate all the numbers so equivalent. The mathematician indicates the equivalence by using three horizontal bars and always indicating in parentheses the modulus with respect to which equivalence is stated. Thus, we state that two numbers, X and X', are congruent as follows:

$$X \equiv X' \equiv x \ (\text{mod } m) \qquad (18.2.1)$$

We are usually interested in the integer which is less than the modulus but greater than or equal to 0; it is called the least positive residue, or simply, the residue of X (or X') with respect to m. Thus, we have, for the residue of x,

$$0 \leq x < m \qquad (18.2.2)$$

Let us examine an example of this concept in numbers rather than abstract symbols.

$$19 \equiv 34 \equiv 4 \pmod{5} \qquad (18.2.3)$$

The residue of 19 or 34 is thus 4 with respect to the modulus 5. In symbolic form, the relationship of (18.2.1) is defined by

$$X = km + x \qquad (18.2.4)$$

and

$$X' = k'm + x \qquad (18.2.5)$$

To provide a full symbolic vocabulary, let us make one more definition. Let us say that when we have a fraction indicated as A, which may be proper or improper, we indicate the integer which is just smaller than this fraction as $[A]$. Thus $[\frac{3}{8}]$ is 0 and $[\frac{17}{2}]$ is 8. Then we can represent (18.2.4), without injecting another constant, simply as

$$X = m \left[\frac{X}{m}\right] + x \qquad (18.2.6)$$

Having become acquainted with the mathematical notation, let us now effect a simplification. Vertical bars subscripted by the modulus indicate the residue relationship in a briefer and easier-to-read notation. Using this notation, we rewrite (18.2.1) as

$$|X'|_m = |X|_m = x \qquad (18.2.7)$$

An example of this usage is

$$|19|_5 = 4 \qquad (18.2.8)$$

A further simplification involves dropping the modulus when its identity is apparent.

Some Rules

In this subsection, we present some of the rules which can be rigorously proven but which are intuitively presented. For the purpose of this presentation, let us define the least positive residue for two quantities, A and B, as

$$|A| = a \qquad |B| = b \qquad (18.2.9)$$

It is easily shown that the residue of the sum of two numbers is the residue of the sum of their residues. It is clearer when this is put in symbolic form as

$$|A + B| = |a + b| \qquad (18.2.10)$$

For example,

$$|19 + 8|_5 = |4 + 3|_5 = 2 = |27|_5 \qquad (18.2.11)$$

Similarly, the residue of the difference of two numbers is the residue of the difference of their residues. In symbolic form,

$$|A - B| = |a - b| \qquad (18.2.12)$$

For example,

$$|19 - 8|_5 = |4 - 3|_5 = 1 = |11|_5 \qquad (18.2.13)$$

Further, the residue of the product of two numbers is the residue of the product of the residues; thus,

$$|AB| = |ab| \qquad (18.2.14)$$

For example,

$$|19 \cdot 8|_5 = |4 \cdot 3|_5 = 2 = |152|_5 \qquad (18.2.15)$$

These equations are the key to the usefulness of modulus arithmetic for application to the computer. Examination of these equations shows that *carries with respect to the modulus can be ignored.*

More Rules

A few of the simple properties of the congruence relationship which may be derived easily are now presented. The residue of the modulus with, respect to itself, is 0, the residue of any multiple of the modulus with respect to itself is also 0. Thus,

$$|m|_m = 0 \qquad |mX|_m = 0 \qquad (18.2.16)$$

The modulus 1 is rather useless for any number when referred to it as a residue of 0; thus,

$$|X|_1 = 0 \qquad (18.2.17)$$

Having generated the concept of least positive residue, it is obvious that if we take the residue with respect to it we should get the same thing—the least positive residue; this leads to

$$\| X \|_m |_m = | X |_m \qquad (18.2.18)$$

For example,

$$\| 19 |_5 |_5 = | 4 |_5 = 4 \qquad (18.2.19)$$

Adding a multiple of the modulus to a number does not affect the number with respect to congruence for that modulus, so that

$$| X \pm km | = | X | \qquad (18.2.20)$$

The residue of a negative integer can be represented in two ways:

$$| -X | = | (m - 1)X | \qquad (18.2.21)$$

$$| -X | = | m - X | \qquad (18.2.22)$$

The latter is more useful than the former and stems from the substitution of $-X$ for X and k for 1 in (18.2.20).
For examples,

$$| -3 |_5 = | 5 - 3 |_5 = 2 \qquad (18.2.23)$$

$$| -9 |_5 = | 1 |_5 = 1 \qquad (18.2.24)$$

Finally, let us generalize (18.2.10) and (18.2.14); they become

$$| \sum X_i | = | \sum x_i | \qquad (18.2.25)$$

$$| \prod X_i | = | \prod x_i | \qquad (18.2.26)$$

These can be read as, "The residue of the sum of a set of numbers is the residue of the sum of the residues of the set of numbers." The second statement is then, "The residue of the product of a set of numbers is the residue of the product of the residues of the numbers."

18.3   MULTIPLE RADIX NOTATION

Discussion

The multiple radix notation postulates a set of radices which we label $m_1, m_2, \cdots, m_n$. To make our representation unique, it is necessary that these m's be relatively prime. This characteristic says that there is no common factor for any two of the m's—there is no number which will divide without remainder more than one of the m's. A more stringent requirement, which is sufficient but not necessary, may be placed on the m's: the m's can be required to be absolutely prime.

Our notational system is capable of representing any positive integer less than the product of the radices. We represent any such number as

$$N \simeq d_n d_{n-1} \cdots d_2 d_1 \tag{18.3.1}$$

Now each digit represents the residue of the number with respect to one of the radices. Thus,

$$d_i = |N|_{m_i} \tag{18.3.2}$$

If we define the compound radix M as the product of the radix set thus,

$$M = m_n m_{n-1} \cdots m_2 m_1 = \prod_1^n m_i \tag{18.3.3}$$

then all uniquely representable numbers N obey the relationship

$$0 \le N < M \tag{18.3.4}$$

Arithmetic Properties

Let us now investigate the advertised arithmetic properties of numbers in radix notation. Consider two numbers, A and B, represented by their residues with respect to the radices, m_n, m_{n-1}, $\cdots$, m_1 as

$$A \simeq a_n \cdots a_1 \tag{18.3.5}$$

$$B \simeq b_n \cdots b_1 \tag{18.3.6}$$

We are interested in their sum or difference, S, and their product, P.

$$S = A \pm B \qquad P = AB \tag{18.3.7}$$

These numbers are represented, to, by their residues with respect the radices as

$$S \simeq s_n \cdots s_1 \qquad P \simeq p_n \cdots p_1 \tag{18.3.8}$$

Then we have the relationships

$$s_i = ||A|_{m_i} \pm |B|_{m_i}|_{m_i} = |a_i \pm b_i| \tag{18.3.9}$$

$$p_i = |a_i b_i| \tag{18.3.10}$$

for $S < M$ and $P < M$. Again, note that *carries can be ignored in examining any one digit of the radix representation.*

Binary-Coded, Radix Notation

In order to place numbers in a form which is satisfactory for computer manipulation, they must be translatable into some binary code. This can be done by taking any given digit of the radix representation and encoding it in some binary code. The initial approach is not fraught with novelty. The code for any digit in a given position is simply the binary number corresponding to it. The number of bits in any given digit position depends on the range of digits used at that position. This in turn depends upon the modulus corresponding to that position. Thus, sufficient bits must be provided to encode all bits from 0 up to 1 less than the modulus.

The ith set of bits corresponding to the ith digit in modulus notation can be set forth as

$$d_i \simeq d_{iq_i} d_{iq_i-1} \cdots d_{i1} \tag{18.3.11}$$

where

$$m_i < 2^{q_i} \tag{18.3.12}$$

and $d_{ij} = 0$ or 1. The q_i bits provide 2^{q_i} combinations. For all of these combinations to be used up, m_i would have to be a power of 2, but to satisfy the condition of being relatively prime, this will only be the case when q_i is 1. In other words, binary-coded, radix notation introduces a certain inherent lack of efficiency. This may very well be tolerable if the advantages for its use can compensate for it. Let us try to write down in symbolic form the representation of a number in binary-coded radix notation,

$$N \simeq d_{n,q_n},\ d_{n,q_n-1},\ \cdots,\ d_{n,1}/d_{n-1,q_{n-1}},\ d_{n-1_{q_{n-1}}-1}\cdots d_{n-1,1}/\cdots/d_{1,q_1},$$

$$d_{1,q_1-1}\cdots d_{1,1} \tag{18.3.13}$$

The slash is used only to facilitate reading.

Examples

The theory is all very well, but now let us illustrate it with a couple of examples. First assume the radices 7 5 3 2. Let us represent the decimal number 16, first in radix notation and then in binary-coded, radix notation. Proceeding from left to right, we find the remainder when 16 is divided respectively by 7, 5, 3, and 2. These remainders are 2, 1, 1, and 0. The binary code of each of these digits can be noted placing a slash between each digit set. Of course, such a slash will not appear in the computer.

$$16 \simeq 2\ 1\ 1\ 0 \simeq 010/011/01/0 \tag{18.3.14}$$

With this set of radices, we have the representation for 5.

$$5 \simeq 5\ 0\ 2\ 1 \simeq 101/000/10/1 \tag{18.3.15}$$

Now, if we add 16 and 5 together, we get

$$16 + 5 = 21 \simeq 0\ 1\ 0\ 1 \simeq 000/001/00/1 \qquad (18.3.16)$$

With reference to the radix 7, we add 5 and 2 which is 0 (mod 7)—we have ignored the carry. We find that $1 + 0$ is 1 (mod 5). Similarly, when we add 1 and 2, the result is 0 (mod 3). Finally, when we add 1 and 0, the answer is 1 (mod 2). These answers are the same whether dealing with the digits or their code representation.

To provide another illustration, we examine the same numbers with reference to the radices 13 and 11.

$$16 \simeq 3/5 \simeq 0011/0101 \qquad (18.3.17)$$

$$5 \simeq 5/5 \simeq 0101/0101 \qquad (18.3.18)$$

$$16 + 5 = 21 \simeq 8/10 \simeq 1000/1010 \qquad (18.3.19)$$

$$16 \cdot 5 = 80 \simeq 2/3 \simeq 0010/0011 \qquad (18.3.20)$$

Just as the word size in a binary computer is stated in terms of bits and for a binary-coded, digital computer in terms of characters, the binary-coded, radix computer can be stated in terms of the number of radices. Thus, when six radices are used and they all lie in the range between 10 and 20, it is easy to obtain a word length equivalent to about one million for a decimal machine. Word size is a consideration in designing any computer, whether it is general-purpose or special-purpose and regardless of the number system contained in the computer. Most computers can handle signed numbers; essentially, it only requires space for an extra bit or character.

18.4 SIGNED NUMBERS, ADDITION AND SUBTRACTION

Representing Negative Numbers

There are two ways of representing negative numbers. The first is determined by sign and magnitude location. An extra bit is used to indicate the sign of the encoded number. It is recorded as a zero for a positive number and a 1 for a negative number. For the 7 5 3 2 system,

$$+16 \simeq 0/2/1/1/0$$

$$-16 \simeq 1/2/1/1/0$$

and, for the 13 11 system,

$$+16 \simeq 0/3/5$$

$$-16 \simeq 1/3/5$$

The second means for representing negative numbers is to use the radix complement. To form the complement we subtract each digit from the corresponding radix. Thus, in symbolic form,

$$-A \simeq m_n - a_n \cdots m_i - a_i \cdots m_1 - a_1 \qquad (18.4.1)$$

No extra bits are required to encode a negative number. However, the range of positive numbers must be diminished. Since we start with a fixed number of representations, we are going to use half of these codes for positive numbers and the other half for negative numbers. This can only be done at the expense of the range of positive numbers represented.

In the 7 5 3 2 system,

$$+16 \simeq 2/1/1/0$$

$$-16 \simeq 5/4/2/0$$

and, in the 13 11 system,

$$+16 \simeq 3/5$$

$$-16 \simeq 10/6$$

Simple Addition of Positive Numbers

To approach addition and subtraction gradually, let us investigate the addition of positive numbers. In this case, it is simply required that addition be performed with regard to each radix but without regard to carry. One radix adder is provided for each radix. A block diagram of such a device for modulus 7 appears as Figure 18.4.1. Since each digit is binary coded, three wires are used to enter the augend digit and three wires for the addend. Addition is performed within the boxes and produces three sum bits labeled S_0, S_1, and S_2. The only other question that must be resolved is with regard to overflow. For as in any computer, addition must indicate overflow before the sum is placed in a register or else the result may be recorded incorrectly.

Addition of Signed Numbers, Sign and Magnitude Notation

As with positive numbers, we must monitor addition to be sure that the word size of the computer is not exceeded. Besides this, we must provide for the determination of sign for the result. Despite the fact that the two operands convey information as to their sign, the sign of the result not only depends on this information but also on magnitude information generated during the process.

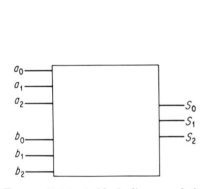

FIGURE 18.4.1 A block diagram of the modulus 7 adder

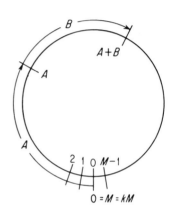

FIGURE 18.4.2 Adding two residue numbers

Let us examine explicit addition or subtraction when addition alone is actually performed. This takes place when we are adding two positive numbers or two negative numbers or when we are subtracting numbers with unlike signs. In the case of subtraction, the sign of the subtrahend is changed and then addition is performed.

Since signed numbers in sign and magnitude notation have their magnitude indicated by the non-sign position of the word, addition is performed by referring only to the non-sign positions. To see this more clearly, let us consider that the residue system numbers are laid out in ascending order clockwise along the perimeter of a circle starting with 0 at the bottom as in Figure 18.4.2. Then as we continue along the circle we approach 0, since the largest representation in this system is $M - 1$. When we add 1 to the *quantity* $M - 1$, we exceed the code size of the computer and the register stores the quantity zero. This holds true when both numbers are positive or both numbers are negative—only the direction of rotation is different.

When subtraction is called for, we are adding differently signed numbers or subtracting numbers having the same sign—then we complement the subtrahend and perform addition. If the number to be complemented is

$$B \simeq b_n b_{n-1} \cdots b_1 \tag{18.4.2}$$

and its complement is

$$B' \simeq b_n' b_{n-1}' \cdots b_1' \tag{18.4.3}$$

where

$$b_i' = m_i - b_i \tag{18.4.4}$$

so that

$$|\, b_i' + b_i \,| = 0 \tag{18.4.5}$$

then, to subtract B from A, we add B' to A. The sign of our result depends on whether it overflows the word size of the computer.

Examine Figure 18.4.3 where again the residue number system has

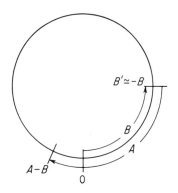
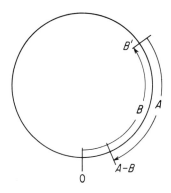

FIGURE 18.4.3 Subtracting B from A for $A > B$ in residue notation

FIGURE 18.4.4 Subtracting B from A for $A < B$ in residue notation

been laid out upon a perimeter of a circle. The number $-B$ is represented by its complement B'. When we add A to B', it causes a clockwise rotation. If A is larger than B, this rotation will bring us past the 0 point. Normally, moving past the zero point will indicate an overflow and an error in addition. In *this* case an overflow indicates that a positive number has been formed.

If, however, the rotation does not bring the result past the 0 point as in Figure 18.4.4, it is because A is smaller than B and the result is therefore negative. Hence, the lack of an overflow indicates that the result is improperly signed and must be complemented to be correct. These operations are summarized in the rules below.

Rules for the Addition or Subtraction of Signed Numbers, Sign and Magnitude Residue Notation

The problem is to perform

$$A \pm B$$

The operations are

1. If subtraction is called for, change the sign of B.
2. If the sign of the two numbers is the same, addition of their magnitude is performed; if the sign of the numbers are different, the second operand is complemented and addition is performed.
3. If no overflow occurs and addition was performed, the result is correct, its sign is that of the augend.
4. If an overflow occurs and addition was performed, the result is incorrect and the computer should be halted.
5. If an overflow occurs preceded by complementation and addition, the result is correct and its sign is that of the augend (minuend).
6. If no overflow occurs and this was preceded by complementation and addition, the result must be complemented and given the sign of the addend (subtrahend).

As can be seen by the rules above, both the problem of sign determination and word-size overflow can be determined by examining the overflow which occurs during the addition process.

Addition of Signed Numbers Using the Complement Notation Residue Representation

Again the same problems present themselves, word size and sign determination. Now, however, a negative number is represented in complement form and does not have a sign *explicitly* associated with it. Addition of two numbers is performed without examining the sign of either.

To perform $A - B$, b_i is complemented regardless of its inherent sign and is then added to a_i for all i.

We find that in this notation both problems can be solved if a method of sign determination is provided. To illustrate this, we use our circle representation. However, the figure is divided into two halves, the left representing a rotation to, but not including 0. $M/2$ includes all the positive numbers; numbers between $M/2$ and $M-1$—the right-hand half of the circle—contains the negative numbers. In Figure 18.4.5, as we add two positive numbers such as A and B, the sum of which does not exceed the word size, the result lies on the left-hand semi-circle; when the sum of A and B exceeds the word size of the computer the result is a negative number whose representation is on the right-hand semi-circle.

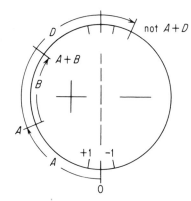

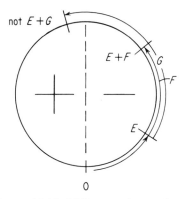

FIGURE 18.4.5 Adding positive numbers, radix complement notation

FIGURE 18.4.6 Adding negative numbers, radix complement notation

Then, to add two negative numbers, the result may be illustrated in Figure 18.4.6. Thus, the two negative numbers E and F form a sum which is also negative, but the figure indicates that the sum does not exceed the word size of the computer; the sum of the two negative numbers E and G is the positive numbers $E + G$. This indicates that the sum exceeds the word size of the computer.

If a similar diagram is drawn for the sum of a negative and a positive number, it can be seen that the word size of the computer will *never* be exceeded in this notation and that the sum will be correct and will require no adjustment.

Rules for addition and subtraction of signed numbers in complement residue notation are

1. To subtract, complement the subtrahend and perform addition. To add, do so directly.

2. If the numbers now added are similarly signed and the result maintains the sign, then the result is correct; if the result is of different sign, it exceeds the word size of the computer and is incorrect.
3. If the numbers are oppositely signed, the result is always correct and properly signed.

Modulo Adders and Four Philosophies for Developing Adder Logic

It must be remembered that we are interested in adding numbers represented in binary-coded, radix notation. The first and most direct approach is to write a separate switching function for each output but in the given radix system. Thus, any sum bit can be represented as a function of each of the augend input bits and each of the addend input bits. Although this method is direct, it is certainly not simple as can readily be seen by trying to implement such a simple device as a mod 7 adder.

The second approach is to decode each set of bits into a 1-out-of-m

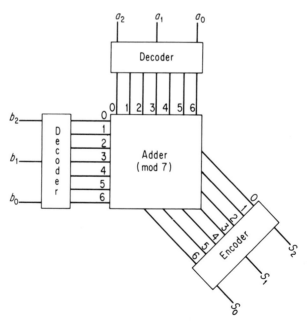

FIGURE 18.4.7   A core matrix adder logic for binary-coded, radix numbers

radix form. One such decoder is provided for the addend and for the augend. These lines are then fed into a core logic adder. From the adder is produced one line for each possible alternative of the sum digit. An encoder is then used to convert from radix to binary-coded, radix notation (this set-up can be seen in Figure 18.4.7).

The third alternative is to add the codes of each digit represented in binary-coded, radix notation. The results are then corrected when required. The fourth alternative is a variation of this by which all addition and subtraction are performed at the same time.

Switching Function Adder

To briefly summarize the process required to design a direct adder, we first set up an addition table. The reader might set up such a table for a mod 7 adder. For each sum bit we must set up a function of the input variables as obtained from the table. Thus, the last significant sum bit can be represented by

$$S_0 = (\bar{a}_2\bar{b}_2)(a_0\bar{b}_0 + \bar{a}_0b_0) + a_2b_2(a_0b_0 + \bar{a}_0\bar{b}_0)$$
$$+ a_2\bar{b}_2(\bar{a}_1\bar{a}_0\bar{b}_1b_0 + \bar{a}_1a_0\bar{b}_1\bar{b}_0 + \bar{a}_1a_0b_1b_0 + a_1\bar{a}_0b_1\bar{b}_0)$$
$$+ \bar{a}_2b_2(\bar{b}_1\bar{b}_0\bar{a}_1a_0 + \cdots) \tag{18.4.6}$$

The next step is to simplify this equation, if possible. Finally, the set of equations must be incorporated into hardware.

The Core Adder

The block diagram of the core adder appears in Figure 18.4.7.

We require two decoders; each of these decoders consists of a number of &-gates. The design for such a decoder is illustrated in Figure 18.4.8. Next the adder is designed, but it merely consists of a number of coincident-current cores. One output line threads all cores for which that particular output digit is called for. Consider when the sum digit by addition is six. This corresponds to entries in the sum that produces 6. These lie on the diagonal labeled "6" in the mod 7 adder table. Finally, use these windings and enter them into an encoder which produces the proper binary-coded, radix bits for output.

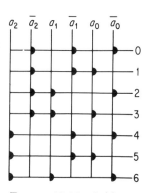

FIGURE 18.4.8 A binary coded residue to residue decoder

Binary Adders with Correction

Let us see what happens when we add two binary-coded, radix numbers. First, assume the sum of these numbers is less than the radix

$$a + b < m \qquad (18.4.7)$$

In this case, adding the codes will produce a code that correctly represents the sum. Next, consider the case where the sum of the digits exceeds the radix. This will undoubtedly require correction unless the radix and the maximum digit represented by the code are identical. That case is only true for the prime radix 2. All other prime radices are odd and, hence, can not be put in the form 2^p. The correction is always made by adding a constant, for the difference between the radix and the maximum code will always be a constant.

To see this, let us examine the construction of a modulus 7 adder. When the sum of two numbers is less than 7, the sum of the code truly represents the sum; when the sum of the numbers exceeds 7, a correction must be made. The three-bit binary adder performs addition modulo 8. The difference between its result and the correction answer is one. So, to correct the output of the modulo 8 adder, we must add a 1 in the least significant bit position. To detect when correction is necessary, we need only examine the carry from the most significant bit, also keeping alert for the combination 111. Should either of these occur, the correction is made. Since it simply consists of adding 001, the whole job can be done with the logic of Figure 18.4.9, if we can afford a carry propagation of as much as three bits or more.

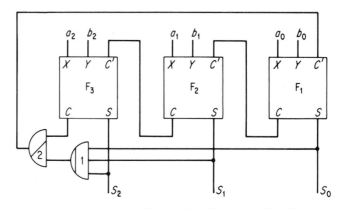

FIGURE 18.4.9   Residue mod 7 adder using full adders

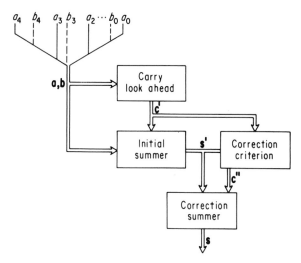

FIGURE 18.4.10   Residue adder block diagram—carry lookahead

In general, a specific code or binary number, instead of the single bit, must be added to the initial sum to produce the proper result. Normally, this would be done with the block logic shown in Figure 18.4.10. Notice that this figure indicates a carry lookahead block so that the initial addition is performed in a single cycle time. The carry correction criterion is applied to the initial sum and the final carry bit. When correction is necessary, it is performed in one additional cycle time by the final adder at the bottom of the diagram.

It might be possible to design a correction factor, lookahead circuit to work with the carry lookahead circuit so that a faster adder would be possible according to the block diagram of Figure 18.4.11.

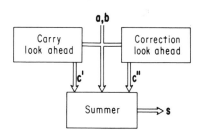

FIGURE 18.4.11   Residue adder with both carry and correction lookahead— block diagram

Multiple Adder Configuration

When using the multiple-base, residue system, the configuration of Figure 18.4.12 might be used to handle the addition of numbers so encoded. There is one adder for each of the radices in the system. There is also an

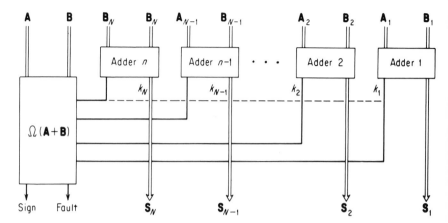

FIGURE 18.4.12 A complete residue system adder—block diagram

overflow detection circuit. It sees both numbers to be added and also special carry functions which are produced by the core matrices at the same time that the individual residues are added by the matrix.

The output of the overflow logic is a single line which detects overflow with regard to the composite modulus M. Techniques for performing this function are discussed in Section 18.8. This output can also be used for sign determination during subtraction and when dealing with signed numbers.

Complementing

When subtraction is required or when negative addition is performed, one of the numbers must be complemented with regard to its radices. This is usually performed by a technique referred to as **wire twisting** which simply means that the identity of the leads are reassigned.

To see this, suppose that we wish to subtract 010 in the binary-coded, radix system with regard to the modulus 7. First, the bits are decoded into a 1-out-of-7 output into the signal *2*. To form the complement, we simply identify this signal with the residue 5 instead of 2. Suppose, for instance, we sish to do the problem 4 − 2. The core adder which is to perform this addition receives as one input a 4, the other input is decoded as a 2; but since a complement is called for, this lead is relabeled and enters the add matrix as 5. Therefore, the subtraction calls for the addition of 4 + 5 (modulo 7) which, in truth, determines the answer, 2.

18.5   MULTIPLICATION

Introduction

To multiply two binary-coded, radix numbers, we simply multiply their residues with respect to each residue modulus and disregard the carries. Therefore, to implement the method, we require one multiplier for each modulus in the system. This multiplier produces a binary-coded, radix product for a pair of binary-coded, radix inputs. The number of bits required on each input line depends on the number of bits required for that radix.

There are two feasible approaches to designing the multiplier. The first determines each output bit as a switching function of the input bits. The second method converts binary-coded, radix information into radix information. Pairs of radix information are fed to a core matrix which produces 1-out-of-m_i lines, one of which contains the signal corresponding to the proper product. Finally, reconversion is required to encode this quantity into binary-coded, radix notation.

The alternative of using a binary-coded multiplier is out. The whole savings in using the radix system is that multiplication can be done in a single clock time. Binary multiplication requires multiple clock times in all but the simplest variations.

There is an important limitation to multiplication that arises in the residue system. The product may not exceed the single word provided for it in the computer. This is different from most commercial designs where multiplication produces two words. The least significant word is usually used for rounding of the most significant word. There are ways of circumambulating this hazard, but a design which avoids especially large numbers is most appropriate to the residue system.

Multiplication Rules

Let us examine in a little more detail the rules with respect to the residue system. Suppose we have a multiplier, A, represented as

$$A \simeq a_n a_{n-1} \cdots a_1 a_0 \qquad (18.5.1)$$

and a multiplicand, B, represented as

$$B \simeq b_n b_{n-1} \cdots b_n b_0 \qquad (18.5.2)$$

so that the product, P, is represented as

$$P \simeq p_n p_{n-1} \cdots p_1 p_0 \qquad (18.5.3)$$

Then, with respect to the radix m_i, we have the product digit, p_i, given by

$$p_i = |a_i b_i| \qquad (18.5.4)$$

which is certainly true for positive numbers.

For negative numbers, multipliers and multiplicands, we wonder if this holds true. Let us represent a negative number in complement form, so that

$$-A \simeq A' \simeq m_n - a_n, \; m_{n-1} - a_{n-1}, \; \cdots m_0 - a_0 \qquad (18.5.5)$$

We form the product of a negative and a positive number just as in (18.5.4). Thus,

$$P = (-A)B$$
$$p_i = ||m_i - a_i|)(b_i)| = |m_i b_i - a_i b_i| = |m_i - a_i b_i|$$
$$(18.5.6)$$

Similarly, the product of two negative numbers turns out to be represented correctly. Thus, we find the product residue with respect to m_i is

$$(-A)(-B) \simeq p_i = |(m_i - a_i)(m_i - b_i)|$$
$$= |m_i^2 - a_i m_i - b_i m_i + a_i b_i| = |a_i b_i| \qquad (18.5.7)$$

To illustrate these rules, examples follow in the 13 11 7 system:

$$15 \simeq 2/4/1 \qquad -15 \simeq 11/7/6 \qquad 20 \simeq 7/9/6 \qquad -20 \simeq 6/2/1$$
$$15 \times 20 \simeq |14|/|36|/|6| = 1/3/6$$
$$-15 \times -20 \simeq |66|/|14|/|6| = 1/3/6$$
$$-15 \times 20 \simeq |77|/|63|/|36| = 12/8/1 \simeq -(15 \times 20)$$
$$-15 \times -20 \simeq |12|/|8|/|1| = 12/8/1$$

TABLE 18.5.1   Multiplication (mod 5)

	0	1	2	3	4
0	0	0	0	0	0
1	0	1	2	3	4
2	0	2	4	1	3
3	0	3	1	4	2
4	0	4	3	2	1

TABLE 18.5.2   Binary-Coded, Radix Multiplier (mod 4)

		00	01	10	11
		0	1	2	3
00	0	0	0	0	0
01	1	0	1	2	3
10	2	0	2	0	2
11	3	1	3	2	1

The Multiplication Table

In designing our multiplier, the first step is to develop a multiplication table. Let us construct such a table with respect to the modulus 5 which appears as Table 18.5.1. Notice that the entries do not precess as nicely as for the addition table. However, one simplification is evident: there is symmetry about one of the diagonals. This redundancy may be useful in implementing some designs.

Direct Product Logic

For a mod 4 multiplier, Table 18.5.2 is appropriate. We wish logic to determine each product bit in terms of the four input bits. This is done if we convert Table 18.5.2 into the Karnaugh table which appears as Table 18.5.3. This is a double map since from it we can determine functions for

TABLE 18.5.3   Karnaugh Map for
Binary-Coded, Radix Multiplier (mod 4)

		10	11	01	00
		2	3	1	0
10	2	0	2	2	0
11	3	2	1	3	0
01	1	2	3	1	0
00	0	0	0	0	0

both output bits. It can be seen from this map that the product bits are

$$p_1 = a_1b_1 \tag{18.5.8}$$

$$p_2 = a_2a_1b_2 + \bar{b}_2b_1a_2 + \cdots \tag{18.5.9}$$

Core Product Logic

To implement a core multiplier, a block diagram very similar to the core adder is developed. This is shown in Figure 18.5.1. Each binary-coded, radix digit is converted to pure radix notation. One set of wires is the horizontal input to the core multiplier; the other set is the vertical input to the core multiplier. The cores correspond exactly to the entries in the multiplication table. Cores corresponding to entries with the same number have a common wire threading them. Thus, if we are constructing a mod 5 multiplier, there are four cores which are threaded by the product lead labeled 3. These correspond to the products 2×4, 4×2, 3×1, and 1×3. Therefore, most wires emanating from this matrix thread four cores; the 0-wire threads nine cores.

Since you see the similarity between the adding and multiplying matrix, it is also apparent that we can use the same set of cores for both purposes! The set of cores is supplied with exactly the same input leads, as shown in Figure 18.5.2. One set of output leads corresponds to the sum and another set to the product. In fact, further leads may be used to product other functions. The carry function, k_i, described later in this chapter, can be implemented using this same matrix.

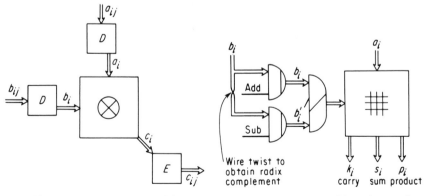

FIGURE 18.5.1 A core multiplier, binary-coded radix notation

FIGURE 18.5.2 An arithmetic matrix,
radix notation

Note also in Figure 18.5.2 that the complement of one of the operands can be obtained simply by relabeling. Thus, the choice of addition or subtraction can be formed with two sets of &-gates and one set of V-mixers, as shown to the left of Figure 18.5.2.

18.6   THE FUNCTIONS $A(x)$ AND $B(x)$

Introduction

The two important considerations which we prepare to examine are those of sign and overflow. To do this we postulate two functions, $A(x)$ and $B(x)$. These functions have other uses; therefore, a whole section is devoted to a discussion of them. It is found that if we are given the residues of a number, x, we can determine what number x was from the residues alone by using two functions. The first of these is called $D(x)$. The trouble is when we compose this function it may not be correct. It may be off by a factor of M (where M is the product of the moduli, $M = \prod m_i$). We must subtract or add a number of multiples of M from this function, $D(x)$. The number of multiples that is subtracted is referred to as $A(x)$. Finally, this may be stated as

$$x = D(x) - MA(x) \tag{18.6.1}$$

Since the functions of which we are speaking apply to numbers which may or may not exceed M, we can make the following definition of another function, $B(x)$:

$$A(x) = B(x) - \left[\frac{x}{M}\right] \tag{18.6.2}$$

Now we can substitute (18.6.2) into (18.6.1).

$$x = D(x) - M\left\{B(x) + \left[\frac{x}{M}\right]\right\} \tag{18.6.3}$$

$$x - M\left[\frac{x}{M}\right] = D(x) - MB(x) \tag{18.6.4}$$

$$|x|_M = D(x) - MB(x) \tag{18.6.5}$$

The last equation indicates that the residue with respect to the product modulus is obtained by taking the D function and subtracting a number of M's designated by the B function. Comparing (18.6.1) and (18.6.5), we conclude that when the number in question is less than M, the A and B function coincide, or,

$$A(\,|\,x\,|_M) \;=\; B(\,|\,x\,|_M) \tag{18.6.6}$$

The D function is defined in terms of each of the moduli of the system as

$$D(x) \;=\; \sum_{i=1}^{n} \hat{m}_i \left|\, \frac{x}{\hat{m}_i}\,\right|_{m_i} \tag{18.6.7}$$

The symbol $\hat{m}_i$ means the product of the moduli with m_i left out or

$$\hat{m}_i \;=\; \prod_{j \neq i}^{M} m_j$$

Equation (18.6.7) is not at all obvious and we will prove in what follows that

$$|\,x\,|_M \;=\; |\,D(x)\,|_M \tag{18.6.8}$$

Preliminaries

In order to prove the theorem above, it is necessary to derive some intermediate results. These are derived in equation form below:

lemma 1

Show $|\,ax\,|_{am} = a\,|\,x\,|_m$

$$|\,ax\,|_{am} \;=\; ax - am\left[\frac{ax}{am}\right] \tag{18.6.9}$$

$$=\; ax - am\left[\frac{x}{m}\right] \tag{18.6.10}$$

$$=\; a\left(x - m\left[\frac{x}{m}\right]\right) \tag{18.6.11}$$

In the parentheses is the definition of the residue of x with respect to m; hence,

$$|\,ax\,|_{am} \;=\; a\,|\,x\,|_m \tag{18.6.12}$$

Call (m_1, m_2) the least common divisor of m_1 and m_2.

If $\mid a \mid_{m_1} = d = \mid a \mid_{m_2}$ and $(m_1, m_2) = 1$ (m_1 and m_2 are relatively prime), then $\mid a \mid_{m_1 m_2} = d$

$$a - m_1 \left[\frac{a}{m_1} \right] = a - m_2 \left[\frac{a}{m_2} \right] = d \qquad (18.6.13)$$

$$m_1 \left[\frac{a}{m_1} \right] = m_2 \left[\frac{a}{m_2} \right] \qquad (18.6.14)$$

$$\left[\frac{a}{m_1} \right] = \frac{m_2}{m_1} \left[\frac{a}{m_2} \right] \qquad (18.6.15)$$

But $(m_1, m_2) = 1$ and m_1 does not divide a. However, since the left side of the above is an integer, then so is the right side. This requires that $[a/m_2](1/m_1)$ be some integer, k. Then,

$$\left[\frac{a}{m_2} \right] = k m_1 \qquad (18.6.16)$$

Now,

$$d = \mid a \mid_{m_2} = a - m_2 \left[\frac{a}{m_2} \right] = a - k m_1 m_2 \qquad (18.6.17)$$

$$a = d + k m_1 m_2 \qquad (18.6.18)$$

hence,

$$\mid a \mid_{m_1 m_2} = d$$

If $\mid \alpha m_1 \mid_{m_1 m_2} = m_1$, $\mid \alpha m_2 \mid_{m_1 m_2} = m_2$, $(m_1, m_2) = 1$, then

$$\mid \alpha \mid_{m_1 m_2} = 1$$

Combining the first assumption with Lemma 1,

$$m_1 = \mid \alpha m_1 \mid_{m_1 m_2} = m_1 \mid \alpha \mid_{m_2} \qquad (18.6.19)$$

$$\mid \alpha \mid_{m_2} = 1 \qquad (18.6.20)$$

Similarly,

$$\mid \alpha \mid_{m_1} = 1. \qquad (18.6.21)$$

Hence, by Lemma 2, $|\alpha|_{m_1 m_2} = 1$

$$|\alpha|_{m_1 m_2} = 1 \tag{18.6.22}$$

theorem 1

$|D(x)|_M = |x|_M$ where M is the product modulus given by

$$M = \prod_{i=1}^{n} m_i$$

and the moduli m_i, $i = 1$ to n are relatively prime with

$$m_n > m_{n-1} > \cdots > m_1$$

and

$$D(x) = \sum_{i=1}^{n} \hat{m}_i \left| \frac{x}{\hat{m}_i} \right|_{m_i}$$

with

$$\hat{m}_i = \prod_{j \neq i}^{n} m_j$$

Proof: By induction, let $i = 1$; then $M = m$ and $\hat{m} = 1$

$$D(x) = 1 \cdot \left| \frac{x}{1} \right|_m = |x|_m \tag{18.6.23}$$

and $|D(x)| = |x|_M$ as was to be shown.

For $i = 2$, $M = m_1 m_2$. Then,

$$D(x) = m_2 \left| \frac{x}{m_2} \right|_{m_1} + m_1 \left| \frac{x}{m_1} \right|_{m_2} \tag{18.6.24}$$

Call

$$a = \left| \frac{1}{m_2} \right|_{m_1} \tag{18.6.25}$$

$$b = \left| \frac{1}{m_1} \right|_{m_2} \tag{18.6.26}$$

Then, by substitution into (18.6.24),

$$D(x) = m_2 a |x|_{m_1} + m_1 b |x|_{m_2} \tag{18.6.27}$$

From the meaning of $\mid x \mid_m$,

$$D(x) \quad m_2\left(ax - m_1\left[\frac{ax}{m_1}\right]\right) + m_1\left(bx - m_2\left[\frac{bx}{m_2}\right]\right) \tag{18.6.28}$$

and

$$\mid D(x) \mid_{m_1m_2} = \left| m_2ax - m_1m_2\left[\frac{ax}{m_1}\right] + m_1bx - m_1m_2\left[\frac{bx}{m_2}\right] \right|_{m_1m_2} \tag{18.6.29}$$

Since the expression $m_1m_2[\quad]$ is divisible by m_1m_2,

$$\mid D(x) \mid_{m_1m_2} = \mid m_2ax + m_1bx \mid_{m_1m_2} \tag{18.6.30}$$

Factoring out x,

$$\mid D(x) \mid_{m_1m_2} = \mid x(am_2 + bm_1) \mid_{m_1m_2} \tag{18.6.31}$$

Define α by

$$\alpha = am_2 + bm_1 \tag{18.6.32}$$

Then (18.6.32) becomes

$$\mid D(x) \mid_{m_1m_2} = \mid \alpha x \mid_{m_1m_2} \tag{18.6.33}$$

From (18.6.24), we know that

$$\mid D(m_1) \mid_{m_1m_2} = m_1 \tag{18.6.34}$$

and

$$\mid D(m_2) \mid_{m_1m_2} = m_2 \tag{18.6.35}$$

Since, by assumption, $(m_1, m_2) = 1$, Lemma 3 holds and

$$\mid \alpha \mid_{m_1m_2} = 1 \tag{18.6.36}$$

Hence,

$$\mid \alpha x \mid_{m_1m_2} = \mid x \mid_{m_1m_2} \tag{18.6.37}$$

and we have shown that $\mid D(x) \mid_{m_1m_2} = \mid x \mid_{m_1m_2}$.

Now to prove the general case of the theorem, assume that it has been shown for $n - 1$. Replace m_1 by $\hat{m}_n$ and m_2 by m_n in (18.6.24), where

$$\hat{m}_n = \prod_{j=1}^{n-1} m_j$$

Then

$$\mid x \mid_{\hat{m}_nm_n} = \mid D(x) \mid_{\hat{m}_nm_n} = \left| m_n\left|\frac{x}{m_n}\right|_{\hat{m}_n} + \hat{m}_n\left|\frac{x}{\hat{m}_n}\right|_{m_n} \right|_M = \mid x \mid_M \tag{18.6.38}$$

We wish to see if this can be put into the form of the theorem. The case for $n - 1$ assumed to be true is written as,

$$| x |_{\hat{m}_n} = | D(x) |_{\hat{m}_n} = \left| \sum_{i=1}^{n-1} \hat{\hat{m}}_i \left| \frac{x}{\hat{\hat{m}}_i} \right|_{m_i} \right|_{\hat{m}_n} \quad (18.6.39)$$

where we define

$$\hat{\hat{m}}_i = \prod_{\substack{j \neq i \\ j=1}}^{n-1} m_j \quad (18.6.40)$$

Substitute (18.6.39) into (18.6.38) so that,

$$| x |_M = \left| m_n \left| \frac{\left| \sum_{i=1}^{n-1} \hat{\hat{m}}_i \left| \frac{x}{\hat{\hat{m}}_i} \right|_{m_i} \right|}{m_n} \right|_{\hat{m}_n} + \hat{m}_n \left| \frac{x}{\hat{m}_n} \right|_{m_n} \right|_M \quad (18.6.41)$$

$$= \left| m_n \left| \sum_{i=1}^{n-1} \hat{\hat{m}}_i \left| \frac{x}{m_n \hat{\hat{m}}_i} \right|_{m_i} \right|_{\hat{m}_n} + \hat{m}_n \left| \frac{x}{\hat{m}_n} \right|_{m_n} \right|_M \quad (18.6.42)$$

Using Lemma 1 in reverse,

$$| x |_M = \left| \left| \sum_{i=1}^{n-1} \hat{m}_i \left| \frac{x}{\hat{m}_i} \right|_{m_i} \right|_M + \hat{m}_n \left| \frac{x}{\hat{m}_n} \right|_{m_n} \right|_M \quad (18.6.43)$$

$$= \left| \sum_{i=1}^{n-1} \hat{m}_i \left| \frac{x}{\hat{m}_i} \right|_{m_i} + \hat{m}_n \left| \frac{x}{\hat{m}_n} \right|_{m_n} \right|_M \quad (18.6.44)$$

$$= \left| \sum_{i=1}^{n} \hat{m}_i \left| \frac{x}{\hat{m}_i} \right|_{m_i} \right|_M \quad (18.6.45)$$

which was to be shown.

Interpretation and Use of These Equations

First let us make a simplification of the equation for $D(x)$. Each of the terms of the summation in the equation for $D(x)$ involves a division. This division is always possible, since the divisor is prime with respect to the modulus. This property will be demonstrated in Section 18.9. To facilitate the expansion of the summation, we are interested in determining the quantity $a \mid 1/n \mid_m$. This is the reciprocal of a number with respect to a modulus. To find this quantity, we note

$$\frac{1}{r} = x \ (\text{mod } m) \tag{18.6.46}$$

$$rx = 1 \ (\text{mod } m) \tag{18.6.47}$$

To indicate the reciprocal of a number, r, with respect to the modulus, we place the asterisk after that number. Then,

$$\mid rr^* \mid_m = 1 \tag{18.6.48}$$

The simplified version of $D(x)$ is

$$D(x) = \sum \hat{m}_i \mid \hat{m}_i^* x \mid_{m_i} \tag{18.6.49}$$

To illustrate these principles, two examples are given below:

example 1

$m_1 = 13, \ m_2 = 11, \ m_3 = 7, \ M = 1001.$

$$\hat{m}_1 = 11 \cdot 7 = 77 \qquad \hat{m}_2 = 13 \cdot 7 = 91 \qquad \hat{m}_3 = 11 \cdot 13 = 143$$

$$\hat{m}_1^* = \left| \frac{1}{77} \right|_{13} = \left| \frac{1}{12} \right|_{13} = 12 \qquad \hat{m}_2^* = \left| \frac{1}{91} \right|_{11} = \left| \frac{1}{3} \right|_{11} = 4$$

$$\hat{m}_3^* = \left| \frac{1}{143} \right|_7 = \left| \frac{1}{3} \right|_7 = 5$$

$$\mid x \mid_{1001} = \mid 77 \mid 12x \mid_{13} + 91 \mid 4x \mid_{11} + 143 \mid 5x \mid_7 \mid_{1001}$$

example 2

Convert 10 3 3 in the 13 11 7 system to a residue with respect to 1001.

$$\mid x \mid_{1001} = \mid 77 \mid 12 \cdot 10 \mid_{13} + 91 \mid 4 \cdot 3 \mid_{11} + 143 \mid 5 \cdot 3 \mid_7 \mid_{1001}$$

$$= \mid 77 \cdot 3 + 91 \cdot 1 + 143 \cdot 1 \mid_{1001}$$

$$= \mid 231 + 91 + 143 \mid_{1001} = 465$$

Check: $\mid 465 \mid_{13} = 10; \mid 465 \mid_{11} = 3; \mid 465 \mid_7 = 3.$

The Determination of the Function A(x)

Looking from outside of the system, we have now determined how to calculate $A(x)$. The difficulty arises when we only have the residues of a number to work with and wish to determine this function. Currently, research is going on in the field to find effective means for doing this. Several methods have been developed, but each has its own defects. We shall examine one of these methods which requires the use of a *super-modulus*. This is an extra modulus which has been appended to the system only for the purpose of aiding us in determining such functions as $A(x)$ with the ultimate goal of fabricating a complete system where sign and overflow are quickly ascertainable.

Consider the super-modulus, m_S. We convert the defining equation into residue form with respect to the super-modulus.

$$| X |_{m_S} = | D(x) - MA(x) |_{m_S} \qquad (18.6.50)$$

Transposition within the residue signs is permissible, so that

$$| MA(x) |_{m_S} = | D(x) - | X |_{m_S} |_{m_S} \qquad (18.6.51)$$

Performing division yields

$$| A(x) |_{m_S} = \left| \frac{1}{M} D(x) - \frac{1}{M} | X |_{m_S} \right|_{m_S} \qquad (18.6.52)$$

$$= \left| \frac{1}{M} \sum \hat{m}_i | \hat{m}_i{}^* |_{m_i} - \frac{1}{M} | X |_{m_S} \right|_{m_S} \qquad (18.6.53)$$

$$= \left| \sum \frac{\hat{m}_i}{M} | \hat{m}_i{}^* |_{m_i} - \frac{1}{M} | X |_{m_S} \right|_{m_S} \qquad (18.6.54)$$

$$= \left| \sum \frac{1}{m_i} | \hat{m}_i{}^* |_{m_i} - \frac{1}{M} | X |_{m_S} \right|_{m_S} \qquad (18.6.55)$$

Equation (18.6.55) can be simplified if we can provide the reciprocals of each of the moduli with respect to the super-modulus. Let us label these reciprocals μ_i. Then,

$$\mu_i = \left| \frac{1}{m_i} \right|_{m_S} \qquad (18.6.56)$$

or

$$| m_i \mu_i |_{m_S} = 1 \qquad (18.6.57)$$

Further, we require the negative reciprocal of the modulus product with respect to the super-modulus. We define this as

$$\mu_S = \left| \frac{-1}{M} \right|_{m_S} \tag{18.6.58}$$

$$| M\mu_S | = -1 \tag{18.6.59}$$

Finally, we have an expression for the function $A(x)$ with respect to the super-modulus and in terms of the new definition,

$$| A(x) |_{m_S} = | \sum \mu_i | \hat{m}_i^* |_{m_i} + \mu_S | x |_{m_S} |_{m_S} \tag{18.6.60}$$

The two examples below first give the equation for $A(x)$ for one residue system and then find this function for a specific number:

example 1

Find the equation for $| A(x) |_9$ for the 13, 11, 7 system.

$$| 13\mu_1 |_9 = 1 \qquad \mu_1 = 7$$

$$| 11\mu_2 |_9 = 1 \qquad \mu_2 = 5$$

$$| 7\mu_3 |_9 = 1 \qquad \mu_3 = 4$$

$$| 1001\mu_S |_9 = -1 \qquad | 2\mu_S |_9 = -1 \qquad \mu_S = 4$$

$$| A(x) |_9 = | 7 | 12x |_{13} + 5 | 4x |_{11} + 4 | 5x |_7 + 4 | x |_9 |_9$$

example 2

Find $| A(x) |_9$ for $65 \simeq 0/10/2/2$ for the 13 11 7 9 system.

$$| A(x) |_9 = | 0 + 5 | 40 |_{11} + 4 | 10 |_7 + 4 | 2 |_9 |_9$$

$$= | 5 \cdot 7 + 4 \cdot 3 + 4 \cdot 2 |_9 = | 55 |_9$$

$$= 1$$

18.7 CONVERSION

Need

The computer does tasks set up for it by the human. Both the statement of the problem and the data itself are known to the human and documented by him in human language. When numerical quantities are dealt with, they appear in the system most familiar to the human, the decimal system. When the computer uses a residue notation, conversion must be provided to present the data to the computer in residue form. Similarly, the output of the computer in residue notation must be converted for printout on decimal equipment so that the answers can be consumed by the human in decimal form.

Although these two conversions are required, it is possible that the computer can be freed of these tasks. This can be done with separate off-line conversion equipment or by programming a separate satellite computer whose sole function is to perform the input and output processing of both data and program required by the computer. In some instances, the use of an intermediate system, such as the mixed radix system, may be appropriate.

The rest of this section is devoted to explaining an input conversion system method and the output conversion method. It should be borne in mind that conversion by means of a mixed radix system is also feasible and may, in some cases, have advantages.

Input Conversion

A number, X, is represented in a fixed radix notation as

$$X \simeq \sum_0^N d_i r^i \qquad (18.7.1)$$

where r is the radix of the system under consideration; r is 10 for the decimal system and 2 for the binary system, both of which are amenable to the method discussed here. The digits of the representation are labeled d_i, where d_N is the most significant digit, d_0 is the least significant digit, and i ranges from 0 to N. Therefore, N is 1 less than the number of digits.

Next, consider the representation of the same number in the residue system,

$$X \simeq X_n X_{n-1} \cdots X_1 \qquad (18.7.2)$$

where x_n corresponds to the modulus m_n, and so forth, x_1 corresponding to m_1.

The residue with respect to the modulus m_i is represented as

$$X_i = |X|_{m_i} = |d_n r^n + d_{n-1} r^{n-1} + \cdots + r_0|_{m_i} \qquad (18.7.3)$$

It is a simple matter to consider this as the residue of the sum of residues. Therefore, x_i can be determined from the original number.

$$x_i = |X|_{m_i} = ||d_n r^n| + |d_{n-1} r^{n-1}| + \cdots + |d_1 r| + |d_0||_{m_i} \quad (18.7.4)$$

Any one of these residues along the line is now the subject for analysis. Look at the term $|d_j r^j|$. The exponentiated base is constant for all numbers subject to conversion. Let us label the residue with respect to this number, ρ_j. Then,

$$\rho_j = |r^j| \quad (18.7.5)$$

The jth digit of the number we are converting has a residue with respect to the ith radix which is indicated by δ_j; thus,

$$\delta_j = |d_j| \quad (18.7.6)$$

which is a variable depending upon the number. The new number, δ_j, is obtained from d_j simply by relabeling.

Finally, we are interested in the residue of the product of these two

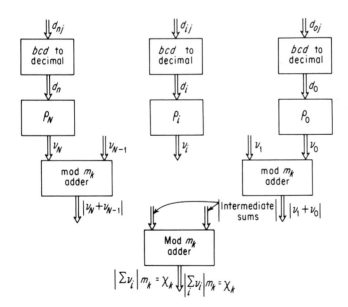

FIGURE 18.7   Conversion to one digit radix of radix notation for a number entered in binary-coded decimal notation

residues. Labeling that quantity ν_j, we have,

$$\nu_j = |\,\rho_j \delta_j\,| \qquad (18.7.7)$$

We are looking for the residue of a constant times a number. This again is obtained by wire twisting or relabeling. Thus, the whole conversion from d_j to ν_j can simply be done by a relabeling of the input lines for the given digit with respect to the given modulus.

The sum of these residues must be taken with respect to the modulus m_i. This leads to the expression,

$$x_i = \Big|\sum_{j=0}^{N} \nu_j\,\Big|_{m_i} \qquad (18.7.8)$$

which is the addition of residues with respect to the modulus m_i and, therefore, requires the repeated use of a mod m_i adder. The process may be expedited by performing several of the additions in parallel; for conversion of small numbers, serial operation of the adder is effective. To see this principle of conversion, examine the following example:

example

Convert 931_{10} to the 13 11 7 system

$\rho_1 = 1$

$\rho_{23} = |\,10\,|_{13} = 10 \qquad \rho_{22} = |\,10\,|_{11} = 10 \qquad \rho_{21} = |\,10\,|_7 = 3$

$\rho_{33} = |\,100\,|_{13} = 9 \qquad \rho_{32} = |\,100\,|_{11} = 1 \qquad \rho_{31} = |\,100\,|_7 = 2$

$X_3 = |\,9 \cdot 9 + 3 \cdot 10 + 1 \cdot 1\,|_{13} = |\,81 + 30 + 1\,|_{13} = |\,102\,|_{13} = 8$

$X_2 = |\,9 \cdot 1 + 3 \cdot 10 + 1\,|_{11} \qquad\qquad\qquad = |\,40\,|_{11} = 7$

$X_1 = |\,9 \cdot 2 + 3 \cdot 3 + 1\,|_7 = |\,18 + 9 + 1\,|_7 \qquad = |\,0\,|_7 = 0$

$X = 8/7/0$

The block diagram for parallel conversion is shown in Figure 18.7.

When information is arriving continuously, it may be entered directly into counters. Thus, a set of n counters that operate mod m_i incoming information, supplied to each one, will cause them to count to the correct residue at any given number. To do this, each time the reading is changed by a unit, this unit must be added to every counter. It is obvious that the counters will always store the residue with respect to the total reading. If readings can change in either direction, then bi-directional counters are necessary.

Sometimes it may be required to convert information from mixed radix notation to residue notation. Naturally, the radices chosen are the same in both cases. A radix number is represented as

$$x \simeq r_1 \cdots r_n \qquad (18.7.9)$$

Each digit, r_i, of this representation, when multiplied by the corresponding radix product and added to other terms of this sort, yields the original number. Thus,

$$x = r_1 + m_1 r_2 + \cdots + \prod_1^{n-1} m_i r_n \qquad (18.7.10)$$

or

$$= \sum_1^n r_i \prod_1^{i-1} m_j \qquad (18.7.11)$$

The residue representation can be obtained directly from partial sums of these terms by using the following relations.

$$x_1 = |X|_{m_1} = r_1 \qquad (18.7.12)$$

$$x_2 = |X|_{m_2} = |r_1 + r_2 m_1|_{m_2} \qquad (18.7.13)$$

$$x_3 = |X|_{m_i} = |\sum_1^i r_j \prod_1^{j-1} m_j|_{m_i} \qquad (18.7.14)$$

Finally, a word should be said about direct readout devices. Thus, when the input to the computer consists of a shaft notation, a digitizer can be connected directly to the shaft so that binary-coded, residue outputs can be read directly from the encoder. Another way to use such readouts is by incrementally feeding sets of counters as noted above.

Output

The output conversion process is a little bit more complicated, but since it is less frequently used in general scientific applications, it may be possible to allow more time for this conversion to achieve a savings in the equipment used.

The method discussed subsumes the knowledge of $A(x)$. When this is not immediately present, it can be determined by the methods discussed in the last section. In converting a number, x, which does not exceed the product modulus, M, the following relation prevails.

$$x = D(x) - MA(x) \qquad (18.7.15)$$

The function $A(x)$ is required to determine how many times the product modulus, M, must be subtracted from the function $D(x)$.

To perform our conversion, we use a super-modulus for determining the function $A(x)$ and for finding the residue of x with respect to 10. This method is applicable as long as the radices are prime to 10. The key to the transformation is found by performing manipulations on (18.7.15). Let us take the residue with respect to 10 of both sides of that expression. Thus,

$$d_0 = |\,x\,|_{10} = |\,D(x) - MA(x)\,|_{10} \qquad (18.7.16)$$

Substituting the equation for $D(x)$,

$$d_0 = |\,\sum \hat{m}_i\,|\,\hat{m}_i{}^*x\,|_{m_i} - MA(x)\,|_{10} \qquad (18.7.17)$$

It is permissible to take residues within the residue sign, so that (18.7.17) becomes

$$d_0 = |\,\sum |\,\hat{m}_i\,|_{10}\,|\,\hat{m}_i{}^*x\,|_{m_i} - |\,M\,|_{10}A(x)\,|_{10} \qquad (18.7.18)$$

Since all the factors in (18.7.18) except x are constants, this provides a means for determining the units digit in the decimal system of the number to be transformed. To determine other digits, we subtract the value of the units digit from the original number. Call the remainder y_1; then,

$$y_1 = x - d_0 \qquad (18.7.19)$$

which is represented in residue notation; in fact, the subtraction is performed in residue notation. Each residue digit of y_1 is then represented by

$$y_{1i} = |\,x_i - d_0\,|_{m_i} \qquad (18.7.20)$$

The next thing we do is to divide y_1 by 10. It must be divisible by 10, for we have removed from x the residue with respect to 10. It is possible to perform a division in the residue system as long as we are sure that the result is integral.

The quotient is labeled x_1. Thus,

$$x_1 = \frac{y_1}{10} \qquad (18.7.21)$$

Each residue of the quotient is determined by a multiplication of y_{1i} by the inverse of 10 with respect to the modulus m_i. Thus,

$$x_{1i} = \delta_i y_{1i} \qquad (18.7.22)$$

where δ_i is the solution of the modulus equation given as

$$| \, 10\delta_i \, |_{m_i} = 1 \qquad\qquad (18.7.23)$$

We continue this processing, finding successive decimal digits. Each cycle requires that we find a new function $A(x_i)$. Then we determine the residue with respect to 10 which is the next decimal digit, d_j. We subtract d_j from x_j to obtain a new number, y_{j+1}. Finally, this number is divided by 10 to yield the number used in the next cycle, x_{j+1}.

This method is best illustrated by the sample conversion applied below.

example

Convert $8/7/0/4$ in the 13 11 7 9 system to decimal.

$$| \, A(x) \, |_9 = | \, 7 \, | \, 12x \, |_{13} + 5 \, | \, 4x \, |_{11} + 4 \, | \, 5x \, |_7 + 4 \, | \, x \, |_9 \, |_9$$

$$= | \, 7 \, | \, 96 \, |_{13} + 5 \, | \, 28 \, |_{11} + 4 \, | \, 4 \, |_9 \, |_9$$

$$= | \, 7{\cdot}5 + 5{\cdot}6 + 16 \, |_9$$

$$= | \, 35 + 30 + 16 \, |_9 = 0$$

$$d_0 = | \, x \, |_{10} = | \, 77 \, | \, 12x \, |_{13} + 91 \, | \, 4x \, |_{11} + 143 \, | \, 5x \, |_7 + 1001 A(x) \, |_{10}$$

$$= | \, 7 \, | \, 12X \, |_{13} + | \, 4x \, |_{11} + 3 \, | \, 5x \, |_7 + 9A(x) \, |_{10}$$

$$= | \, 7{\cdot}5 + 6 + 0 + 0 \, |_{10} = | \, 41 \, |_{10} = 1$$

$$y_1 = x - d_0$$

$$= 7/6/6/3$$

$$x_1 = y_1/10$$

$$x_{1i} = \delta_i y_{1i} \qquad | \, 10\delta_3 \, |_{13} = 1 \qquad \delta_3 = 4$$

$$| \, 10\delta_2 \, |_{11} = 1 \qquad \delta_2 = 10 \qquad | \, 10\delta_1 \, |_7 = 1 \qquad \delta_1 = 5$$

$$| \, 10\delta_S \, |_9 = 1 \qquad \delta_S = 1$$

$$x_{23} = | \, 7\delta_3 \, |_{13} = | \, 28 \, |_{13} = 2 \qquad x_{12} = | \, 6\delta_2 \, |_{11} = | \, 60 \, |_{11} = 5$$

$$x_{11} = | \, 6\delta_1 \, |_7 = | \, 30 \, |_7 = 2 \qquad x_{1S} = | \, 3\delta_S \, |_9 = 3$$

$$x_1 \simeq 2/5/2/3$$

$$A(x_1) = | \, 7 \, | \, 12x \, |_{13} + 5 \, | \, 4x \, |_{11} + 4 \, | \, 5x \, |_7 + 4 \, | \, x \, |_9 \, |_9$$

$$= 2$$

$$d_1 = |\; x_1 \;|_{10} = |\; 7 \;|\; 12x_1 \;|_{13} + |\; 4x_1 \;|_{11} + 3 \;|\; 5x_1 \;|_7 + 9A\,(x_1)\; |_{10}$$

$$= |\; 7 \;|\; 12\cdot2 \;|_{13} + |\; 4\cdot5 \;|_{11} + 3 \;|\; 5\cdot2 \;|_7 + 9\cdot2 \;|_{10}$$

$$= |\; 7\cdot11 + 9 + 3\cdot3 + 18 \;|_{10}$$

$$= |\; 77 + 9 + 9 + 18 \;|_{10} = |\; 113 \;|_{10} = 3$$

$$y_2 = x_1 - d_1 \simeq 12/2/6/0$$

$$x_{23} = |\; 12\delta_3 \;|_{13} = |\; 43 \;|_{13} = 9 \qquad x_{22} = |\; 2\delta_2 \;| = |\; 20 \;|_{11} = 9$$

$$x_{21} = |\; 6\delta_1 \;|_7 = |\; 30 \;|_7 = 2 \qquad x_{2S} = |\; 0\delta_S \;| = 0$$

$$x_2 \simeq 9/9/2/0$$

$$|\; A\,(x_2)\; |_9 = |\; 7 \;|\; 12\cdot9 \;|_{13} + 5 \;|\; 4\cdot9 \;|_{11} + 4 \;|\; 5\cdot2 \;|_7 + 4 \;|\; 0 \;|_9 \;|_9$$

$$= |\; 7\cdot4 + 5\cdot3 + 4\cdot3 \;|_9 = |\; 55 \;|_9 = 1$$

$$d_2 = |\; x_2 \;|_{10} = |\; 7 \;|\; 12\cdot9 \;|_{13} + |\; 4\cdot9 \;|_{11} + 3 \;|\; 5\cdot2 \;|_7 + 9\cdot1 \;|_{10}$$

$$= |\; 7\cdot4 + 3 + 3\cdot3 + 9 \;|_{10} = 9$$

$$8/7/0/4 \simeq 931_{10}$$

18.8   OVERFLOW AND SIGN DETECTION

Introduction

Either overflow or sign detection is required to make a workable addition system. Thus, when dealing with sign and magnitude notation, the function $\Omega(x)$ detects both overflow of word size and the proper sign of the result. Conversely, when using the radix complement notation, the sign function detects both overflow and the correct sign for the result. At least one of these functions is necessary, for the correctness of the sign and of the result is never obtained without charge—we must pay for it.

The overflow function, $\Omega(x)$, is now defined. If we add two numbers, a and b, both of which are less than M, the product modulus, and the result, c, is less than M also. Then, $\Omega(c)$ is defined as 0. However, if c is greater than or equal to M, the overflow function, $\Omega(c)$, is defined as 1. Put more precisely,

$$\Omega(c) = \left[\frac{c}{M}\right] \tag{18.8.1}$$

Unfortunately, it is not possible to determine $\Omega(c)$ by observing the carries produced when adding the residues with respect to any or all of the moduli. For instance, if we add the numbers 76 and 37 encoded in the 13 11 7 system, we have the following result:

$$76 = 11/10/6$$

$$37 = 11/4/2$$

$$\overline{}$$

$$113 = 9/3/1$$

Notice that there are overflows with respect to 13, 11, and 7—all the moduli; however, 113 is less than the product moduli $M(=1001)$.

In order to obtain an expression for $\Omega(c)$, let us recall the representation of each number in terms of the D and B function. Thus,

$$a = D(a) - MB(a) \tag{18.8.2}$$

$$b = D(b) - MB(b) \tag{18.8.3}$$

$$c = D(a) + D(b) - MB(a) - MB(b) \tag{18.8.4}$$

When we expand (18.8.4) in terms of the D function,

$$c = \sum \hat{m}_i \mid \hat{m}_i{}^* a_i \mid_{m_i} + \sum \hat{m}_i \mid \hat{m}_i{}^* b_i \mid_{m_i} - M[B(a) + B(b)] \tag{18.8.5}$$

To simplify our expressions, let us recall the bracket notation for the integer just less than the number contained in the brackets. By putting a subscript outside and to the right of the brackets, we indicate the integer just less than the residue with respect to the radix used as the subscript. Thus,

$$[x]_m = [\mid x \mid_m]_m = \left[\frac{x}{m}\right] \tag{18.8.6}$$

This facilitates matters when we are dealing with sums of residues.

$$\left[\frac{\mid x \mid_m + \mid y \mid_m}{m}\right] = [\mid x \mid + \mid y \mid]_m \tag{18.8.7}$$

Now the equation (18.8.5) is not the only expression for c. We have, directly,

$$c = \sum \hat{m}_i \mid \hat{m}_i{}^* c_i \mid_{m_i} - MA(c) = D(c) - MA(c) \tag{18.8.8}$$

$$= \sum \hat{m}_i \mid \hat{m}_i{}^* (a_i + b_i) \mid_{m_i} - MA(c) \tag{18.8.9}$$

Let us examine the difference between the two sums in (18.8.5) and the single sum of (18.8.9). By definition, a residue must be less than the modulus, $| X |_m < m$. But the sum of two residues may be greater than the modulus. Thus, any time for a given i we find

$$[\, | \, \hat{m}_i {}^* a_i \, | + | \, \hat{m}_i {}^* b_i \, | \,]_{m_i} = 0$$

we know that $| \, \hat{m}_i {}^* a_i \, |_{m_i} + | \, \hat{m}_i {}^* b_i \, |_{m_i}$ may replace $| \, \hat{m}_i {}^* (a_i + b_i) \, |_{m_i}$. However, when

$$[\, | \, \hat{m}_i {}^* a_i \, | + | \, \hat{m}_i {}^* b_i \, | \,]_{m_i} = 1$$

we know that $\hat{m}_i (\, | \, \hat{m}_i {}^* a_i \, |_{m_i} + | \, \hat{m}_i {}^* b_i \, |_{m_i})$ exceeds $\hat{m}_i (\, | \, \hat{m}_i {}^* (a_i + b_i) \, |_{m_i}$ by exactly $M = \hat{m}_i m_i$.

Define k_i by

$$k_i = [\, | \, \hat{m}_i {}^* a_i \, | + | \, \hat{m}_i {}^* b_i \, | \,]_{m_i} \tag{18.8.10}$$

Then,

$$\sum \hat{m}_i \, | \, \hat{m}_i {}^* a_i \, |_{m_i} + \sum \hat{m}_i \, | \, \hat{m}_i {}^* b_i \, |_{m_i} = \sum \hat{m}_i \, | \, \hat{m}_i {}^* (a_i + b_i) \, |_{m_i} + M \sum k_i \tag{18.8.11}$$

Making this substitution in (18.8.5),

$$c = \sum \hat{m}_i \, | \, \hat{m}_i {}^* (a_i + b_i) \, |_{m_i} + M (\sum k_i - B(a) - B(b)) \tag{18.8.12}$$

$$= D(c) + M (\sum k_i - B(a) - B(b)) \tag{18.8.13}$$

Recalling that

$$A(c) = B(c) - \left[\frac{c}{M} \right] \tag{18.8.14}$$

we combine (18.8.8), (18.8.13), and (18.8.14).

$$c = D(c) - M \left\{ B(c) - \left[\frac{c}{M} \right] \right\} = D(c) + M (\sum k_i - B(a) - B(b))$$

$$\tag{18.8.15}$$

Then

$$\left[\frac{c}{M} \right] = B(c) - B(a) - B(b) + \sum k_i \tag{18.8.16}$$

We define the K function of x as the B function of x with respect to the modulus 2. Thus,

$$K(x) = | \, B(x) \, |_2 \tag{18.8.17}$$

Then the carry function is defined as

$$\Omega = |K(c) + K(b) + K(a) + \sum k_i|_2 \qquad (18.8.18)$$

To illustrate these principles and the derivation, we work out two examples. The functions $K(x)$ are supplied.

example 1

Given 13 11 7 system

$$\begin{array}{lll} a = & 76 = 11/10/6 & K(a) = 1 \\ b = & 36 = 11/4/2 & K(b) = 1 \\ \hline c = 113 = & 9/3/1 & K(c) = 1 \end{array}$$

Find $\Omega(c)$

$$\hat{m}_1 = 11 \cdot 7 = 77 \qquad |12\hat{m}_1^*|_{13} = 1 \qquad \hat{m}_1^* = 12$$

$$\hat{m}_2 = 13 \cdot 7 = 91 \qquad |3\hat{m}_2^*|_{11} = 1 \qquad \hat{m}_2^* = 4$$

$$\hat{m}_3 = 13 \cdot 11 = 143 \qquad |3\hat{m}_3^*|_7 = 1 \qquad \hat{m}_3^* = 5$$

$$k_1(c) = [\,|12 \cdot 11\,| + |12 \cdot 11\,|\,]_{13} = [\,|132\,| + |132\,|\,]_{13}$$
$$= [2 + 2]_{13} = 0$$

$$k_2(c) = [\,|4 \cdot 10\,| + |4 \cdot 4\,|\,]_{11} = [\,|140\,| + |16\,|\,]_{11}$$
$$= [8 + 5]_{11} = 1$$

$$k_3(c) = [\,|5 \cdot 6\,| + |5 \cdot 2\,|\,]_7 = [\,|30\,| + |10\,|\,]_7$$
$$= [2 + 3]_7 = 0$$

$$\Omega(c) = |K(a) + K(b) + K(c) + \sum k_i|_2$$
$$= |1 + 1 + 1 + 0 + 1 + 0|_2$$
$$= 0$$

example 2

Given 13 11 7 system

$$\begin{array}{ll} a = 76 \simeq 11/10/6 & K(a) = 1 \\ d = 990 \simeq 2/0/3 & K(d) = 0 \\ \hline e = 1066 \simeq 0/10/2(\simeq 65) & K(e) = 1 \end{array}$$

$$k_1 = [\,|\,12{\cdot}11\,| + |\,12{\cdot}21\,|\,]_{13} = [\,|\,132\,| + |\,24\,|\,]_{13}$$
$$= [2 + 11]_{13} = 1$$
$$k_2 = [\,|\,4{\cdot}10\,| + |\,4{\cdot}0\,|\,]_{11} = [\,|\,40\,|\,]_{11} = 0$$
$$k_3 = [\,|\,5{\cdot}6\,| + |\,5{\cdot}3\,|\,]_7 = [\,|\,30\,| + |\,15\,|\,]_7$$
$$= [2 + 1]_7 = 0$$
$$\Omega(e) = |\,K(a) + K(d) + K(e) + \sum k_i\,|_2$$
$$= |\,1 + 0 + 1 + 1 + 0 + 0\,|_2$$

Implementing A(x) and $k_i(a + b)$

The function $A(x)$ can be determined by using the super-modulus and the expressions of previous sections. The total requirements for this process are relabeling and adding with respect to the super-modulus, m_S. Figure 18.8.1 illustrates how relabeling and adders are utilized in the formation of the function $A(x)$ with respect to the super-modulus.

The function $k_i(c)$ is given by (18.8.8). The implementation of this

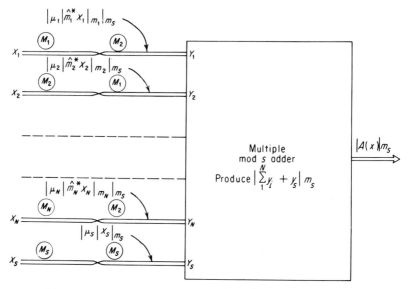

FIGURE 18.8.1 Logic to determine $|\,A(x)\,|_{m_S}$ from the residue representation $x_N,\ \dots x_1$, and the residue x_S with respect to the supermodulus M_S

TABLE 18.8.1 The Carry Function, k_3 for Addition (mod 7);
$$k_3 = [|5a_3| + |5b_3|]_7$$

$|a_3\hat{M}_3{}^*|_7$	0	3	6	2	5	1	4	b_3
a_3	0	1	2	3	4	5	6	$|b_3\hat{M}_3{}^*|_7$
0 0								
3 1						√		
6 2					√	√		
2 3				√	√	√		
5 4			√	√	√	√		
1 5		√	√	√	√	√		
4 6	√	√	√	√	√	√		

can best be seen by an example. First, let us made an addition table for the modulus 7, as illustrated in Table 18.8.1. Notice that the carry function k_3 contains in it the constant $\hat{m}_3{}^*$. Calculation shows this constant to be 5. The labels for the columns and rows can be worked backwards to determine the values of a_3 and b_3. This is the case with Table 18.8.1. It is a simple matter to translate that table into one where the rows and columns are ordered with respect to a_3 and b_3; this is the case for Table 18.8.2. The

TABLE 18.8.2 The Carry Function, k_3
Directly in Terms of the Augend and
Addend Digits of mod 7 Addition

	b_3						
	0	1	2	3	4	5	6
a_3 0							
1		√	√		√	√	√
2		√			√	√	
3					√		
4		√	√	√	√	√	√
5		√	√		√	√	
6		√			√		

checked cells in Table 18.8.2 indicate combinations for which the value of k_3 is 1. It is now a simple matter to thread a wire through all the checked cores, which wire will then produce a signal when the augend and addend residues cause the function k_3 to be 1. This concept was illustrated in block form in Figure 18.5.2.

Implementing $\Omega(a + b)$

To implement the overflow function, we require the radix carry functions, k_i, which are obtained as above. The addend and augend carry functions, $K(a)$ and $K(b)$, can be developed using the functions $A(a)$ and $B(b)$. However, it is simpler to append an extra bit which conveys whether these functions are 1 or 0. All that is left to determine is $K(a + b)$. It might be assumed that this could be prepared from the function $A(a + b)$. However, it should be noted that when a number, x, is less than M, the A function and the B function are identical; when the number x is greater than or equal to M, these functions differ. Verily, if we knew $B(a + b)$ we could determine $A(a + b)$, compare the two, and determine if an overflow occurs.

However, if by some means we can determine $K(a + b)$, we can plug it into the equation for Ω, which is given in (18.8.14), and obtain the proper result. An entirely different method for determining the overflow function is to convert the sum into mixed radix notation using a super-modulus. Then the most significant digit, x_{n+1}, indicates the number of multiples of M in the sum.

Sign Determination

For numbers in the radix complement notation, sign determination is the key to arithmetic. One way to make this determination is to perform a complete conversion to a mixed radix system which will indicate the sign or whether the result has landed in a forbidden zone.

Another method is to make a partial conversion which might take less time and which would indicate the size of the most significant digit in mixed radix notation. Using the circle to represent the range of numbers which the computer handles, Figure 18.8.2 indicates how this circle is divided into sectors by determining the most significant mixed radix digit. Since the radices are usually odd, the number of sectors produced will also be odd. All but one of these sectors will leave no question as to the size of the number. The top sector with the question mark in Figure 18.8.2 does not delineate the sign. Another digit in radix notation must be examined to get

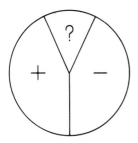

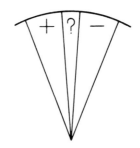

FIGURE 18.8.2 Initial sign determination, iterative technique

FIGURE 18.8.3 Intermediate sign determination, iterative technique

further information. The sector is subdivided as in Figure 18.8.3. This will usually give a definitive answer; however, there is a subsector which leaves a question. This iterative procedure is continued until the sign is definitely determined.

Summary

In general, the techniques for sign and overflow determination are neither quick nor efficient. This is true especially when a method of general applicability is sought. Methods for handling systems of specific radices have been developed, and these may be fruitful in specific applications. Certainly, further research in this area should prove fruitful.

18.9 OTHER CONSIDERATIONS

Introduction—Considerations In Using the "Foreign-Number System"

In planning a system which uses the residue number representation, the three functional aspects of the computer still apply: the computer is still required to perform the input/output function, refer to a memory for memorization and remembering, and to use the processor for performing the arithmetic and editing functions, the heart of the computer.

The input/output system requires translation from one representation to another. Again intermediate languages, such as punch cards, magnetic tape, and so forth, may be present in the system. Conversion is required into and from the residue notation. Translation methods were discussed in Section 18.7. Faster translation methods would make the system more attractive.

Reference to memory requires a memory address and a data word entered into or received from the memory. The data word would have the format of the residue system. Memory addressing can be performed in binary, decimal, or other notation. The memory system may be considered separate from the arithmetic unit. However, during memory reference it is frequently required to perform operand address modification. This requires alteration of the operand address by addition of an index number. For this reason, it may be more convenient to maintain a radix notation throughout. In this fashion, radix adders could be used for address modification also. Detection of 0, frequently required for branching during operand address modification, could be implemented with no difficulty, since 0 appears as a set of 0-bits in all notations (with few exceptions).

Processing in residue presents a number of limitations. The most annoying of these revolves around division. Also, there are limitations for which the program may bear the brunt when multiplication is to be performed. A subsection is devoted below to the discussion of division. There are other factors relative to the selection of a code for a computer. These may be divided into two classes according to whether they pertain to alphabetic or numeric information.

Alphabetic information seems to require a uniform character size, although this is not completely obligatory. There is no reason why such a structure could not be superimposed over the radix notation when the computer is told that alphabetic information is present. The fixed word length of the computer fits into a proper pattern for alphabetic information, although a variable format might be more desirable.

Numeric quantities must be considered in terms of scaling, floating-point notation, and representation of fractions; these topics are treated below.

Division

The process of division amounts to the solution of an equation in one of the terms below,

$$| \, x \, | \; = \; \left| \frac{b}{a} \right| \qquad | \, ax \, | \; = \; | \, b \, | \qquad (18.9.1)$$

It has been shown in the literature that there is a unique solution for this equation only when a and the modulus, m, are relatively prime, written as $(a, m) = 1$. Further, it has been shown that if a and m have a common divisor, d, written as $(a, m) = d$, there are exactly d solutions possible, if

d divides b, and there is absolutely no solution if d does not divide b. The following examples illustrate this principle:

example 1

$$x = \left| \frac{19}{3} \right|_{11}$$

First,

$$| \, 3y \, |_{11} = 1 \qquad y = 4$$

$$x = | \, 4 \cdot 19 \, |_{11} = | \, 4 \cdot 8 \, |_{11} = | \, 32 \, |_{11} = 10$$

Check:

$$| \, 3 \cdot 10 \, |_{11} = | \, 19 \, |_{11} = 8$$

example 2

Solve $| \, 3x \, |_{15} = | \, 21 \, |_{15}$

$$x = \left| \frac{21}{3} \right|_{15} = 7$$

Check:

$$| \, 3 \cdot 7 \, |_{15} = | \, 21 \, |_{15} = 6$$

but

$$x = \left| \frac{21 + 15k}{3} \right|_{15}$$

is also valid

$$x = 7 + 5 = 12$$

$$x = | \, 7 + 10 \, |_{15} = 2$$

Since $d = 3$, this accounts for the three solutions.

Check:

$$| \, 3 \cdot 12 \, |_{15} = | \, 21 \, |_{15} = 6$$

$$| \, 3 \cdot 2 \, |_{15} = | \, 21 \, |_{15} = 6$$

example 3

Solve $\big|\ 6x\ \big|_{15} = \big|\ 7\ \big|_{15}$.

$$(6, 15) = 3 \quad \text{(common divisor 3)}$$

$$(3, 7) = 1 \quad \text{(no common divisor of } d \text{ and } b)$$

There is no number x such that $\big|\ 6x\ \big|_{15} = \big|\ 7\ \big|_{15}$

The problem of division with residue numbers does not frequently present a simple solution. Only when the quotient of two numbers is an integer is a quick solution guaranteed. In that case, each residue of the dividend is multiplied by the reciprocal of the residue of the divisor. It is apparent that when any of the divisor residues are 0, division is impossible, since a reciprocal for 0 is undefined. When all of the divisor residues are non-0 but the quotient is non-integral, a result can be obtained, but it will not be correct.

Approximate solutions for the division problem have been found. These use iterative techniques, table lookups, or combinations of the two. This kind of solution is several times longer than the equivalent division in a parallel binary machine. However, when the frequency of division in a general scientific problem is considered, the time disadvantage for division may be more than compensated for by the speed in multiplication and addition.

Scaling

Scaling of numbers is defined as multiplication or division by a constant. In fixed-point machines, scaling is almost always performed by multiplication using a power of the base. Thus, decimal machines scale by a factor of 10^K and binary machines, by a factor of 2^K. For the residue system there is no such fixed base; therefore, scaling is done with respect to arbitrary numbers. Actually, this process is best performed when these numbers are not so arbitrary—when they are one of the radices or a product of several of the radices. Scaling by arbitrary factors is usually very slow. If a radix or a radix product is used, this can be done much faster. In fact, scaling can be performed with respect to one radix in n cycles, where n is the number of radices in a representation.

Floating-Point

In fixed-base systems, floating-point is conceived of with respect to the base quantity. For the residue system, we can conceive of a floating representation which refers to the product modulus, M. Thus, a number, $\mathbf{A}$, can be thought of as

$$\mathbf{A} = A \cdot M^{\alpha} \qquad (18.9.2)$$

Fractions

It is possible to conceive of residue notation applying to the numerator of a fraction for which the denominator is the product modulus, M. Arithmetic can be performed in this system analogously to that described earlier in a chapter. The advantage of such a system has not been demonstrated as yet.

18.10 DISCUSSION

Present Applications

There are two systems using this method. The first is a correlator built at Lockheed Space and Missiles and described by Cheney. This equipment does auto-correlation and cross-correlation. This processing requires the sum of a large number of products. The number of such products is fixed. The range of numbers is also fixed and known. This determines that the range of result is also known. The design provides a proper word size so that the result will never exceed the capacity.

The input for this device was performed by the sampling of an analog waveform, with conversion directly to binary and eventually into residue notation. Calculation was performed using residue adders and multipliers. The setup used logic blocks rather than cores to achieve the desired speed. Output was done by converting from residue to mixed residue notation. This was then recorded or else converted into analog form for a display presentation.

This system operated very effectively with a hardware cost much smaller than a comparable fixed-base system.

Another application used the residue system only as a small subsystem of a large general-purpose computer. Decimal addition was performed in this subsystem with respect to the residues 5 and 2.

Present Usefulness

The residue system could be applied to a range of problems. At present, this range is limited but not infinitesimal. On the contrary, there are a good number of military problems which would lend themselves to this type of solution.

Some of the qualities of a problem tractable to a residue system are examined. Certainly, if the range of numbers and the range of the results is known, this could be of definite advantage. If translation could be per-performed facilely, time would be saved. Thus, if an input were derived from a shaft rotation, a shaft encoder could be immediately converted to binary-coded, radix notation. Another alternative is where the system would not require rapid input/output translation.

Residue notation is ideal for fast multiplication and addition. Therefore, the problem statement should contain little and preferably no divisions. Simple decisions and branching are easily accomplished when a stored-program computer is postulated.

The reader can certainly think of some definite areas where this system might take hold. For instance, there is navigation, anti-submarine warfare, simulation where the range of variables is known (such as for training exercises) and control where an analog output is desirable. Other problem classes of this nature in the military and scientific domain may be apparent.

Problems For Research

This is certainly an area where many unsolved problems exist. Fast and efficient methods for several kinds of operations are desirable; namely,

1. Sign determination.
2. Overflow.
3. Auxiliary functions such as $A(x)$, $B(x)$, $D(x)$, etc.
4. Conversion.
5. Division.

It is my prediction that the usefulness of this notation will not be exploited for a long time, for usually much time elapses before such a tool as this enters the engineer's bag of tricks. Certainly within a decade, several special-purpose computers will be built incorporating this system.

The applicability of this notation to the general-purpose computer will depend upon the effectiveness of research in the areas itemized above.

PROBLEMS

18.1 Find the representation of the numbers below in two systems: the 11, 7, 3 mixed-base system; the 11, 7, 3 residue system.

a.	163	d.	5
b.	77	e.	13
c.	40	f.	200

18.2 Show that for the residue system, if the m_i are not relatively prime, the representation is not unique.

18.3 Comment on the efficiency in information content of the binary-coded residue system. How can the choice of the m_i improve this efficiency (measured in the number of bits required to convey numbers of maximum size, M).

18.4 What pros and cons can you advance for a 2's complements BCR representation?

18.5 Add the fifteen possible pairs of numbers of Problem 18.1 in the residue system, 11, 7, 3. What about overflow? Try the 11, 7, 5, 3 system.

18.6 Design a mod 5 adder
   a. With core logic.
   b. With gate by first writing a Karnaugh map.

18.7 Design a mod 7 multiplier as above
   a. With cores.
   b. With gates.

18.8 Design a serial-by-character arithmetic unit using a core adder/multiplier with whatever gating is required. Use the moduli 32, 31, 29, and complement numbers. Assume the results are always within the wordlength provided. Include information on
   a. Registers.
   b. Timing.

18.9 Design an input to the above for a rotating shaft reading.

18.10 Design a decimal output for the unit above.

18.11 What could be done about overflow detection?

18.12 Convert 3, 6, 2 in the 11, 7, 5 system to decimal
   a. Directly.
   b. Find $\mid A(x) \mid_9$ (determine $\mid X \mid_{MS}$ from a).
   c. Find $\mid A(x) \mid_9$ for $1/2/3/4$ in the 11, 7, 5, 9 system.

18.13 Convert 201_{10} to the 11, 7, 5 system.

BIBLIOGRAPHY

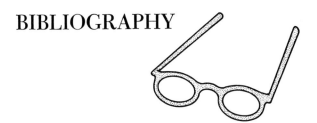

The bibliography consists of the most important articles and books about fast digital arithmetic. A long list with no remarks would present much toil to the reader who finds further research necessary. In writing this text, I have had to review the literature completely; I feel I can serve the reader best by presenting my opinions on these works.

Each title is summarized and often commented upon. To relate the references to the text, Table A on the next page may be consulted.

1. Aiken, H., and Semon, W. *Advanced Digital Computer Logic*, Report WADC TR-59-472, Wright Air Development Center, Wright-Patterson Air Force Base, Ohio.
The finest description of modular arithmetic—the whole volume, about 100 pages, is devoted to this topic. The explanation starts from the beginning and presents the theoretical and practical groundwork.

2. Akushsky, I. Y., Emelianov-Yaroslavsky, L. B. Klyamko, E. K., Linsky, V. S., and Monakhof, G. D. "Methods of Speeding Up the Operation of Digital Computers," *Proc. Intern. Conf. Information Processing.* Paris: UNESCO House, 1959.
The Russians are aware of some of the arithmetic algorithms, too.

3. Avizienis, A. "Signed-Digit Number Representation For Fast Parallel Arithmetic," *IRE, Trans. Prof. Group on Electronic Computers*, V. 10 No. 3 (September 1961), pp. 389–399.
See (4).

4. Avizienis, A. *A Study of Redundant Number Representation For Parallel Digital Computers*, Report No. 101. Digital Computer Laboratory, University of Illinois, Urbana, Illinois (May 1960), 76 pp.
This study investigated the possibility of incorporating redundancy in representation to eliminate the carry ripple. The conclusions did not show an advantage in time or hardware for the method under consideration.

TABLE A References by reference number for
each Chapter

Chapter	References Numbers
1	7, 12, 17, 30, 34, 40
2	17, 25, 28
3	17, 25, 26, 28, 32
4	3, 4, 7, 12, 16, 17, 27, 30
5	20, 24, 27, 41, 42
6	29, 36, 37
7	7, 12, 17, 34, 38, 40
8	8, 11, 24, 30
9	5, 24
10	18, 19, 24, 27
11	2, 3, 4, 11, 17, 24, 35, 39
12	8, 24, 30, 33
13	15, 24, 33, 43
14	2, 3, 4, 15, 17, 24, 31, 39, 43
15	6, 17
16	6
17	21
18	1, 9, 10, 13, 14, 22, 23

5. Booth, A. D. "A Signed Binary Multiplication Technique," *Quart. J. Mech. and Appl. Math.*, V. 4, Part 2 (1951), p. 236.
A simple description of ternary multiplication.

6. Bucholtz, Werner. *Planning a Computer System*. New York: McGraw-Hill, 1962, 322 pp.
This book is concerned *only* with STRETCH. It has much valuable system design information. It has one of the few sources on floating-point, Chapter 8. Also, arithmetic unit design of the STRETCH is found in Chapter 14.

7. Burks, A. W., Goldstine, H. H., and von Newman, J. *Preliminary Discussion of the Logical Design of an Electronic Computing Instrument*. Princeton, N. J.: Institute of Advanced Study, 1947.
Noteworthy from an historical viewpoint. The IAS computer is the precursor of the modern binary machine; the ingenuity of its formulators demands respect.

8. Burtsev, V. S. "Accelerating Multiplication and Division Operations in High Speed Digital Computers," *Exact Mechanics and Computing Techniques*. Moscow: Academy of Science, 1958.
Includes carry-save adders and the use of multiples in division and multiplication.

9. Computational Laboratory, Harvard University. *Notes on Modular Number System*, Report No. ASD 61–12, 254 pp. Electronic Technology Laboratory, Aero Systems Division, Air Force Systems Command, Wright-Patterson Air Force Base, Ohio.

New theorems developed at Harvard University relating to modular arithmetic are compiled here. Each note is a mathematical entity. Usually independent theory is the emphasis here.

10. Driese, E. C., Glen, and Young, Jr. *Computer Applications of Residue Class Notations*, ASD Technical Report No. 61–189, Electronic Technology Laboratory, Aero Systems Division, Air Force Systems Command, Wright-Patterson Air Force Base, Ohio.

The attempt here is to develop a complete system in theory to perform computer arithmetic. The fixed-residue, radix notation and floating-gamut principle are introduced for this purpose. Although the discourse leaves many questions unanswered, the ideas are certainly well worth considering.

11. Estrene, G., Gilchrist, B., and Pomerene, J. H. "A Note on High-Speed Multiplication," *IRE Trans. Prof. Group on Electronic Computers*, V. 5, No. 3 (September 1956), p. 140.

First discussion of the carry-save adder used for multiplication.

12. Flores, Ivan. *Computer Logic*. Englewood Cliffs, N. J.: Prentice-Hall, Inc., 1960, Chapters 10, 11.

While serial arithmetic is covered in detail here, there is little said about parallel arithmetic. As is the policy in computer design, this volume and *The Logic of Computer Arithmetic* are compatible even with respect to their symbology. Nevertheless, a good introduction to logical design.

13. Garner, Harvey L. "A Ring Model for the Study of Multiplication for Complement Codes" *IRE Trans. Prof. Group on Electronic Computers*, V. 8, No. 1 (March 1959), pp. 25–30.

Explains the diminished-radix, complement representation of negative numbers for residue notation, analogous to 1's complement for natural numbers. Shows multiplication in this representation when a correction less time-consuming than using full binary is applied.

14. Garner, Harvey L. "The Residue Number System," *Proc. Western Joint Computer Conf.* (March 1959), pp. 146–153.

A fine introductory article.

15. Freiman, C. V. "Statistical Analysis of Certain Binary Division Algorithms," *Proc. IRE*, V. 49, No. 1 (January 1961), pp. 91–103.

The theoretical basis for the multiples method for shifting over 0's and 1's.

16. Gilchrist, B. Pomerene, J. H., and Wong, S. Y. "Fast Carry Logic for Digital Computers," *IRE Trans. Prof. Group on Electronic Computers*, V. EC-4, No. 4 (December 1955), pp. 133–136.

The asynchronous adder is first published here.

17. Ledley, Robert S. *Digital Computer and Control Engineering*. New York: Mc-Graw-Hill Book Co., Inc., 1960. pp. 485–542.

Sometimes another explanation of the same material may serve to clarify a point. Shifting over 0's and 1's is explained here, as well as lookahead adders. Some material on floating-point arithmetic is included.

18. Lehman, M. "High-Speed Multiplication," *IRE Trans. Prof. Group on Electronic Computers*, V. 6, No. 3 (1957), pp. 204–205.

Improved shifting over 0's and 1's for multiplication first described.

19. Lehman, M. "Short-cut Multiplication and Division in Automatic Binary Digital Computers," *Proc. Inst. Elec. Eng.*, Paper No. 2693M, V. 105B (September 1958), pp. 496–503.

Shifting over 0's and 1's, improved method, is encountered here again.

20. Lehman, M., and Burla, N. "Skip Techniques for High-Speed Carry Propagation in Binary Arithmetic Units," *IRE Trans. Prof. Group on Electronic Computers*, V. EC-10, No. 4 (December 1961), pp. 691–698.

This is a review and re-evaluation of adder logic. It is mainly concerned with the lookahead method which the authors call the *skip* technique. They analyze groups of unequal size. What they seem to forget is that the critical number is the *largest* group size and consistency requires a comparison between an adder with maximum equal group sizes to one of same maximum but unequal group sizes. This comparison would make the apparent speed advantage disappear.

21. Lemaerts, E. H. "Automatic Square-Rooting," *Electronic Engineering* (July 1955), pp. 287–289.

The only known description about a square-root algorithm for incorporation in digital computer hardware. The explanation is good, but the example is a little difficult to follow.

22. Lockheed Missiles and Space, *Interim Technical Report on Modular Arithmetic Techniques*, ASD Technical Report No. 61–472, December 1961, 151 pp. Electronic Technology Laboratory, Aero Systems Division, Air Force Systems Command, Wright-Patterson Air Force Base, Ohio.

A few new theorems on modular arithmetic are presented.

23. Maclean, M. A., and Aspinall, D. "A Decimal Adder Using a Stored Addition Table," *Proc. Inst. Elec. Eng.* V. 105B (July 1958), pp. 129–135, 144–146.

An adder for numbers coded in 2–5 residue code. Shows ways of surmounting the carry difficulty between radices when needed.

24. MacSorley, O. L. "High-speed Arithmetic in Binary Computers," *Proc. IRE*, V. 49, No. 1 (January 1961), pp. 67–91.

The most inclusive discussion of modern computer arithmetic. Because of its compactness there are portions which lack clarity. It should be considered as the best supplement to this text, however.

25. Metze, G. *A Study of Parallel One's Complement Arithmetic Units with Separate Carry or Borrow Storage, Report No. 81.* Digital Computer Laboratory, University of Illinois, Urbana, Illinois (November 11, 1957), 77 pp.
Shows the advantages and disadvantages of an arithmetic unit using 1's complement notation. The conclusion is that the disadvantages predominate.

26. Metze, G. and Robertson, J. E. "Elimination of Carry Propagation in Digital Computers," *Proc. Intern. Conf. Information Processing.* Paris: UNESCO House, 1959.
An arithmetic using a redundant representation.

27. National Bureau of Standards, *Methods for High-Speed Addition and Multiplication,* NBS Circ. No. 591, 1958. 20 cents from U. S. Superintendent of Documents.
Really two articles:
a. A fine explanation of the look-ahead adder, also found elsewhere in the literature.
b. A good explanation of improved shift over 0's and 1's for multiply.

28. Reitwiesner, George W. "Binary Arithmetic," in *Advances in Computers,* ed. Franz L. Alt. New York: Academic Press, 1960, pp. 232–308.
An attempt to rigorize binary arithmetic—to put into notation all binary arithmetic and arithmetic algorithms. The notation is unwieldy and hard to follow. Besides, no new algorithm is forthcoming.

29. Reitwiesner, George W. "The Determination of Carry Propagation Length for Binary Addition," *IRE Trans. Prof. Group on Electronic Computers,* V. EC-9, No. 1 (March 1960), pp. 35–38.
The author derives an expression for the average maximum number of ripple stages in an asynchronous adder. This figure differs only slightly from others proposed. He calculates and graphs adders of from 2- to 39-bit words. Why didn't he go on to 60 or 70?

30. Richards, R. K. *Arithmetic Operations in Digital Computers.* New York: D. Van Nostrand Co., Inc., 1955.
The explanations in this one are easy to follow and the neophyte will find it an invaluable background source. Eight years is a long time in the computer field, so you could hardly expect this volume to contain any of the later sophistications in logic. In fact, observe that almost all the other references in this list are of later vintage.

31. Robertson, J. E. "A New Class of Division Methods," *IRE Trans. Prof. Group on Electronic Computers,* V. 7, No. 3 (1958), pp. 218–222.
Speed may be gained in division by representing the quotient digits differently from the divisor and dividend and then converting. The paper describes how this concept is applied to different number systems.

32. Robertson, J. E. "Two's Complement Multiplication in Binary Parallel Digital Computers," Correspondence, *IRE Trans. Prof. Group on Electronic Computers,* V. EC-4, No. 3 (September 1955), pp. 118–119.
The first occurrence in the literature for the second method of 2's complement multiplication.

33. Saltman, R. G. "Reducing Computing Time for Synchronous Binary Division," *IRE Trans. Prof. Group on Electronic Computers,* V. EC-10, No. 2 (June 1961), pp. 169–174.
A description of the non-restoring method of multiples.

34. Shaw, R. F. "Arithmetic Operations in Binary Computers," *Rev. Sci. Instr.,* V. 21 (August 1950), pp. 687–693.
An early approach describing the first crude algorithms (as method 1 multiply).

35. Shimshoni, M. "An Improved Technique for Fast Multiplication on Serial Digital Computers," *Electron. Eng.,* V. 30 (August 1958), pp. 504–505.
Speed up of *serial* multiplication by truncating multiples.

36. Sklansky, J. "Conditional-sum Addition Logic," *IRE Trans. Prof. Group on Electronic Computers,* V. EC-9, No. 2 (June 1960), pp. 226–231.
The first and only CSA publication.

37. Sklansky, J. "An Evaluation of Several Two-Summand Binary ·Adders," *IRE Trans. Prof. Group on Electronic Computers,* V. EC-9, No. 2 (June 1960), pp. 213–226.
The review of different types of adders. The evaluation is based upon two input-only gates and the results are vitiated since this assumption is so absurd with present circuitry. It may become important if we find very high-speed logic has this limitation. The author points out the way to extension and the approximate direction of change of his results as better (more inputs) gates are used.

38. Tocher, K. D. and Lehman, M. "A Fast Parallel Arithmetic Unit," *Proc. Inst. Elec. Eng.,* Paper No. 2108M, V. 103B, Supplement No. 3 (November 1956), p. 520.
Description of arithmetic unit in the Imperial College computer.

39. Tocher, K. D. "Techniques of Multiplication and Division for Automatic Binary Computer," *Quart. J. Mech. and App. Math.,* XI, Part 3 (1958), pp. 364–384.
A review of some methods but written with a mathematical approach and notational system.

40. University of Illinois. *On the Design of a Very High-Speed Computer, Report No. 80,* second edition. Digital Computer Laboratory, University of Illinois, Urbana, Illinois, April 1958, 220 pp.
Examines many aspects in the design of a binary computer among which is the arithmetic unit. Here is method approach to the many different decisions which must be made during the initial phase of engineering.

41. Weinberger, A. and Smith, J. L. "The Logical Design of a One-Microsecond Adder Using One-Megacycle Circuitry," *Proc. Western Joint Computer Conf.* (1956), pp. 103–108.
See (27).

42. Weinberger, A. and Smith, J. L. "The Logical Design of a One-Microsecond Adder Using One-Megacycle Circuitry" *IRE Trans. Prof. Group on Electronic Computers*, V. EC-5, No. 2 (June 1956), pp. 65–73.
See (27).

43. Wilson, J. B. and Ledley, R. S. "An Algorithm for Rapid Binary Division," *IRE Trans. Prof. Group on Electronic Computers*, V. EC-10, No. 4 (December 1961), pp. 662–670.
Shifting over 0's and 1's, the improved method discussed earlier by MacSorley.

INDEX